Middle School 2-1

기말고사 완벽대비

적중100

영어 기출 문제집

중2

동아 | 이병민

Best Collection

구성과 특징

교과서의 주요 학습 내용을 중심으로 학습 영역별 특성에 맞춰 단계별로 다양한 학습 기회를 제공하여 단원별 학습능력 평가는 물론 중간 및 기말고사 시험 등에 완벽하게 대비할 수 있도록 내용을 구성

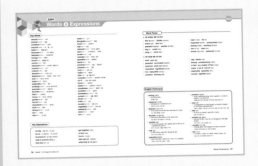

Words & Expressions

Step1 Key Words 단원별 핵심 단어 설명 및 풀이
Key Expression 단원별 핵심 숙어 및 관용어 설명
Word Power 반대 또는 비슷한 뜻 단어 배우기
English Dictionary 영어로 배우는 영어 단어

Step2 실력평가 단원별 수시평가 대비 주관식, 객관식 문제풀이

Step3 서술형 대비 학업성취도 및 수행능력평가 대비 서술형 문제풀이

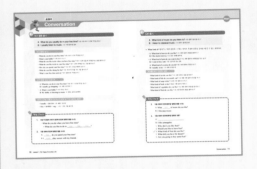

Conversation

Step1 핵심 의사소통 의사소통에 필요한 주요 표현 방법 요약
핵심 Check 기본적인 표현 방법 및 활용능력 확인

Step2 대화문 익히기 상황에 따른 대화문 활용 및 연습

Step3 기본평가 시험대비 기초 학습 능력 평가

Step4 실력평가 단원별 수시평가 대비 주관식, 객관식 문제풀이

Step5 서술형 대비 학업성취도 및 수행능력평가 대비 서술형 문제풀이

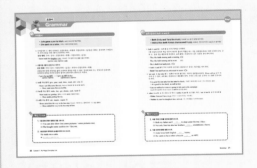

Grammar

Step1 주요 문법 단원별 주요 문법 사항과 예문을 알기 쉽게 설명
핵심 Check 기본 문법사항에 대한 이해 여부 확인

Step2 기본평가 시험대비 기초 학습 능력 평가

Step3 실력평가 단원별 수시평가 대비 주관식, 객관식 문제풀이

Step4 서술형 대비 학업성취도 및 수행능력평가 대비 서술형 문제풀이

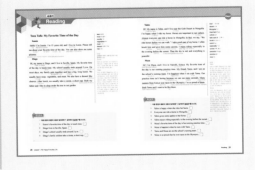

Reading

Step1 구문 분석 단원별로 제시된 문장에 대한 구문별 분석과 내용 설명
확인문제 문장에 대한 기본적인 이해와 인지능력 확인

Step2 확인학습A 빈칸 채우기를 통한 문장 완성 능력 확인

Step3 확인학습B 제시된 우리말을 영어로 완성하여 작문 능력 키우기

Step4 실력평가 단원별 수시평가 대비 주관식, 객관식 문제풀이

Step5 서술형 대비 학업성취도 및 수행능력평가 대비 서술형 문제풀이
교과서 구석구석 교과서에 나오는 기타 문장까지 완벽 학습

Composition

|영역별 핵심문제|

단어 및 어휘, 대화문, 문법, 독해 등 각 영역별 기출문제의 출제 유형을 분석하여 실전에 대비하고 연습할 수 있도록 문제를 배열

|서술형 실전 및 창의사고력 문제|

학교 시험에서 점차 늘어나는 서술형 시험에 집중 대비하고 고득점을 취득하는데 만전을 기하기 위한 학습 코너

|단원별 예상문제|

기출문제를 분석한 후 새로운 시험 출제 경향을 더하여 새롭게 출제될 수 있는 문제를 포함하여 시험에 완벽하게 대비할 수 있도록 준비

|단원별 모의고사|

영역별, 단계별 학습을 모두 마친 후 실전 연습을 위한 모의고사

on the textbook

교과서 파헤치기

- 단어Test1~2 영어 단어 우리말 쓰기와 우리말을 영어 단어로 쓰기
- 대화문Test1~2 대화문 빈칸 완성 및 전체 대화문 쓰기
- 본문Test1~5 빈칸 완성, 우리말 쓰기, 문장 배열연습, 영어 작문하기 복습 등 단계별 반복 학습을 통해 교과서 지문에 대한 완벽한 습득
- 구석구석지문Test1~2 지문 빈칸 완성 및 전문 영어로 쓰기

Lesson 3

The Music Goes On

 의사소통 기능

• 선호 말하기
  A: Which sport do you like best?
  B: I like tennis best.

• 이유 말하기
  A: Why do you want to visit Canada?
  B: Because I want to see Niagara Falls.

🖋 언어 형식

• 수동태
  The Beatles **were loved** by many people.

• If 조건절
  If you like today's idols, you will love the original idol.

Words & Expressions

Key Words

- **amazing** [əméiziŋ] 형 놀라운
- **audience** [ɔ́ːdiəns] 명 청중, 관람객
- **ballet** [bǽlei] 명 발레
- **become** [bikʌ́m] 동 ~이 되다
- **breath** [breθ] 명 숨, 호흡
- **composer** [kəmpóuzər] 명 작곡가
- **concert** [káːnsərt] 명 연주회, 음악회, 콘서트
- **creation** [kriéiʃən] 명 창조물, 창작
- **cry** [krai] 동 울다, 외치다
- **definitely** [défənitli] 부 단연, 틀림없이
- **down** [daun] 형 우울한
- **drummer** [drʌ́mər] 명 북 연주자, 드러머
- **even** [íːvən] 부 ~조차
- **face** [feis] 명 얼굴 동 ~을 마주 보다[향하다]
- **fall** [fɔːl] 동 떨어지다
- **fan** [fæn] 명 팬, 부채, 선풍기
- **fantastic** [fæntǽstik] 형 환상적인
- **flea market** 벼룩시장
- **funny** [fʌ́ni] 형 재미있는, 우스운
- **giraffe** [dʒərǽf] 명 기린
- **grape** [greip] 명 포도, 포도나무
- **greeting** [gríːtiŋ] 명 인사
- **hall** [hɔːl] 명 집회장, 홀
- **heal** [hiːl] 동 고치다, 낫게 하다
- **Hungary** [hʌ́ŋgəri] 명 헝가리
- **idol** [áidl] 명 (많은 사랑을 받는) 우상
- **invent** [invént] 동 발명하다, 창안하다
- **liberty** [líbərti] 명 자유

- **machine** [məʃíːn] 명 기계, 기계장치
- **madly** [mǽdli] 부 미친 듯이, 열렬하게
- **meeting** [míːtiŋ] 명 만남, 모임
- **memory** [méməri] 명 기억, 추억
- **miss** [mis] 동 놓치다, 그리워하다
- **movement** [múːvmənt] 명 움직임
- **novel** [návəl] 명 소설
- **note** [nout] 명 음, 음표 동 적어두다, 주목하다
- **original** [ərídʒənl] 형 본래의
- **paper folding** 종이접기
- **performance** [pərfɔ́ːrməns] 명 공연, 연극, 실행
- **pianist** [piǽnist] 명 피아니스트, 피아노 연주자
- **place** [pleis] 명 곳, 장소
- **prepare** [pripέər] 동 준비하다
- **recent** [ríːsnt] 형 최근의
- **scream** [skriːm] 동 소리치다, 괴성을 지르다
- **seat** [siːt] 명 자리, 죄석
- **sheet music** 악보
- **signature** [sígnəʃər] 명 서명
- **single** [síŋgl] 형 단 하나의, 혼자의
- **softly** [sɔ́ːftli] 부 부드럽게, 상냥하게
- **strawberry** [strɔ́ːbèri] 명 딸기
- **sunny** [sʌ́ni] 형 화창한
- **throw** [θrou] 동 던지다
- **unlike** [ənláik] 전 ~와는 달리
- **vacation** [veikéiʃən] 명 방학, 휴가
- **wall** [wɔːl] 명 벽, 담
- **zebra** [zíːbrə] 명 얼룩말

Key Expressions

- **at once** 동시에, 한꺼번에
- **because of** ~ 때문에
- **build up** 점점 높이다
- **cheer up** 격려하다, 힘을 북돋우다
- **from memory** 기억해서, 외워서

- **go wild** ~에 열중하다, ~에 열광하다
- **hold one's breath** 숨을 참다, 숨을 죽이다
- **listen to** ~을 듣다
- **in person** 직접
- **press down** 누르다

Word Power

※ 서로 반대되는 뜻을 가진 어휘

- □ **early** (일찍) ↔ **late** (늦게)
- □ **strong** (힘 있는, 강한) ↔ **weak** (약한)
- □ **funny** (재미있는) ↔ **boring** (지루한)
- □ **like** (좋아하다) ↔ **dislike** (싫어하다)
- □ **definitely** (단연, 틀림없이) ↔ **indefinitely** (불명확하게)
- □ **best** (가장 좋은) ↔ **worst** (가장 나쁜)

- □ **softly** (부드럽게) ↔ **roughly** (거칠게)
- □ **fold** (접다) ↔ **spread** (펼치다)
- □ **like** (~와 같이) ↔ **unlike** (~와는 달리)
- □ **send** (보내다) ↔ **receive** (받다)
- □ **single** (단 하나의) ↔ **multiple** (다수의)
- □ **pull** (끌다) ↔ **push** (밀다)

English Dictionary

- □ **audience** 청중, 관람객
  → the group of people who have gathered to watch or listen to something
  무언가를 보거나 듣기 위해 모인 사람들의 무리

- □ **ballet** 발레
  → a style of dancing that tells a dramatic story with music but no talking or singing
  이야기하거나 노래하지 않고 음악과 함께 극적인 이야기를 하는 춤

- □ **breath** 숨, 호흡
  → the air that you take into your lungs and send out again
  당신이 폐로 들이마시고 다시 내뱉는 공기

- □ **composer** 작곡가
  → a person who writes music
  음악을 쓰는 사람

- □ **creation** 창조물
  → the act or process of making something that is new, or of causing something to exist that did not exist before
  새롭거나 전에 존재하지 않았던 무언가를 만들어 내는 과정이나 행위

- □ **fall** 떨어지다
  → to drop down from a higher level to a lower level
  높은 곳에서 낮은 곳으로 떨어지다

- □ **flea market** 벼룩시장
  → an outdoor market that sells second-hand goods at low prices
  중고 물건들을 낮은 가격에 판매하는 야외 시장

- □ **hall** 홀, 집회장
  → a space or passage inside the entrance or front door of a building
  건물 정문이나 입구 안의 공간이나 통로

- □ **heal** 고치다, 낫게 하다
  → to become healthy again; to make something healthy again
  다시 건강하게 되다; 다시 건강하게 만들다

- □ **idol** 우상
  → a person or thing that is loved and admired very much
  매우 많은 사랑을 받거나 존경받는 사람이나 사물

- □ **performance** 공연
  → the act of performing a play, concert or some other form of entertainment
  연극, 콘서트 또는 다른 형태의 연회를 공연하는 활동

- □ **pianist** 피아니스트
  → a person who plays the piano
  피아노를 연주하는 사람

- □ **prepare** 준비하다
  → to make something or somebody ready to be used or to do something
  사용되거나 또는 무언가 하기 위해 어떤 사물이나 사람을 준비시키다

- □ **signature** 서명
  → your name as you usually write it, for example, at the end of a letter
  예를 들어, 편지 끝에 당신이 보통 적는 당신의 이름

서답형

01 다음 짝지어진 단어의 관계가 같도록 빈칸에 알맞은 말을 쓰시오.

> early : late = _____ : multiple

서답형

[02~04] 다음 영영풀이에 해당하는 말을 쓰시오.

02

> the air that you take into your lungs and send out again

➡ _____

03

> an outdoor market that sells second-hand goods at low prices

➡ _____

04

> a person who writes music

➡ _____

중요

05 다음 중 밑줄 친 부분의 뜻풀이가 바르지 <u>않은</u> 것은?

① Necessity is the mother of the <u>invention</u>.
(발명)
② It's not easy for me to <u>memorize</u> the musical notes. (기억하다)
③ Please hold your <u>breath</u> for a moment.
(숨, 호흡)
④ This building <u>faces</u> south. (얼굴)
⑤ He'll <u>scream</u> with excitement during the surprise party. (외치다, 소리치다)

06 다음 주어진 문장의 밑줄 친 의미와 같은 의미로 쓰인 것은?

> Some <u>fans</u> screamed madly at concerts.

① Hundreds of football <u>fans</u> were gathered in the stadium.
② The Korean traditional <u>fans</u> are quite popular among foreigners.
③ <u>Fans</u> were used by our ancestors during hot summer.
④ I need the <u>fans</u> to dry my hair.
⑤ People should use <u>fans</u> rather than air conditioners to protect the earth.

중요

07 다음 문장의 빈칸에 공통으로 들어갈 말로 적절한 것은?

> • I need your _____ on the cheque.
> • You should write your _____ on two copies of the contract.
> • He was writing his _____ at the bottom of the paper.

① idol ② creation
③ sheet ④ hall
⑤ signature

서답형

08 다음 대화의 밑줄 친 부분을 주어진 단어를 사용하여 의미가 같도록 바꾸어 쓰시오.

> Jack: Which book do you like best?
> Sumin: I like *Charlotte's Web* best. (favorite)

➡ _____

01 다음 짝지어진 단어의 관계가 같도록 빈칸에 알맞은 말을 쓰시오.

> teach : teacher = compose : _____

[02~03] 다음 영영풀이에 해당하는 단어를 쓰시오.

02

> the act or process of making something that is new, or of causing something to exist that did not exist before

➡ _____

03

> the group of people who have gathered to watch or listen to something

➡ _____

04 다음 문장의 빈칸에 들어갈 말을 〈보기〉에서 골라 쓰시오.

> ┌── 보기 ──┐
> breath / audience / down

(1) Whenever it rains, I'm usually _____.

(2) Take a deep _____ when you feel nervous.

(3) The _____ was touched by his speech.

05 다음 우리말을 주어진 어구를 모두 배열하여 영작하시오.

(1) 벼룩시장이 공원에서 열릴 것이다.
(market / will / in / held / the park / flea / the / be)
➡ _____

(2) 그녀는 악보 없이 피아노를 연주하였다.
(music / played / she / without / sheet / the / piano)
➡ _____

06 다음 우리말에 맞게 빈칸에 알맞은 말을 쓰시오.

(1) 당신이 문을 열고 싶다면, 버튼을 누르세요.
➡ If you want to open the door, _____ _____ the button please.

(2) 선수들은 결승선을 향해 속도를 점점 높일 것이다.
➡ The players will _____ _____ _____ toward the finish line.

(3) Mike는 한꺼번에 두 가지 일을 다루는 일을 잘한다.
➡ Mike is good at dealing with two things _____ _____.

07 다음 빈칸에 들어갈 말을 순서대로 쓰시오.

> • Jane is a teacher, writer and designer (A)_____ once.
> • Because the car is broken down, I can't build (B)_____ speed.
> • You have to deliver this document (C)_____ person.

(A) _____ (B) _____ (C) _____

교과서
Conversation

1 선호 말하기

> **A** Which sport do you like best? 너는 어느 운동을 가장 좋아하니?
> **B** I like tennis best. 나는 테니스를 가장 좋아해.

■ 'Which ~ do you like best[most]?' 또는 'What's your favorite ~?'으로 상대방이 선호하는 것을 물어볼 수 있다.

선호 묻기

- What kind of sports do you like best? 너는 어떤 종류의 운동을 가장 좋아하니?
- Which do you prefer, oranges or apples? 너는 오렌지와 사과 중 어느 것을 더 좋아하니?
- Do you like watching TV more than listening to the radio?
  너는 라디오를 듣는 것보다 TV 보는 것을 더 좋아하니?

선호 말하기

- I like ~ most[best]. 나는 ~을 가장 좋아한다.
- I love ~. 나는 ~을 매우 좋아한다.
- I'm fond of ~. 나는 ~을 좋아한다.
- My favorite ... is ~. 내가 가장 좋아하는 …는 ~이다.
- I enjoy ~ (very much). 나는 ~을 (매우) 즐긴다.

핵심 Check

1. 다음 우리말과 일치하도록 빈칸에 알맞은 말을 쓰시오.

(1) **A:** _____ _____ do you like best? (당신은 어느 동물을 가장 좋아하나요?)

    B: I like cats best. (저는 고양이를 가장 좋아합니다.)

(2) **A:** What is your _____ _____? (당신이 가장 좋아하는 과목은 무엇입니까?)

    B: My favorite subject is English. (제가 가장 좋아하는 과목은 영어입니다.)

(3) **A:** Which flower do you _____? (당신은 어떤 꽃을 아주 좋아합니까?)

    B: I love roses. (저는 장미를 아주 좋아합니다.)

② 이유 말하기

> **A** Why do you want to visit Canada? 너는 왜 캐나다를 방문하고 싶니?
>
> **B** Because I want to see Niagara Falls. 왜냐하면 나이아가라 폭포를 보고 싶기 때문이야.

■ 'Why do you ~?', 'Can you tell me the reason why ~?' 또는 'What's the reason why ~?' 등으로 이유를 물어볼 수 있다.

이유 말하기

- Because 주어 + 동사 ~. ~이기 때문이다.
- It is because of+명사(구) ~. 그것은 ~ 때문이다.
- The reason why ~ is because ~. ~한 이유는 ~이다.

핵심 Check

2. 다음 우리말과 일치하도록 빈칸에 알맞은 말을 쓰시오.

(1) A: _____ do you want to buy some flowers? (왜 당신은 꽃을 사기를 원하나요?)

B: _____ I want to give them to my mother. (나는 그것들을 어머니에게 주고 싶기 때문이에요.)

(2) A: Can you tell me _____ _____ _____ you want to visit the museum?
(당신은 왜 박물관을 방문하고 싶어 하는지 이야기해 줄 수 있나요?)

B: _____ _____ _____ _____ _____ _____ _____ is

because I like history. (제가 그곳에 방문하고 싶은 이유는 제가 역사를 좋아하기 때문입니다.)

(3) A: What's _____ _____ _____ _____ _____ _____ _____

to the city? (당신이 그 도시로 이사하고 싶은 이유가 무엇인가요?)

B: The reason why I want to move there is _____ _____ education.
(제가 그곳으로 이사하고 싶은 이유는 교육 때문입니다.)

A. Listen and Speak 1-A

> **Jack:** Hi, Sumin. ❶How's the book club going?
>
> **Sumin:** It's fun. ❷I read lots of interesting books.
>
> **Jack:** ❸Which book do you like best?
>
> **Sumin:** ❹I like *Charlotte's Web* best.

Jack: 안녕, 수민아. 책 동아리는 어때?
Sumin: 재미있어. 나는 흥미로운 책들을 많이 읽어.
Jack: 어떤 책을 가장 좋아하니?
Sumin: 나는 'Charlotte's Web'을 가장 좋아해.

❶ How is ~ going?: ~는 어때?
❷ lots of: 많은 (= a lot of)
❸ Which ~ do you like best?: '너는 어느 ~을 가장 좋아하니?'라는 뜻으로 상대방의 선호를 묻는 표현이다.
❹ 선호를 묻는 질문에 대한 대답으로는 Yes나 No로 답하지 않으며 'I like ~ best.'와 같이 대답할 수 있다.

Check(√) True or False

(1) Sumin read many interesting books in the book club.　　　　T ☐ F ☐

(2) Sumin likes *Charlotte's Web* best.　　　　T ☐ F ☐

A. Listen and Speak 1-B

> **Amy:** ❶Jiho, what are you going to do this Saturday?
>
> **Jiho:** ❷I'm going to Blue Sky's fan meeting with my friends.
>
> **Amy:** ❸Wow, I'm also a big fan of the band.
>
> **Jiho:** Really? Which member do you like best, Amy?
>
> **Amy:** I like Lucy best. She sings really well.
>
> **Jiho:** ❹I like the drummer, Mike, best. ❺He's fantastic! Do you want to join us?
>
> **Amy:** Sure, I'd love to. ❻I can't wait!

Amy: 지호야, 이번 주 토요일에 뭐 할 거니?
Jiho: 나는 친구들이랑 Blue Sky 팬 모임에 갈 거야.
Amy: 와, 나도 그 밴드의 열렬한 팬이야.
Jiho: 정말? 너는 어느 멤버를 가장 좋아하니, Amy?
Amy: 나는 Lucy를 가장 좋아해. 그녀는 노래를 정말 잘해.
Jiho: 나는 드러머인 Mike를 가장 좋아해. 그는 환상적이야. 우리와 함께 갈래?
Amy: 물론이지, 너무 좋아. 기대된다!

❶ What are you going to do ~?: 상대방의 계획을 묻는 표현이다.
❷ I'm going to ~ = I'm going to go to ~
❸ big: 열렬한, 매우 좋아하는
❹ the drummer와 Mike는 동격이다.
❺ fantastic: 환상적인
❻ I can't wait!: 기대감을 나타내는 표현으로 I'm looking forward to it!으로 바꾸어 쓸 수 있다.

Check(√) True or False

(3) Lucy and Mike are the members of the band Blue Sky.　　　　T ☐ F ☐

(4) Amy cannot go to Blue Sky's fan meeting with Jiho.　　　　T ☐ F ☐

Listen and Speak 1-C

A: Do you like sports?

B: Yes, I do.

A: ❶Which sport do you like best?

B: I like tennis best. ❷It's so exciting!

❶ Which ~ do you like best?: '너는 어느 ~을 가장 좋아하니?'라는 뜻으로 상대방의 선호를 묻는 표현이다.

❷ It's so exciting!: 그것은 매우 흥미진진하다!

Listen and Speak 2-A

B: ❶Why do you have all those old clothes?

G: ❷I'm going to sell them at the flea market.

B: Really? I have some old clothes, too.

G: ❸Then why don't you join me this Saturday?

B: Okay.

❶ 'all those+형용사+명사'의 어순이다., clothes: 의류, 옷

❷ them = all those old clothes, flea market: 벼룩 시장

❸ Why don't you ~?: '~하는 게 어때?'라고 제안할 때 쓰는 표현이다.

Listen and Speak 2-B

Sujin: ❶Tom, why do you have so many paper flowers?

Tom: They're for my mom's birthday.

Sujin: They're so beautiful. Where did you get them?

Tom: I made them.

Sujin: Wow, you're really good.

Tom: Thanks. ❷I'm taking a paper folding class these days.

Sujin: They are going to be the perfect gift for your mom.

Tom: ❸I hope so, too.

❶ so many: 그토록 많은

❷ take a class: 수업을 듣다, paper folding: 종이 접기, these days: 요즘

❸ so는 앞 문장의 내용을 받는 지시대명사이다.

Listen and Speak 2-C

A: ❶Which country do you want to visit for your dream vacation?

B: I want to visit Canada.

A: ❷Why do you want to visit Canada?

B: ❸Because I want to see Niagara Falls.

❶ Which country do you want to ~?: '어느 나라를 ~하고 싶니?'라고 의견을 묻고 있다.

❷ '왜 캐나다를 방문하고 싶니?'라는 뜻으로 상대방에게 이유를 묻는 표현이다.

❸ because 뒤에는 '주어+동사'를 포함한 절이 오지만 'because of' 뒤에는 명사(구)가 이어진다. 이때 because를 생략하고 이유만 말할 수 있다.

Real Life Talk

Mina: Good afternoon, friends. I'm Mina with the school radio show. Today Mr. Smith, our English teacher, is here with us. Hi, Mr. Smith.

Mr. Smith: Hello, everyone. I'm happy to be here with you.

Mina: Let's talk about music. Mr. Smith, ❶what's your favorite band?

Mr. Smith: ❷Definitely The Beatles.

Mina: Oh, I like them, too. Which song do you like best?

Mr. Smith: I like most of their songs, but I like *Hey Jude* best.

Mina: Why do you like it?

Mr. Smith: ❸Because the song makes me feel better when I'm down.

Mina: That's great! Let's listen to the song.

❶ What's your favorite ~?: '당신이 가장 좋아하는 ~은 무엇입니까?'라고 선호 표현을 묻는 질문으로 'Which band do you like best?'라고 바꾸어 물어 볼 수 있다.

❷ definitely: 단연, 틀림없이

❸ down: 우울한(= depressed)

다음 우리말과 일치하도록 빈칸에 알맞은 말을 쓰시오.

Listen & Speak 1 A

Jack: Hi, Sumin. _____ the book club going?

Sumin: It's fun. I read lots of interesting books.

Jack: _____ _____ do you like best?

Sumin: I like *Charlotte's Web* _____.

Jack: 안녕, 수민아. 책 동아리는 어때?
Sumin: 재미있어. 나는 흥미로운 책들을 많이 읽어.
Jack: 어느 책을 가장 좋아하니?
Sumin: 나는 'Charlotte's Web'을 가장 좋아해.

Listen & Speak 1 B

Amy: Jiho, _____ _____ _____ _____ _____ _____ this Saturday?

Jiho: I'm going to Blue Sky's fan meeting with my friends.

Amy: Wow, I'm also _____ _____ _____ of the band.

Jiho: Really? _____ _____ do you like best, Amy?

Amy: I like Lucy best. She sings really well.

Jiho: I like the _____, Mike, best. He's fantastic! Do you want to join us?

Amy: Sure, I'd love to. _____ _____ _____!

Amy: 지호야, 이번 주 토요일에 뭐 할 거니?
Jiho: 나는 친구들이랑 Blue Sky 팬 모임에 갈 거야.
Amy: 와, 나도 그 밴드의 열렬한 팬이야.
Jiho: 정말? 너는 어느 멤버를 가장 좋아하니, Amy?
Amy: 나는 Lucy를 가장 좋아해. 그녀는 노래를 정말 잘해.
Jiho: 나는 드러머인 Mike를 가장 좋아해. 그는 환상적이야. 우리와 함께 갈래?
Amy: 물론이지, 너무 좋아. 기대된다!

Listen & Speak 1 C

A: Do you like sports?

B: Yes, I do.

A: _____ _____ do you like best?

B: I like _____ best. It's so _____!

A: 운동을 좋아하니?
B: 응, 좋아해.
A: 어느 운동을 가장 좋아하니?
B: 나는 테니스를 가장 좋아해. 그것은 매우 흥미진진해!

Listen & Speak 2 A

B: _____ do you have all those old clothes?

G: I'm going to sell them at the _____ _____.

B: Really? I have some old clothes, too.

G: Then _____ _____ _____ join me this Saturday?

B: Okay.

B: 너는 왜 저 모든 헌 옷들을 가지고 있니?
G: 나는 벼룩시장에 그 옷들을 팔 거야.
B: 정말? 나도 헌 옷들이 좀 있어.
G: 그러면 이번 주 토요일에 나와 함께 팔면 어때?
B: 좋아.

Listen & Speak 2 B

Sujin: Tom, _____ do you have so many paper flowers?

Tom: They're _____ my mom's birthday.

Sujin: They're so beautiful. _____ did you get them?

Tom: I made them.

Sujin: Wow, you're really good.

Tom: Thanks. I'm taking _____ _____ _____ _____ these days.

Sujin: They are going to be _____ _____ _____ for your mom.

Tom: I hope so, too.

Listen & Speak 2 C

A: _____ _____ do you want to visit for your dream vacation?

B: I want to visit Canada.

A: _____ _____ _____ _____ _____ visit Canada?

B: _____ I want to see Niagara Falls.

Real Life Talk

Mina: Good afternoon, friends. I'm Mina _____ _____ _____ _____. Today Mr. Smith, your English teacher, is here with us. Hi, Mr. Smith.

Mr. Smith: Hello, everyone. I'm happy to be here with you.

Mina: Let's talk about music. Mr. Smith, _____ _____ _____ _____?

Mr. Smith: _____ The Beatles.

Mina: Oh, I like them, too. _____ _____ _____ _____ _____ _____?

Mr. Smith: I like most of their songs, but I like *Hey Jude* best.

Mina: _____ _____ _____ _____ _____ _____?

Mr. Smith: _____ the song makes me feel better _____ _____ _____.

Mina: That's great! Let's listen to the song.

01 다음 빈칸에 들어갈 말로 적절하지 <u>않은</u> 것은?

> A: Which sport do you like best?
>
> B: _____

① I like tennis best.

② I love baseball.

③ I enjoy badminton very much.

④ My favorite sport is soccer.

⑤ I would like to play basketball.

02 다음 대화의 빈칸에 들어갈 말로 적절한 것은?

> A: _____ do you want to visit Canada?
>
> B: Because I want to see Niagara Falls.

① Why   ② When   ③ Which

④ Who   ⑤ What

[03~04] 다음 대화를 읽고, 물음에 답하시오.

> Jack: Hi, Sumin. (A)[How's / What's] the book club going?
>
> Sumin: It's fun. I read lots of (B)[interested / interesting] books.
>
> Jack: (C)[Which / Why] book do you like best?
>
> Sumin: I like *Charlotte's Web* best.

03 위 대화의 빈칸 (A)~(C)에 알맞은 말을 쓰시오.

(A) _____ (B) _____ (C) _____

04 위 대화의 내용과 일치하지 <u>않는</u> 것은?

① Sumin is a member of the book club.

② Sumin has fun in the book club.

③ Sumin read many interesting books.

④ Sumin loves *Charlotte's Web*.

⑤ Sumin's book club is *Charlotte's Web*.

서답형

01 다음 대화의 빈칸에 주어진 단어를 사용하여 대답을 완성하시오.

> A: Which sport do you like best?
> B: _____ (tennis, like)

➡ _____

[02~05] 다음 대화를 읽고, 물음에 답하시오.

> Amy: Jiho, _____ⓐ_____
> Jiho: I'm going to Blue Sky's fan meeting with my friends.
> Amy: Wow, I'm also a big fan of the band.
> Jiho: Really? Which member do you like best, Amy?
> Amy: I like Lucy best. She sings really well.
> Jiho: I like the _____ⓑ_____, Mike, best. He's fantastic! Do you want to join us?
> Amy: Sure, I'd love to. ⓒI can't wait!

02 위 대화의 빈칸 ⓐ에 들어갈 말로 어색한 것은?

① what are you going to do this Saturday?
② what are you planning to do this Saturday?
③ what are you supposed to do this Saturday?
④ what's your plan for this Saturday?
⑤ what are you doing now for this Saturday?

서답형

03 위 대화의 빈칸 ⓑ에 주어진 영영풀이에 해당하는 말을 쓰시오.

> a person who plays a drum or drums

➡ _____

중요

04 위 대화의 밑줄 친 ⓒ와 바꾸어 쓸 수 있는 것은?

① I cannot go with you.
② I'm really looking forward to it.
③ I'm sorry, but I can't.
④ I'm afraid not.
⑤ I have no doubt.

05 위 대화를 읽고 대답할 수 <u>없는</u> 질문은?

① What are Jiho and Amy going to do at Blue Sky's fan meeting?
② Which member of Blue Sky does Jiho like best?
③ Which instrument does Mike play?
④ Which band is Amy a big fan of?
⑤ Who is Amy's favorite member of Blue Sky?

[06~07] 다음 대화를 읽고, 물음에 답하시오.

> B: Why do you have all those old clothes?
> G: I'm going to sell them at the flea market.
> B: Really? I have some old clothes, too.
> G: ⓐ그러면 이번 주 토요일에 나와 함께 팔면 어때? (them, join, why)
> B: Okay.

서답형

06 위 대화의 밑줄 친 우리말 ⓐ에 맞게 주어진 단어를 사용하여 영어로 쓰시오.

➡ _____

서답형

07 What is the boy going to bring to the flea market?

➡ _____

[08~09] 다음 대화를 읽고, 물음에 답하시오.

> Sujin: Tom, why do you have so many paper flowers?
> Tom: They're for my mom's birthday. (A)
> Sujin: They're so beautiful. (B)
> Tom: I made them. (C)
> Sujin: Wow, you're really good. (D)
> Tom: Thanks. I'm taking a paper folding class these days. (E)
> Sujin: They are going to be the perfect gift for your mom.
> Tom: I hope so, too.

서답형

08 위 대화의 (A)~(E) 중 주어진 문장이 들어가기에 가장 적절한 곳은?

> Where did you get them?

① (A) ② (B) ③ (C) ④ (D) ⑤ (E)

09 위 대화의 내용과 일치하지 <u>않는</u> 것은?

① Tom made many paper flowers for himself.
② Tom prepared paper flowers as his mom's birthday gift.
③ Tom brought some paper from his class to make paper flowers.
④ Tom learned how to make paper flowers in a paper folding class.
⑤ Sujin is sure that Tom's paper flowers will be the perfect gift for his mom.

[10~12] 다음 대화를 읽고, 물음에 답하시오.

> Mina: Good afternoon, friends. I'm Mina ⓐ<u>with</u> the school radio show. Today Mr. Smith, our English teacher, is here with us. Hi, Mr. Smith.
> Mr. Smith: Hello, everyone. I'm happy ⓑ<u>to be</u> here with you.
> Mina: Let's talk about music. Mr. Smith, what's your favorite band?
> Mr. Smith: ⓒ<u>Definite</u> The Beatles.
> Mina: Oh, I like them, too. ⓓ<u>Which</u> song do you like best?
> Mr. Smith: I like most of their songs, but I like *Hey Jude* best.
> Mina: Why do you like it?
> Mr. Smith: ⓔ<u>Because of</u> the song makes me feel better when I'm down.
> Mina: That's great! Let's listen to (A)<u>the song</u>.

서답형

10 위 대화의 ⓐ~ⓔ 중 어법상 어색한 것을 <u>모두</u> 찾아 바르게 고치시오.

➡ _____

서답형

11 위 대화의 밑줄 친 (A)가 가리키는 것을 찾아 쓰시오.

➡ _____

중요

12 위 대화를 읽고 대답할 수 <u>없는</u> 질문은?

① Who is the guest on the school radio show?
② What does Mr. Smith teach at school?
③ Which band does Mr. Smith like best?
④ Why does Mr. Smith love *Hey Jude*?
⑤ How does Mina feel when listening to *Hey Jude*?

01 다음 밑줄 친 우리말을 주어진 단어를 사용하여 영어로 쓰시오.

> A: 너는 어느 운동을 가장 좋아하니? (best, like)
> B: I like tennis best.

➡ _____

02 다음 대화의 밑줄 친 우리말을 영어로 쓰시오.

> A: Why do you want to visit Canada?
> B: 왜냐하면 나는 나의 친구를 방문하고 싶기 때문이야.

➡ _____

03 다음 대화를 읽고 대화의 내용과 일치하도록 빈칸을 완성하시오.

> Mina: Good afternoon, friends. I'm Mina with the school radio show. Today Mr. Smith, our English teacher, is here with us. Hi, Mr. Smith.
> Mr. Smith: Hello, everyone. I'm happy to be here with you.
> Mina: Let's talk about music. Mr. Smith, what's your favorite band?
> Mr. Smith: Definitely The Beatles.
> Mina: Oh, I like them, too. Which song do you like best?
> Mr. Smith: I like most of their songs, but I like *Hey Jude* best.
> Mina: Why do you like it?
> Mr. Smith: Because the song makes me feel better when I'm down.
> Mina: That's great! Let's listen to the song.

> Did you hear the school radio show today? There was a special guest on the show. He is (1)_____, our English teacher. Mina and Mr. Smith talked about (2)____. Mr. Smith said that his favorite band is (3)_____. Among their songs, he liked (4)_____ best, because (5)_____. The song was beautiful. I liked it so much, too.

(1) _____ (2) _____ (3) _____

(4) _____ (5) _____

[04~05] 다음 대화를 읽고, 물음에 답하시오.

> Sujin: Tom, why do you have so many paper flowers?
> Tom: They're for my mom's birthday.
> Sujin: They're so beautiful. Where did you get them?
> Tom: I made them.
> Sujin: Wow, you're really good.
> Tom: Thanks. (A)나 요즘 종이접기 수업을 듣고 있어.
> Sujin: They are going to be the perfect gift for your mom.
> Tom: I hope so, too.

04 Why did Tom make lots of paper flowers?

➡ _____

 05 위 대화의 밑줄 친 우리말 (A)에 맞게 〈보기〉에 있는 단어를 모두 배열하시오.

> ┤ 보기 ├
> taking / these / I'm / folding / days / a / class / paper

➡ _____

Grammar

① 수동태

- Tom **built** this house. [능동태] Tom은 이 집을 지었다.
- This house **was built** by Tom. [수동태] 이 집은 Tom에 의해 지어졌다.

■ 수동태는 능동태의 목적어를 주어로 만들고 동사를 'be+p.p.' 형태로 만든 후, 능동태의 주어를 'by+목적격' 형태로 하여 '주어가 ~되다'라고 해석한다. 능동태 문장의 시제에 따라 수동태 시제를 결정한다.
- Jane **cleans** the room every day. Jane은 매일 그 방을 청소한다.
- The room **is cleaned** by Jane every day. 그 방은 Jane에 의해 매일 청소된다.

■ 4형식 문장의 수동태는 두 가지 형태를 갖는다. 직접목적어를 주어로 한 수동태에서는 간접목적어에 특정 전치사를 부여한다. 전치사 to를 쓰는 동사는 'give, tell, teach, show, bring' 등이고, 전치사 for를 쓰는 동사는 'buy, make, cook, get' 등이며, 전치사 of를 쓰는 동사는 'ask'가 있다.
- English **is taught to** us by Ms. Kim. 영어는 Kim 선생님에 의해서 우리에게 가르쳐진다.
- Pizza **was cooked for** her yesterday by my mom. 피자는 어제 그녀를 위해 나의 엄마에 의해 만들어졌다.

■ 5형식 문장의 목적격보어가 원형부정사인 경우, 수동태 문장에서는 to부정사로 만들어 준다. 그 외에는 모든 목적격보어를 그대로 쓸 수 있다.
- He **is called** Smiley by us. 그는 우리에 의해 Smiley라고 불린다.
- I **was made to do** the job by her. 나는 그녀에 의해 그 일을 하도록 강요받았다.

■ 조동사의 수동태는 '조동사+be+p.p.' 형태를 취한다.
- A new supermarket **will be built** next year. 새로운 슈퍼마켓이 내년에 지어질 것이다.
- The chairs **can be replaced** with other ones. 그 의자들은 다른 것들로 교체될 수 있다.

■ by 이외의 전치사를 사용하는 수동태에 유의한다.
- I **am interested in** reading books. 나는 책 읽는 것에 흥미가 있다.
- Cheese **is made from** milk. 치즈는 우유로 만들어진다.
- Jason **was surprised at** the news. Jason은 뉴스에 놀랐다.

핵심 Check

1. 다음 우리말과 같도록 빈칸에 알맞은 말을 쓰시오.
(1) 지구 표면의 대부분이 물로 덮여 있다.
➡ Most of the earth's surface _____ _____ with water.
(2) 그는 나로부터 질문 하나를 받았다.
➡ He _____ _____ a question by me.

❷ If 조건절

> • **If** you watch this movie, you will love it. 네가 만약 이 영화를 본다면. 너는 그것을 좋아할 거야.
>
> • **If** I have time to do this, I will let you know. 내가 이걸 할 시간이 있다면, 너에게 알려 줄게.

■ 조건의 부사절에서는 현재시제를 사용하여 미래를 나타내며 '만약 ~라면'이라고 해석한다.

   • **If** we go by bus, it will be comfortable. 우리가 버스를 타고 간다면. 편할 거야.

   • **If** you are hungry, I will make some sandwiches. 네가 배고프다면. 내가 샌드위치를 만들게.

■ If절이 명사 역할을 하는 경우도 있다. 명사절 접속사 if와 부사절 접속사 if의 쓰임을 구별하자. 명사절 접속사 if의 경우 '~인지 아닌지'로 해석하며 미래를 나타낼 때에는 미래시제를 써야 한다.

   • **If** he has some rest, he will be much better. 그가 조금 쉰다면, 훨씬 더 좋아질 거야.

   • I wonder **if** you will come or not. 나는 당신이 올지 안 올지가 궁금합니다.

■ If ~ not은 '만약 ~하지 않으면'의 의미인 Unless로 쓸 수 있다. unless 역시 조건절이므로 현재시제로 미래를 나타낸다.

   • **If** you **don't** hurry, you will be late for class. 서두르지 않으면. 수업에 늦을 거야.

   • **Unless** you hurry, you will be late for class. 서두르지 않으면, 수업에 늦을 거야.

핵심 Check

2. 다음 우리말과 같도록 빈칸에 알맞은 말을 쓰시오.

   (1) 내가 일찍 도착한다면, 너에게 전화할게.

   ➡ If I _____ early, I _____ _____ you.

   (2) 네가 그녀의 파티에 온다면, 그녀는 아주 행복할 거야.

   ➡ If you _____ to her party, she _____ _____ very happy.

   (3) 나는 네가 교회에 갈 건지 알고 싶어.

   ➡ I want to know _____ you _____ _____ to church.

01 다음 문장에서 어법상 <u>어색한</u> 부분을 바르게 고쳐 쓰시오.

(1) Jimmy born in 2005 in Seoul.

　　_____ ➡ _____

(2) A letter was sent for her yesterday.

　　_____ ➡ _____

(3) If you will leave a message, I will give it to Kim.

　　_____ ➡ _____

(4) I don't know if he visits her this weekend.

　　_____ ➡ _____

02 주어진 동사를 어법에 맞게 빈칸에 쓰시오.

(1) If you _____ this magazine, I will lend it to you. (want)

(2) Many accidents _____ _____ by careless driving. (cause)

(3) You can _____ the difficult problem. (solve)

(4) I _____ _____ to the party, but I didn't go. (invite)

(5) If you don't hurry, you _____ _____ the train. (miss)

03 다음 우리말에 맞게 주어진 단어를 바르게 배열하시오. (필요하면 어형을 바꿀 것)

(1) 유리는 어떻게 만들어지나요?

　　(how / be / make / glass)

　　➡ _____

(2) 나는 이곳에 고용될 거야.

　　(be / I / here / will / employ)

　　➡ _____

(3) 네가 달리면, 내가 따라갈게.

　　(if / follow / you / I / run / will / you)

　　➡ _____

(4) 네가 약간의 음식을 가지고 올 건지 알려 줘.

　　(if / you / let / know / me / bring / some / food / will)

　　➡ _____

01 다음 우리말을 바르게 영작한 것은?

> 그 편지는 일주일 전에 너에게 부쳐졌다.

① The letter is sent you a week ago.
② The letter has been sent to you a week ago.
③ The letter sent to you a week ago.
④ The letter was sent to you a week ago.
⑤ The letter was sent for you a week ago.

02 다음 중 수동태로의 전환이 바르지 <u>않은</u> 것은?

① Did somebody clean the restroom?
　→ Was the restroom cleaned by somebody?
② Ted broke my camera.
　→ My camera was broken by Ted.
③ Jane made me so happy.
　→ I was made so happy by Jane.
④ My grandparents brought me up.
　→ I was brought up my grandparents.
⑤ He showed me some pictures.
　→ I was shown some pictures by him.

03 다음 중 밑줄 친 if의 쓰임이 <u>다른</u> 하나는?

① <u>If</u> anyone calls, I will tell you.
② I will be sad <u>if</u> you leave.
③ I wonder <u>if</u> she liked it or not.
④ He will stay longer <u>if</u> she wants him to.
⑤ <u>If</u> it rains tomorrow, we won't go out.

04 서답형 주어진 단어를 이용하여 다음 우리말을 영어로 쓰시오.

> 네가 그 파티에 초대받는다면 너는 그곳에 갈 거니?
> (invite, will, go)

➡ _____

05 다음 중 어법상 옳은 것은?

① The glass is filled by milk.
② If I make some mistakes, can you help me?
③ I wonder if you meet him tomorrow.
④ He was made do the homework first.
⑤ Some cookies were made to me by Julia.

06 다음 중 어법상 바르지 <u>않은</u> 것은?

> ①<u>Will</u> you call ②<u>me</u> ③<u>if</u> I ④<u>will give</u> you ⑤<u>my phone number</u>?

①　　　②　　　③　　　④　　　⑤

07 다음 빈칸에 공통으로 들어갈 말로 가장 적절한 것은?

> • The mountain is covered _____ snow.
> • She was pleased _____ the news.

① by　　　② at　　　③ with
④ in　　　⑤ from

08 주어진 어구를 바르게 배열하여 다음 우리말을 영어로 쓰시오.
서답형

> 우리가 그 길을 못 찾으면 무엇을 해야 할지 모르겠어.
> (don't know / will / we / I / what / we / don't find / the way / do / if)

➡ _____

09 다음 두 문장이 같은 의미가 되도록 빈칸에 알맞은 말을 고르면?

> He saw the child playing the violin alone.
> = The child _____ the violin alone by him.

① was seen play   ② is seen to play
③ was seen playing   ④ saw playing
⑤ is seen playing

10 다음 중 if의 쓰임이 같은 것끼리 바르게 묶으시오.
서답형

> ⓐ He will come here if he gets up early tomorrow.
> ⓑ If songs are chosen, we can practice together.
> ⓒ I wonder if there is some food to eat.
> ⓓ If you need money, I will lend you some.
> ⓔ She couldn't tell if he said the truth.

➡ _____

11 다음 두 문장의 의미가 같도록 빈칸에 알맞은 말을 쓰시오.
서답형

> If you don't do your best, you will not pass the test.
> = _____ you do your best, you will not pass the test.

12 다음 중 어법상 바르지 않은 것은?

① If you use my computer again, I will punish you.
② Tom was made to fix the radio.
③ Did the building designed by a famous architect?
④ I'm not sure if he wants me to teach him English.
⑤ A present is given to her by her friends.

13 다음 중 빈칸에 들어갈 말이 다른 하나는?
중요

① My mom was disappointed _____ me.
② Jason was satisfied _____ the test result.
③ His clothes are covered _____ dirt.
④ Jessy was worried _____ her dog.
⑤ I filled the bucket _____ various flowers.

14 주어진 단어를 이용하여 다음 문장을 수동태로 쓰시오.
서답형

> Nobody told me about the class meeting.
> (wasn't)

➡ _____

15 다음 빈칸에 적절하지 않은 것은?
중요

> _____ you arrive here, we will start to eat the food.

① If   ② After
③ As soon as   ④ When
⑤ Though

16 다음 밑줄 친 문장을 수동태로 바르게 전환한 것을 모두 고르시오.

> The CEO offered Tom the job, but he refused it.

① The job offered to Tom by the CEO,
② The job was offered to Tom by the CEO,
③ Tom was offered the CEO to the job,
④ Tom was offered the job by the CEO,
⑤ The job was offered for Tom by the CEO,

서답형
17 주어진 단어를 활용하여 다음 우리말을 영어로 쓰시오.

> 너에게 자전거 한 대가 주어진다면, 너는 무엇을 할 거니? (bike / give / to / do)

➡ _____

중요
18 다음 빈칸에 들어갈 말이 다른 하나는?

① Math is taught _____ us by Mr. Henderson.
② A book was given _____ me by John.
③ The ball was thrown _____ him by a boy.
④ A delicious meal was cooked _____ me yesterday.
⑤ Dolls were sold _____ a lot of children at the hospital.

19 다음 빈칸에 들어갈 말이 바르게 짝지어진 것은?

> A: Who took the picture?
> B: The picture _____ Harry.

① was taken to   ② was taken by
③ is taken to   ④ is taken by
⑤ was taken in

20 다음 중 어법상 바르지 않은 것은?

> I ①am worried ②about your health. If I ③make a doctor's appointment, ④do you ⑤go see the doctor?

①   ②   ③   ④   ⑤

서답형
21 주어진 단어를 주어로 하여 다음 물음에 답하시오.

> A: Can you tell me who invented Hangeul?
> B: Hangeul _____.

➡ _____

서답형
22 주어진 어구를 활용하여 다음 우리말을 영어로 쓰시오.

> 내가 당신을 직접 만나게 된다면, 당신에게 많은 질문을 할 거예요.
> (meet / in person / ask / many)

➡ _____

서답형
23 다음 주어진 문장과 같은 의미가 되도록 빈칸에 알맞은 말을 쓰시오.

> Your clothes won't get clean if you don't use soap.
> = If soap _____, your clothes _____.

➡ _____

서답형
24 다음 문장에서 틀린 부분을 찾아 바르게 고치시오.

> If it doesn't rain, the party will hold outside.

_____ ➡ _____

01 주어진 단어를 활용하여 다음 우리말을 영어로 쓰시오.

> 그 기계가 사람들에 의해 사용된다면, 그들은 행복할 거야. (use / be)

➡ _____

02 다음 대화의 빈칸에 알맞은 말을 쓰시오.

> **A:** Who wrote *Romeo and Juliet*?
> **B:** *Romeo and Juliet* _____ Shakespeare.

➡ _____

03 다음 문장을 주어진 단어로 시작하는 문장으로 다시 쓰시오.

> Jimmy's sister made him feel comfortable.

➡ Jimmy _____.

04 주어진 동사를 어법에 맞게 빈칸에 쓰시오.

(1) If you _____ _____ early, please wake me up. (get up)

(2) I'm not sure if Katherine _____ _____ a tree tomorrow. (plant)

(3) Amy _____ _____ by a bee yesterday. (sting)

05 다음 문장을 두 가지 형태의 수동태로 쓰시오.

> Somebody gave the police the important evidence.

➡ _____

➡ _____

06 두 개의 문장을 연결하여 자연스러운 하나의 문장으로 만드시오.

> • You need money.
> • You want those pictures.
> • You are busy now.

> • You can have them.
> • I will call you later.
> • I will lend you some.

➡ _____

➡ _____

➡ _____

07 주어진 문장을 수동태로 쓰시오.

> Liszt's music really moved me.

➡ _____

08 괄호 안에 주어진 단어를 활용하여 빈칸 ⓐ~ⓒ에 알맞은 말을 쓰시오.

A: What will you do if it rains tomorrow?
B: If ⓐ_____ (rain) tomorrow, I ⓑ_____ (take) my umbrella.
A: Who bought you the umbrella?
B: The umbrella ⓒ_____ (be / me) by my dad.

09 주어진 단어를 어법에 맞도록 빈칸에 쓰시오.

invent / surround / divide / surprise / build

• The electric light bulb _____ by Thomas Edison in 1879.
• I didn't expect Jane to come to the meeting yesterday, but she was there. I _____ to see her.
• An island _____ by water.
• The class was too large last semester, so it _____ into two sections.
• If construction costs aren't high, they _____ a new dormitory.

10 주어진 단어를 활용하여 다음 우리말을 영어로 쓰시오.

• 불이 난다면, 화재경보기가 울릴 거야. (there / a fire / the alarm)
• 내가 너를 도와주길 원한다면, 도와줄게. (want / to / help)
• 내일 몸이 좋지 않으면, 집에 머물 거야. (feel well / stay at)

➡ _____
➡ _____
➡ _____

11 다음 상황을 읽고 주어진 단어를 어법에 맞게 쓰시오.

Next week Mina is going to Paris.
She has a friend, Jimmy, who lives in Paris, but Jimmy is also going away – to New York. So they won't see each other in Paris.
If Jimmy (arrive) in Paris next week, they (see) each other.

➡ _____

12 다음 우리말에 맞도록 빈칸에 알맞은 말을 쓰시오.

• _____ you hurry, you _____ the bus.
서두르지 않으면, 너는 버스를 놓칠 거야.
• If you win the prize, I _____.
네가 그 상을 탄다면, 나는 매우 놀랄 거야.
• If the museum _____ many people, I _____ to another museum.
내일 그 박물관이 많은 사람들로 붐빈다면, 나는 다른 박물관으로 갈 거야.

The Star of Stars

Do you have a favorite K-pop idol? Many students will answer, "Yes."

These students often show great love for their stars. Some scream
　　　　　　　빈도부사(일반 동사 앞에 위치)　　　　　　　　　　　어떤 학생들은(부정대명사)

madly at concerts. Others wait hours to take pictures of their stars.
　　　　　다른 어떤 학생들은(부정대명사)　　　to부정사의 부사적 용법(목적)

Some students even travel to another city to see their favorite stars.
　　　　　　심지어(부사)　　　　　　to부정사의 부사적 용법(목적)

Are idols a recent creation? No way! Did idols begin with The Beatles
　　　　　　　　　　　　　절대 아니다!

in the 1960's? They were loved by many, but they were not the first.
　1960년대의　 =The Beatles　수동태　 = many people

How about Elvis Presley in the 1950's? Not even close. To find the
How about+명사 ~?: ~는 어때?　　　　　　　Not 앞에 The answer is 생략

answer, let's take a time machine to a concert hall in Vienna in 1845.
　　　let's+동사원형: ~하자　　　　　　　　전치사 in: 도시이름, 연도 앞에 사용

All the seats are filled. Unlike other concerts, the side of the piano
All the +복수명사: 모든 ~

faces the audience. This way, the audience can see the handsome
~을 마주본다　　　　이렇게 함으로써

185cm pianist better. He doesn't have any sheet music with him. He
　piano에 접미사 -ist 붙인 직업 명사

begins to play from memory.
　　to부정사의 명사적 용법(begins의 목적어)

favorite 가장 좋아하는
answer 대답하다
often 종종
scream 괴성을 지르다
madly 미친 듯이, 마구
concert 콘서트
even 심지어
travel 여행하다
another 또 다른, 또 하나의
idol 우상
recent 최근의
first 첫 번째의; 최초의 인물
close 가까운
take ~을 타다
seat 좌석
unlike ~와 달리
audience 청중, 관객
sheet music 악보
from memory 기억을 더듬어

 확인문제

● 다음 문장이 본문의 내용과 일치하면 T, 일치하지 <u>않으면</u> F를 쓰시오.

1 Many students have their favorite idols. ☐

2 In order to see the concert, some students are willing to wait hours. ☐

3 There are some students who travel to another city to see their favorite idols. ☐

4 It is hard to say that idols were created recently. ☐

5 In 1845, audience could usually see the side of the piano at all concerts. ☐

He starts slowly by softly touching the keys. All the people hold
their breath because they don't want to miss a single note. He builds
up speed, and his long fingers press down on many keys at once. This
makes the music very powerful and rich.

The audience pays attention to his every little body movement. His
long beautiful hair flies everywhere. It's like watching a piano and
ballet performance at once. Time flies and the concert ends. People
scream and throw flowers and pieces of clothing onto the stage. The
concert hall goes wild!

Who was this amazing star? His name was Franz Liszt and he was
born in 1811 in Hungary. He first started playing the piano when he
was seven. Liszt later became a great pianist, composer and teacher.
But many people think of him as the first idol. Why don't you give his
music a listen? If you like today's idols, you will love the original idol.

---

hold one's breath 숨을 죽이다

note (음악) 음, 음표

build up 점점 높이다

key 건반

at once 한꺼번에, 동시에

powerful 강력한

pay attention to ~에 주의를 기울
이다

little 작은

movement 움직임

like ~와 같은

performance 공연

throw ~을 던지다

go wild 열광하다

amazing 놀라운

become ~이 되다

think of A as B A를 B라고 여기다

listen 듣다; 듣기

original 원래의, 본래의

📎 **확인문제**

● 다음 문장이 본문의 내용과 일치하면 T, 일치하지 않으면 F를 쓰시오.

1 The pianist starts to play the piano slowly. ☐

2 Pressing down on many keys at once makes the music powerful. ☐

3 The pianist has short beautiful hair. ☐

4 The audience is satisfied with the concert. ☐

5 Franz Liszt was a Hungarian pianist who was born in 1811. ☐

6 Liszt paid attention to only composing music later in life. ☐

● 우리말을 참고하여 빈칸에 알맞은 말을 쓰시오.

1 Do you have _____ _____ K-pop _____? Many students _____ _____, "Yes."

2 These students _____ _____ great love _____ their stars.

3 Some _____ _____ _____ concerts.

4 _____ wait _____ _____ _____ pictures of their stars.

5 Some students _____ _____ _____ another city _____ _____ their favorite stars.

6 Are idols _____ _____ _____ _____? No way!

7 _____ idols _____ _____ The Beatles in the 1960's?

8 They _____ _____ _____ many, but they were not _____ _____.

9 _____ _____ Elvis Presley _____ the 1950's? Not even close.

10 _____ _____ the answer, _____ _____ a time machine _____ a concert hall _____ Vienna _____ 1845.

11 All the seats _____ _____.

12 _____ other concerts, _____ _____ of the piano _____ the audience.

13 This way, the audience _____ _____ the handsome 185cm pianist _____.

14 He doesn't have _____ _____ _____ with him.

15 He begins _____ _____ _____ _____.

16 He starts slowly _____ _____ _____ _____ _____.

1 여러분은 가장 좋아하는 K팝 아이돌이 있는가? 많은 학생들이 "그렇다."라고 답할 것이다.

2 이 학생들은 종종 자신들의 스타를 향해 큰 애정을 보인다.

3 어떤 학생들은 콘서트에서 미친 듯이 괴성을 지른다.

4 어떤 학생들은 스타의 사진을 찍기 위해 몇 시간을 기다린다.

5 어떤 학생들은 심지어 가장 좋아하는 스타를 보기 위해 다른 도시로 여행을 가기까지 한다.

6 아이돌이 최근의 창조물일까? 아니다!

7 아이돌은 1960년대의 The Beatles부터 시작됐을까?

8 그들은 많은 사람들에게 사랑받았지만, 최초는 아니다.

9 1950년대의 Elvis Presley는 어떤가? 완전히 헛짚었다.

10 답을 찾기 위해서 1845년에 빈에 있는 한 콘서트홀로 타임머신을 타고 가 보자.

11 모든 좌석이 꽉 차 있다.

12 다른 연주회와는 달리 피아노의 옆면이 청중을 향해 있다.

13 이렇게 함으로써, 청중은 잘생긴 185cm의 피아니스트를 더 잘 볼 수 있다.

14 그는 어떠한 악보도 가지고 있지 않다.

15 그는 기억으로 연주하기 시작한다.

16 그는 건반을 부드럽게 누르면서 천천히 시작한다.

17 All the people _____ _____ _____ they don't want to miss _____ _____ _____.

18 He _____ _____ speed, and his long fingers _____ _____ _____ many keys _____ _____.

19 This _____ the music very _____ and _____.

20 The audience _____ _____ _____ his every little _____.

21 His _____ _____ _____ _____ everywhere.

22 It's _____ _____ a piano and ballet _____ _____ _____.

23 Time _____ and the concert _____.

24 People scream and _____ _____ and pieces of clothing _____ _____ _____.

25 The concert hall _____ _____!

26 Who was _____ _____ _____ _____?

27 His name _____ Franz Liszt and he _____ _____ _____ 1811 in Hungary.

28 He first started _____ _____ _____ _____ _____ he was seven.

29 Liszt _____ _____ a great pianist, _____ and _____.

30 But many people _____ _____ him _____ the first idol.

31 _____ _____ _____ _____ _____ his music a listen?

32 If you _____ today's idols, you _____ _____ the _____ idol.

17 모든 사람들이 단 하나의 음도 놓치고 싶지 않아서 숨을 죽인다.

18 그는 속도를 점점 올리고, 그의 긴 손가락으로 많은 건반을 한 꺼번에 누른다.

19 이것은 음악을 아주 힘 있고 풍성하게 만든다.

20 청중들은 그의 모든 작은 몸짓에 주의를 집중한다.

21 그의 길고 아름다운 머리카락이 사방에 날린다.

22 이것은 마치 피아노와 발레 공연을 동시에 보는 것 같다.

23 시간은 쏜살같이 흐르고 연주회가 끝난다.

24 사람들은 소리를 지르며 꽃과 옷을 무대로 던진다.

25 콘서트홀은 열광의 도가니가 된다!

26 이 놀라운 스타는 누구였을까?

27 그의 이름은 Franz Liszt였고 그는 1811년에 헝가리에서 태어났다.

28 그는 7살에 처음 피아노를 치기 시작했다.

29 Liszt는 나중에 훌륭한 피아니스트이며 작곡가이자 선생님이 되었다.

30 그러나 많은 사람들은 그를 첫 번째 아이돌이라고 생각한다.

31 그의 음악을 한번 들어보는 게 어떤가?

32 만약 당신이 요즘의 아이돌을 좋아한다면, 원래의 아이돌도 좋아할 것이다.

● 우리말을 참고하여 본문을 영작하시오.

1 여러분은 가장 좋아하는 K팝 아이돌이 있는가? 많은 학생들이 "그렇다."라고 답할 것이다.

➡ _____

2 이 학생들은 종종 자신들의 스타를 향해 큰 애정을 보인다.

➡ _____

3 어떤 학생들은 콘서트에서 미친 듯이 괴성을 지른다.

➡ _____

4 어떤 학생들은 스타의 사진을 찍기 위해 몇 시간을 기다린다.

➡ _____

5 어떤 학생들은 심지어 가장 좋아하는 스타를 보기 위해 다른 도시로 여행을 가기까지 한다.

➡ _____

6 아이돌이 최근의 창조물일까? 아니다!

➡ _____

7 아이돌은 1960년대의 The Beatles부터 시작됐을까?

➡ _____

8 그들은 많은 사람들에게 사랑받았지만, 최초는 아니다.

➡ _____

9 1950년대의 Elvis Presley는 어떤가? 완전히 헛짚었다.

➡ _____

10 답을 찾기 위해서 1845년에 빈에 있는 한 콘서트홀로 타임머신을 타고 가 보자.

➡ _____

11 모든 좌석이 꽉 차 있다.

➡ _____

12 다른 연주회와는 달리 피아노의 옆면이 청중을 향해 있다.

➡ _____

13 이렇게 함으로써, 청중은 잘생긴 185cm의 피아니스트를 더 잘 볼 수 있다.

➡ _____

14 그는 어떠한 악보도 가지고 있지 않다.

➡ _____

15 그는 기억으로 연주하기 시작한다.

➡ _____

16 그는 건반을 부드럽게 누르면서 천천히 시작한다.

➡ _____

17 모든 사람들이 단 하나의 음도 놓치고 싶지 않아서 숨을 죽인다.

➡ _____

18 그는 속도를 점점 올리고, 그의 긴 손가락으로 많은 건반을 한꺼번에 누른다.

➡ _____

19 이것은 음악을 아주 힘 있고 풍성하게 만든다.

➡ _____

20 청중들은 그의 모든 작은 몸짓에 주의를 집중한다.

➡ _____

21 그의 길고 아름다운 머리카락이 사방에 날린다.

➡ _____

22 이것은 마치 피아노와 발레 공연을 동시에 보는 것 같다.

➡ _____

23 시간은 쏜살같이 흐르고 연주회가 끝난다.

➡ _____

24 사람들은 소리를 지르며 꽃과 옷을 무대로 던진다.

➡ _____

25 콘서트홀은 열광의 도가니가 된다!

➡ _____

26 이 놀라운 스타는 누구였을까?

➡ _____

27 그의 이름은 Franz Liszt였고 그는 1811년에 헝가리에서 태어났다.

➡ _____

28 그는 7살에 처음 피아노를 치기 시작했다.

➡ _____

29 Liszt는 나중에 훌륭한 피아니스트이며 작곡가이자 선생님이 되었다.

➡ _____

30 그러나 많은 사람들은 그를 첫 번째 아이돌이라고 생각한다.

➡ _____

31 그의 음악을 한번 들어보는 게 어떤가?

➡ _____

32 만약 당신이 요즘의 아이돌을 좋아한다면, 원래의 아이돌도 좋아할 것이다.

➡ _____

[01~03] 다음 글을 읽고, 물음에 답하시오.

Do you have a favorite K-pop idol? Many students will answer, "Yes." These students often show great love for their stars. Some scream madly at concerts. Others wait hours to take pictures of their stars. Some students even travel to another city ⓐto see their favorite stars.

01 위 글의 내용과 일치하지 않는 것은?

① Many students have a favorite K-pop idol.

② The fans of K-pop idols show great love for their stars.

③ Some students go mad when they see K-pop idols.

④ Some students scream at concerts of their favorite stars.

⑤ There are students who wait hours to take pictures of their stars.

02 위 글의 밑줄 친 ⓐ와 쓰임이 같은 것은?

① She wants you to do your best.

② He bought a book to read on the train.

③ Mrs. Peterson went out to see what happened.

④ Sam forced me to do the work.

⑤ The tool enabled water to flow well.

 서답형

03 주어진 단어를 어법에 맞게 쓰시오.

If students (ask) whether they have a favorite K-pop idol, they (answer) "Yes."

➡ _____

[04~07] 다음 글을 읽고, 물음에 답하시오.

Are idols a recent creation? No way! Did idols begin with The Beatles in the 1960's? They _____ⓐ_____ many, but they were not the first. ⓑHow about Elvis Presley in the 1950's? Not even close. To find the answer, let's take a time machine to a concert hall in Vienna in 1845.

서답형

04 다음 주어진 동사를 이용하여 빈칸 ⓐ를 완성하시오.

(love)

➡ _____

05 위 글의 밑줄 친 ⓑ의 의미로 가장 적절한 것은?

① Did Elvis Presley like The Beatles in the 1950's?

② Did Elvis Presley begin with The Beetles?

③ Did idols begin with Elvis Presley?

④ Did idols want to be like Elvis Presley?

⑤ Was Elvis Presley the most popular singer in the 1950's?

06 위 글에 이어질 내용으로 가장 적절한 것은?

① the origin of a time machine

② a story about the first idol in the world

③ how to build a concert hall in 1845

④ the reason why idols are a recent creation

⑤ how popular the Beatles and Elvis Presley were

서답형

07 위 글의 내용에 맞게 다음 질문에 완전한 문장으로 답하시오.

> Q: Where does the writer want to go with a time machine?

➡ _____

_____

[08~11] 다음 글을 읽고, 물음에 답하시오.

To find the answer, let's take a time machine to a concert hall in Vienna ⓐ 1845.

All the seats are filled. ① This way, the audience can see the handsome 185cm pianist better. ② He doesn't have any sheet music with him. ⓑ그는 기억으로 연주하기 시작한다.

He starts slowly by softly touching the keys. ③ All the people hold their breath because they don't want to miss a single note. ④ He builds up speed, and his long fingers press down on many keys at once. ⑤ This makes the music very powerful and rich.

중요

08 주어진 문장이 들어가기에 가장 적절한 곳은?

> Unlike other concerts, the side of the piano faces the audience.

①　　　②　　　③　　　④　　　⑤

09 위 글의 빈칸 ⓐ에 들어갈 말로 적절한 것은?

① on　　　② by　　　③ in
④ until　　　⑤ to

서답형

10 주어진 단어를 활용하여 밑줄 친 우리말 ⓑ를 영어로 쓰시오.

> (begin / from)

➡ _____

11 위 글을 읽고 답할 수 없는 질문은?

① Where is the concert held?
② How tall is the pianist?
③ How does he start to play the piano?
④ What kind of answer does the writer want to find?
⑤ How does the pianist touch the piano keys?

[12~17] 다음 글을 읽고, 물음에 답하시오.

Are ⓐidols a recent creation? No way! Did idols begin with The Beatles in the 1960's? (A)Many people loved them, but they were not the first. How about Elvis Presley in the 1950's? Not even close. To find (B)the answer, let's take a time machine to a concert hall in Vienna in 1845.

(C)All the seats are taken. Unlike other concerts, the side of the piano faces ⓑthe audience. This way, the audience can see the handsome 185cm pianist better. He doesn't have any ⓒsheet music with him. He begins to play from memory.

He starts slowly by softly touching ⓓthe keys. All the people hold their ⓔbreath because they don't want to miss a single note. He builds up speed, and his long fingers press down on many keys at once. This makes the music very powerful and rich.

12 위 글의 밑줄 친 @~@의 영영풀이가 틀린 것은?

① @: people who are greatly admired or loved by many fans

② ⓑ: the group of people watching or listening to a concert

③ ⓒ: music that is printed on sheets of paper

④ ⓓ: specially shaped pieces of metal that you place in a lock

⑤ ⓔ: the air that you let out through your mouth

서답형

13 위 글의 밑줄 친 (A)를 수동태 문장으로 쓰시오.

➡ _____

14 위 글의 밑줄 친 (B)에 대한 질문으로 가장 적절한 것은?

① When was the first concert held?

② When did the first idol begin?

③ Who wants to be like The Beetles?

④ Who was the first pianist in the world?

⑤ Why weren't idols made recently?

서답형

15 다음 주어진 동사를 이용하여 밑줄 친 (C)와 같은 의미의 문장을 쓰시오.

(fill)

➡ _____

서답형

16 위 글의 내용에 맞도록 아래 질문에 답하시오.

Q: How is the concert different from others?

A: _____

➡ _____

17 위 글의 내용과 일치하지 않는 것은?

① 비틀즈는 1960년대에 활동하였다.

② 피아니스트는 악보 없이 연주했다.

③ 콘서트 연주는 처음부터 끝까지 부드럽게 이어졌다.

④ 청중들에게 피아니스트의 모습이 잘 보였다.

⑤ 청중들은 숨죽여 피아니스트의 연주를 감상하였다.

[18~22] 다음 글을 읽고, 물음에 답하시오.

All the seats are filled. Unlike other concerts, the side of the piano faces the audience. This way, the audience can see the handsome 185cm pianist better. ① He doesn't have any sheet music with him. He begins to play from memory. ②

He starts slowly by softly touching the keys. All the people hold their breath because they don't want to miss a single note. ③ This makes the music very powerful and rich.

The audience pays attention to his every little body movement. ④ His long beautiful hair flies everywhere. ⑤ It's like watching a piano and ballet performance at once. Time flies and the concert ends. People scream and throw flowers and pieces of clothing onto the stage. The concert hall goes _____ @ _____ !

18 주어진 문장이 들어가기에 가장 알맞은 곳은?

He builds up speed, and his long fingers press down on many keys at once.

①　　②　　③　　④　　⑤

중요

19 분위기로 미루어 보아 빈칸 @에 가장 적절한 것은?

① bad　　② wild　　③ blind

④ deaf　　⑤ angry

20 위 글에서 찾아볼 수 없는 것은?

① the concert hall filled with many people
② the handsome pianist playing from memory
③ the audience listening to the music with enthusiasm
④ the audience focusing on a ballet performance
⑤ the pianist who has long hair

21 위 글의 내용과 일치하지 않는 것은?

① The audience wants to hear every single note that the pianist plays.
② The keys are touched softly by the pianist at first.
③ The pianist doesn't have any sheet music.
④ The audience doesn't care about the body movement of the pianist.
⑤ People scream after the concert ends.

서답형
22 위 글의 내용에 맞도록 다음 빈칸에 알맞은 말을 쓰시오.

Flowers _____ onto the stage by people.

➡ _____

[23~24] 다음 글을 읽고, 물음에 답하시오.

Do you have a favorite K-pop idol? Many students will answer, "Yes." (A)These students often show great love for their stars. Some scream madly at concerts. Others wait hours to take pictures of their stars. Some students even travel to another city to see their favorite stars.

Are idols a recent creation? No way! Did idols begin with The Beatles in the 1960's? They were loved by many, but they were not the first. How about Elvis Presley in the 1950's? Not even close. To find the answer, (B)let's take a time machine to a concert hall in Vienna in 1845.

23 위 글의 밑줄 친 문장 (A)를 수동태로 쓰시오.

➡ _____

_____

24 위 글의 글쓴이가 밑줄 친 (B)와 같이 말한 이유로 가장 적절한 것은?

① to ask some questions about music
② to find the first concert in the world
③ to find out who the first idol is
④ to meet the famous K-pop idol
⑤ to see the concert of Franz Liszt

[01~02] 다음 글을 읽고, 물음에 답하시오.

Do you have a favorite K-pop idol? Many students will answer, "Yes." These students often show great love for their stars. (A)몇몇은 콘서트에서 미친 듯이 괴성을 지른다. Others wait hours to take pictures of their stars. Some students even travel to another city to see their favorite stars.

01 다음 단어를 활용하여 밑줄 친 우리말 (A)를 영어로 쓰시오.

| (scream / mad / concerts) |

➡ _____

02 다음 주어진 어구를 바르게 배열하여 빈칸에 알맞은 말을 쓰시오.

| Some students spend hours _____ _____ . (waiting / to take pictures of / their stars / for / them) |

➡ _____

[03~05] 다음 글을 읽고, 물음에 답하시오.

Are idols a recent creation? (A)No way! Did idols begin with The Beatles in the 1960's? They were loved by many, but they were not ⓐthe first. How about Elvis Presley in the 1950's? Not even close. To find the answer, (B)타임 머신을 타고 가보자 to a concert hall in Vienna in 1845.

03 주어진 단어를 활용하여 밑줄 친 (A)와 같은 의미의 문장을 쓰시오.

| Idols (not, create) recently. |

➡ _____

04 위 글의 밑줄 친 ⓐ를 구체적으로 쓰시오.

➡ _____

05 위 글의 밑줄 친 우리말 (B)를 영어로 쓰시오.

➡ _____

[06~10] 다음 글을 읽고, 물음에 답하시오.

To find the answer, let's take a time machine to a concert hall in Vienna in 1845.

All the seats are filled. Unlike other concerts, the side of the piano faces the audience. (A)This way, the audience can see the handsome 185cm pianist better. He doesn't have any sheet music with him. He begins to play from memory.

He starts slowly by softly touching the keys. All the people hold their breath because they don't want to miss a single note. He builds up speed, and his long fingers press down on many keys at once. (B)이것은 그 음악을 매우 힘있고 풍성하게 만든다.

06 위 글의 밑줄 친 (A)가 의미하는 것을 우리말로 쓰시오.

➡ _____

07 위 글의 내용에 맞도록 대화의 빈칸에 알맞은 말을 쓰시오.

A: Why are people holding their breath?
B: It's because ________________.

➡ ________________

08 How does the pianist play without any sheet music?

➡ ________________

중요
09 위 글의 밑줄 친 우리말 (B)를 영어로 쓰시오.

➡ ________________

10 위 글의 내용에 맞도록 다음 기사의 빈칸에 알맞은 말을 쓰시오.

The Star of Our Time
Yesterday Franz Liszt performed his piano concert very successfully in ________. This concert was ________ from others. The side of the piano ________ the audience. They could ________ Liszt better this way. He didn't have any sheet music and ________ from ________. His music was so ________ and rich. When the concert ended, the concert hall went wild.

[11~14] 다음 글을 읽고, 물음에 답하시오.

All the seats are filled. Unlike other concerts, the side of the piano faces the audience. This way, the audience can see the handsome 185cm pianist ⓐbetter. He doesn't have any sheet music with him. He begins ⓑto play from memory.

He starts slowly by softly ___(A)___ the keys. All the people hold their ⓒbreath because they don't want to miss a single note. He builds up speed, and his long fingers press down on many keys at once. This makes the music very powerful and rich.

The audience pays attention to his every little body ⓓmovements. His long beautiful hair flies everywhere. It's like ___(B)___ a piano and ballet performance at once. Time ⓔflies and the concert ends. People scream and throw flowers and pieces of clothing onto the stage. The concert hall ___(C)___ wild!

11 수동태를 사용하여 다음 물음에 완전한 문장으로 답하시오.

What is thrown onto the stage?

➡ ________________
____

12 위 글의 ⓐ~ⓔ 중에서 어법상 바르지 않은 것의 기호를 쓰고 바르게 고치시오.

➡ ________________

중요
13 주어진 단어를 어법에 맞게 빈칸 (A)~(C)에 쓰시오.

go / touch / watch

(A)________ (B)________ (C)________

14 위 글의 내용에 맞도록 다음 대화의 빈칸에 들어갈 말을 쓰시오.

A: Where is the concert held?
B: It ________________.
A: How does the music sound?
B: It ________________.

Real Life Talk - Step 2

A: Which singer do you like best?
= Who's your favorite singer?

B: I like John Lennon best.

A: Why do you like him?
John Lennon을 가리킨다.

B: Because he is a great singer.
Because+주어+동사

A: Which song do you like best?
= most

B: I like *Imagine* best. It cheers me up.

구문해설 • cheer up: 기운 나게 하다

A: 어느 가수를 가장 좋아하니?
B: 나는 John Lennon을 가장 좋아해.
A: 왜 그를 좋아해?
B: 왜냐하면 그는 훌륭한 가수이기 때문이야.
A: 너는 어느 곡을 가장 좋아하니?
B: 나는 Imagine을 가장 좋아해. 그것은 내게 힘을 북돋아 줘.

Think and Write

Dear Sandra,

Hello, my name is Jina and I'm a big fan of you. I watched all of your movies
당신의 열렬한 팬
and I love "Into the Sky" best. I think that your acting is so real. How do you
명사절 접속사 that
prepare for your roles? If I meet you in person, I will ask you many more
~를 준비하다   조건의 부사절에서 현재시제가 미래를 표현
questions. I hope to see you soon.
hope의 목적어

Love, Jina

구문해설 • a big fan: 열렬한 팬 • acting: 연기 • real: 진짜의 • prepare: 준비하다 • role: 배역
• in person: 직접 • soon: 곧

Sandra 씨에게.
안녕하세요. 제 이름은 Jina이고 저는 당신의 열렬한 팬이에요. 저는 당신이 출연한 모든 영화를 다 봤고요 "Into the Sky"를 가장 좋아해요. 저는 당신의 연기가 매우 진정성 있다고 생각해요. 당신이 맡은 역할을 어떻게 준비하나요? 제가 당신을 직접 만나게 된다면, 저는 당신에게 더 많은 질문을 할 거예요. 당신을 곧 만나길 바랍니다.
사랑을 담아. Jina

Read and Write

The Star of Our Time
시대
Yesterday Franz Liszt performed his piano concert very successfully in
범위가 넓은 장소 앞에서 쓰는 전치사
Vienna. This concert was different from others. The side of the piano faced the
~와는 달랐다   = other concerts
audience. They could see Liszt better this way. He didn't have any sheet music
well의 비교급
and played from memory. His music was so powerful and rich. When the
매우   ~할 때
concert ended, the concert hall went wild.

구문해설 • perform: 공연하다 • successfully: 성공적으로 • others: 다른 것들 • face: ~을 마주보다
• better: 더 잘 • go wild: 열광하다

우리 시대의 스타
어제 Franz Liszt가 Vienna에서 매우 성공적으로 피아노 연주회를 하였습니다. 이 콘서트는 다른 콘서트들과 달랐습니다. 피아노의 측면이 청중을 향해 있었습니다. 청중들은 이런 식으로 Liszt를 더 잘 볼 수 있었습니다. 그는 어떠한 악보도 가지고 있지 않았고 기억으로 연주했습니다. 그의 음악은 매우 힘 있고 풍성했습니다. 콘서트가 끝날 때. 콘서트홀은 열광의 도가니가 되었습니다.

Words & Expressions

01 다음 〈보기〉의 주어진 단어와 관계가 다른 것은?

> ┤ 보기 ├
> recent – recently

① mad – madly
② original – originally
③ definite – definitely
④ careful – carefully
⑤ friend – friendly

02 다음 영영풀이에 해당하는 단어를 쓰시오.

> your name as you usually write it, for example at the end of a letter

➡ _____

03 다음 중 밑줄 친 부분의 뜻풀이가 바르지 않은 것은?

① My parents are <u>madly</u> in love with each other. 열렬히
② <u>Unlike</u> his father, he is not good at sports. 싫어하다
③ I need the most <u>recent</u> information. 최신의
④ It's not my <u>original</u> plan to do. 본래의
⑤ One of the biggest mysteries is about the <u>creation</u> of life. 창조

04 다음 문장의 빈칸에 들어갈 말을 〈보기〉에서 골라 쓰시오. (필요하면 어형을 바꿀 것)

> ┤ 보기 ├
> sheet music / go wild / in person

(1) Only ten pieces of _____ _____ existed.
(2) When the singer came on the stage, the fans _____ _____.
(3) You need to bring your letter _____ _____.

05 다음 주어진 문장의 밑줄 친 단어와 같은 의미로 쓰인 것은?

> They don't want to <u>miss</u> a single note.

① He completely <u>missed</u> the joke.
② I don't know why she didn't <u>miss</u> her mother so much.
③ What did you <u>miss</u> most when you were in Canada?
④ He must have <u>missed</u> a chance to go abroad.
⑤ After my English teacher left, many students <u>missed</u> her.

06 다음 대화의 밑줄 친 우리말을 영어로 쓰시오. (4 단어)

> A: Which song do you like best?
> B: I like *Imagine* best.
> <u>그것은 내게 힘을 북돋아 줘.</u>

➡ _____

Conversation

07 다음 대화의 밑줄 친 우리말을 영어로 쓰시오.

> Jack: 너는 어느 책을 가장 좋아하니?
> Sumin: I like *Charlotte's Web* best.

➡ _____

[08~09] 다음 대화를 읽고, 물음에 답하시오.

> Amy: Jiho, what are you going to do this Saturday?
> Jiho: I'm going to Blue Sky's fan meeting with my friends. (A)
> Amy: Wow, I'm also a big fan of the band. (B)
> Jiho: Really? Which member do you like best, Amy? (C)
> Amy: I like Lucy best. She sings really well. (D)
> Jiho: I like the drummer, Mike, best. He's fantastic! (E)
> Amy: Sure, I'd love to. I can't wait!

08 위 대화의 (A)~(E) 중 주어진 문장이 들어가기에 적절한 곳은?

> Do you want to join us?

① (A) ② (B) ③ (C) ④ (D) ⑤ (E)

09 Which instrument does Mike play in Blue Sky band?

➡ _____

[10~11] 다음 대화를 읽고, 물음에 답하시오.

> B: Why do you have all those old clothes?
> G: I'm going to sell them at the ___(A)___ .
> B: Really? I have some old clothes, too.
> G: Then why don't you join me this Saturday?
> B: Okay.

10 위 대화의 빈칸 (A)에 '벼룩시장'을 의미하는 말을 영어로 쓰시오.

➡ _____

11 What are they going to do this Saturday together?

➡ _____

[12~13] 다음 대화를 읽고, 물음에 답하시오.

> Mina: Good afternoon, friends. I'm Mina with the school radio show. Today Mr. Smith, our English teacher, is here with us. Hi, Mr. Smith.
> Mr. Smith: Hello, everyone. I'm happy to be here with you.
> Mina: Let's talk about music. Mr. Smith, what's your favorite band?
> Mr. Smith: Definitely The Beatles.
> Mina: Oh, I like them, too. Which song do you like best?
> Mr. Smith: I like most of their songs, but I like *Hey Jude* best.
> Mina: Why do you like it?
> Mr. Smith: Because the song makes me feel better when I'm (A)down.
> Mina: That's great! Let's listen to the song.

12 위 대화의 밑줄 친 (A)와 바꾸어 쓸 수 없는 것은?

① depressed   ② gloomy
③ satisfied   ④ discouraged
⑤ blue

13 위 대화의 내용과 일치하지 않는 것은?

① Mr. Smith is a guest on the school radio show.
② Mr. Smith likes The Beatles best.
③ Mina likes most of The Beatles' songs.
④ They are going to listen to *Hey Jude*.
⑤ *Hey Jude* makes Mr. Smith feel better when he feels down.

Grammar

14 다음 빈칸에 들어갈 말로 알맞지 <u>않은</u> 것을 <u>모두</u> 고르시오.

_____ you come back, I won't leave here.

① Unless   ② If   ③ That
④ Until   ⑤ For

15 다음 중 어법상 옳지 <u>않은</u> 것은?

① If you like today's idols, you will love the original idol.
② My camera was disappeared from my classroom.
③ Her father has been told about the work for three hours.
④ The music is played by the most famous pianist.
⑤ I will be a doctor when I grow up.

16 다음 문장의 빈칸에 들어갈 말로 가장 적절한 것은?

_____ late this evening, I won't wait for you.

① Because you were ② If you are
③ If you will be   ④ When you will be
⑤ Though you are

17 다음 주어진 동사를 어법에 맞게 쓰시오.

We (play) football yesterday. The match (cancel).

➡ _____

18 다음 중 수동태로의 전환이 바르지 <u>않은</u> 것은?

① A loud noise woke us up.
   → We were woken up by a loud noise.
② How do people learn languages?
   → How are languages learned by people?
③ Somebody recorded our conversation.
   → Our conversation is recorded by somebody.
④ We must do something before it's too late.
   → Something must be done before it's too late.
⑤ I will give you plenty of time to decide.
   → You will be given plenty of time to decide.

19 다음 우리말을 영어로 바르게 옮긴 것은?

내 차가 고장 나면, 나는 그것을 수리할 거야.

① If my car broke, I repair it.
② If my car was broken, I will repair it.
③ If my car will be broken, I will repair it.
④ If my car is broken, I will repair it.
⑤ If my car break, I will repair it.

20 다음 문장에서 어법상 옳지 <u>않은</u> 것은?

Nothing ①has been said ②about the incident ③since it ④was happened ⑤last year.

①   ②   ③   ④   ⑤

21 다음 문장과 같은 의미의 문장을 주어진 어구를 주어로 하여 쓰시오.

> If you take care of your sister, I will be really relieved.
> = If your sister _____, I will be really relieved.

➡ _____

22 다음 중 밑줄 친 부분의 쓰임이 다른 하나는?

① If it is sunny tomorrow, will you go out with me?
② I will go there if you let me go there.
③ I wonder if he is going to join us.
④ You will look good if you wear glasses.
⑤ If you solve this problem, I will admit that you are a genius.

23 다음 우리말을 영어로 잘못 옮긴 것은?

① 그가 너에게 그 사진을 보여주었니?
  → Was the picture shown to you by him?
② 내일 널 만나면, 그걸 줄게.
  → If I see you tomorrow, I will give it to you.
③ 그녀가 그에게 시계 하나를 사 줬어.
  → A watch was bought for him by her.
④ BTS는 아이돌 그룹으로 알려져 있다.
  → BTS is known to an idol group.
⑤ 그는 나로부터 몇 가지 질문을 받았다.
  → He was asked some questions by me.

24 다음 문장을 수동태로 전환하시오.

> My mom didn't allow me to go to the park alone.

➡ _____

Reading

[25~27] 다음 글을 읽고, 물음에 답하시오.

Do you have a favorite K-pop idol? Many students will answer, "Yes." These students often show great love for their stars. Some scream madly at concerts. __(A)__ wait hours to take pictures of their stars. Some students ⓐeven travel to __(B)__ city to see their favorite stars.

25 위 글의 내용과 일치하지 않는 것은?

① 많은 학생들이 K-pop 아이돌을 좋아한다.
② 스타를 향한 사랑을 표현하는 방법이 학생들마다 다양하다.
③ 어떤 학생은 콘서트에서 스타를 향해 비명을 지르기도 한다.
④ 콘서트에 입장하기 위해 몇 시간을 기다리는 학생들도 있다.
⑤ 어떤 학생들은 스타를 보기 위해 다른 도시로 여행을 한다.

26 위 글의 밑줄 친 ⓐ와 의미가 같은 것은?

① You need an even surface to work on.
② She spoke in a steady, even voice.
③ You know even less about it than I do.
④ It is unattractive and even ugly.
⑤ That was an even decision.

27 위 글의 빈칸 (A)와 (B)에 들어갈 말로 바르게 짝지어진 것은?

① Some – other
② Another – another
③ Others – the other
④ Others – other
⑤ Others – another

[28~29] 다음 글을 읽고, 물음에 답하시오.

Are idols a recent creation? No way! Did idols begin with The Beatles in the 1960's? They were loved by many, but they were not the first. How about Elvis Presley in the 1950's? Not even close. ⓐTo find the answer, let's take a time machine to a concert hall in Vienna in 1845.

28 위 글의 내용과 일치하는 것은?

① Idols were made lately.
② The Beatles were the first idol in the world.
③ Many people loved The Beatles.
④ Elvis Presley liked The Beatles.
⑤ Idols in the 1960's were very popular.

[30~32] 다음 글을 읽고, 물음에 답하시오.

All the seats are filled. Unlike other concerts, the side of the piano faces the audience. This way, the audience can see the handsome 185cm pianist better. He doesn't have any sheet music with him. He begins to play from memory.

He starts slowly by softly touching the keys. All the people hold their breath because they don't want to miss a single note. He builds up speed, and his long fingers press down on many keys at once. ⓐThis makes the music very powerful and rich.

The audience pays attention to his every little body movement. His long beautiful hair flies everywhere. It's like watching a piano and ballet performance ___ⓑ___ . Time flies and the concert ends. People scream and throw flowers and pieces of clothing onto the stage. The concert hall goes wild!

30 위 글의 밑줄 친 ⓐ가 의미하는 것을 우리말로 쓰시오.

➡ _____

31 위 글의 빈칸 ⓑ에 들어갈 알맞은 말을 위 글에서 찾아 쓰시오.

➡ _____

29 위 글의 밑줄 친 ⓐ와 쓰임이 같은 것은?

① There are many problems to solve.
② He studied hard to become a great teacher.
③ Jason hoped to meet her again.
④ She allowed me to go out with him.
⑤ Karen tried to help her friends.

32 위 글을 읽고 답할 수 없는 질문은?

① How is the concert different from others?
② How tall is the pianist?
③ How does the pianist start to play?
④ How does the pianist move his body?
⑤ Why do people scream?

출제율 95%

01 다음 문장의 빈칸에 공통으로 들어갈 말로 적절한 것은?

> • The government is going to _____ the same risk.
> • There are no eyebrows on the _____ of *Mona Lisa*.
> • Why the long _____?

① miss   ② scream   ③ face
④ breath   ⑤ note

출제율 90%

02 다음 대화의 밑줄 친 부분을 주어진 단어를 이용하여 다시 쓰시오.

> **A:** Which sport do you like?
> **B:** I like tennis very much. (fond, very)

➡ _____

출제율 90%

03 다음 문장의 빈칸에 들어갈 말을 〈보기〉에서 골라 쓰시오.

> ┌─ 보기 ─┐
> paper folding / at once / pay attention to / from memory

(1) You should _____ the teacher in class.
(2) I learned how to make a paper flower in _____ class.
(3) He began to play _____ on the stage.

출제율 90%

04 다음 우리말을 주어진 단어를 활용하여 영어로 쓰시오.

(1) 나는 벼룩시장에서 그 신발을 샀다. (flea)
➡ _____

(2) 마지막 주자는 속도를 높이기 시작했다. (build, runner)
➡ _____

(3) 운전자는 브레이크를 밟았다. (pressed, brake, on)
➡ _____

[05~06] 다음 대화를 읽고, 물음에 답하시오.

> **Mina:** Good afternoon, friends. I'm Mina with the school radio show. Today Mr. Smith, our English teacher, is here with us. Hi, Mr. Smith. (A)
> **Mr. Smith:** Hello, everyone. I'm happy to be here with you. (B)
> **Mina:** Let's talk about music. Mr. Smith, what's your favorite band?
> **Mr. Smith:** Definitely The Beatles. (C)
> **Mina:** Oh, I like them, too. (D)
> **Mr. Smith:** I like most of their songs, but I like *Hey Jude* best. (E)
> **Mina:** Why do you like it?
> **Mr. Smith:** Because the song makes me feel better when I'm down.
> **Mina:** That's great! _____ ⓐ _____

출제율 100%

05 위 대화의 (A)~(E) 중 주어진 문장이 들어가기에 가장 적절한 곳은?

> Which song do you like best?

① (A)   ② (B)   ③ (C)   ④ (D)   ⑤ (E)

출제율 85%

06 위 대화의 빈칸 ⓐ에 들어갈 말로 나머지와 의미가 다른 것은?

① Let's listen to the song.
② How about listening to the song?
③ Why don't we listen to the song?
④ What about listening to the song?
⑤ Why did you listen to the song?

07 다음 대화의 밑줄 친 우리말 (A)를 주어진 단어를 이용하여 영어로 쓰시오.

> A: (A)너는 어떤 과일을 가장 좋아하니? (best, which)
>
> B: I like apples best.

➡ _____

08 다음 대화가 자연스럽게 이어지도록 순서대로 배열하시오.

> (A) I like Lucy best. She sings really well.
> (B) Wow, I'm also a big fan of the band.
> (C) What are you going to do this Saturday?
> (D) Really? Which member do you like best, Amy?
> (E) I'm going to Blue Sky's fan meeting with my friends.

➡ _____

[09~10] Read the dialogue and answer the questions.

> Jack: Hi, Sumin. How's the book club going?
> Sumin: It's fun. I read lots of interesting books.
> Jack: Which book do you like best?
> Sumin: I like *Charlotte's Web* best.

09 What did Sumin think about her book club?

➡ _____

10 What is Sumin's favorite book?

➡ _____

11 다음 중 어법상 바른 것은?

① The house was painted by he.
② By whom did the bridge constructed?
③ The project can't be finished on time.
④ Karen is locking up in the room.
⑤ My decision will not change by anything.

12 주어진 단어를 어법에 맞게 각각 쓰시오.

> (disappoint)
> If you give up, you _____ me.
> = If you give up, I _____ you.

➡ _____

13 다음 중 어법상 바르지 않은 것은?

> We ①are scheduled ②to go on ③a field trip. But if it ④will rain on the day, we ⑤will change the plan.

①   ②   ③   ④   ⑤

14 주어진 단어를 활용하여 다음 우리말을 영어로 쓰시오.

> 눈이 오면 도로가 폐쇄될 거야. (close)

➡ _____

15 다음 중 어법상 바른 문장의 개수는? 출제율 90%

ⓐ Emma can't close the window. It is stuck.
ⓑ Could you give me directions? I lost.
ⓒ I will fix your bike if I have a screwdriver.
ⓓ I love my wife. I am married a wonderful woman.
ⓔ King Sejong was born in 1397.

① 1개   ② 2개   ③ 3개
④ 4개   ⑤ 5개

16 다음 중 밑줄 친 부분이 어법상 옳은 것은? 출제율 95%

① Tim was made <u>clean</u> the window.
② I <u>called</u> Puppy by my dad.
③ <u>Did</u> the lights turned off?
④ Is the book <u>borrowed</u> from the library?
⑤ If they <u>will throw</u> a party, will you go there?

17 주어진 단어를 이용하여 다음 빈칸에 알맞은 말을 쓰시오. 출제율 90%

block / call

A: The water won't go down the drain. The drain _____ with food.
B: Don't worry. I _____ a plumber.

[18~20] 다음 글을 읽고, 물음에 답하시오.

To find the answer, let's take a time machine to a concert hall in Vienna in 1845.

All the seats are filled. ⓐ<u>Unlike</u> other concerts, the side of the piano faces the audience. This way, the audience can see the handsome 185cm pianist better. He doesn't have any sheet music with him. He begins to play ⓑ<u>from memory</u>.

He starts slowly by softly touching the keys. All the people ⓒ<u>hold</u> their breath because they ⓓ<u>want</u> to miss a single note. He ⓔ<u>builds up</u> speed, and his long fingers press down on many keys at once. This (A)<u>makes</u> the music very powerful and rich.

18 위 글의 ⓐ~ⓔ 중 글의 흐름상 어색한 것은? 출제율 100%

① ⓐ   ② ⓑ   ③ ⓒ   ④ ⓓ   ⑤ ⓔ

19 위 글의 내용과 일치하지 않는 것은? 출제율 90%

① The concert is held in Vienna.
② The pianist is tall and handsome.
③ The pianist memorizes what he has to play.
④ The pianist starts to play fast.
⑤ The performance is getting faster.

20 위 글의 밑줄 친 (A)와 쓰임이 같은 것은? 출제율 95%

① He <u>made</u> it by himself.
② The computer <u>makes</u> our work easy.
③ She <u>makes</u> me delicious cookies all the time.
④ My mom <u>makes</u> her own clothes.
⑤ I wanted to <u>make</u> a good impression on you.

[21~24] 다음 글을 읽고, 물음에 답하시오.

All the seats ⓐ<u>are filled</u>. Unlike other concerts, the side of the piano faces the audience. This way, the audience can see the handsome 185cm pianist better. He doesn't have ⓑ<u>any</u> sheet music with him. He begins to play from memory.

He starts ⓒ<u>slowly</u> by softly touching the keys. All the people hold their ⓓ<u>breathe</u> because they don't want to miss a single note. He ⓔ<u>builds up</u> speed, and his long fingers press down on many keys at once. This makes the music very powerful and rich.

(A)청중들은 그의 모든 작은 몸짓에 주의를 집중한다. His long beautiful hair flies everywhere. It's like watching a piano and ballet performance at once. Time flies and the concert ends. People scream and throw flowers and pieces of clothing onto the stage. The concert hall goes wild!

21 위 글의 밑줄 친 ⓐ~ⓔ 중 바르지 <u>않은</u> 것은?

① ⓐ ② ⓑ ③ ⓒ ④ ⓓ ⑤ ⓔ

22 주어진 단어를 써서 밑줄 친 우리말 (A)를 영어로 쓰시오.

pay, every, little, movement

➡ _____

_____

23 다음을 읽고 해당하는 단어를 위 글에서 찾아 쓰시오.

This word is used when someone entertains an audience by doing something such as singing, dancing, or playing a musical instrument.

➡ _____

24 위 글의 내용과 일치하는 것은?

① The side of the piano usually faces the audience in the concerts.
② The pianist tries hard to see the sheet music.
③ The pianist presses lots of keys at one time.
④ The audience feels bored with the concerts.
⑤ The concert shows a piano performance with a ballet show.

25 다음 밑줄 친 (A)를 주어진 말로 시작하여 문장을 완성하시오.

The Star of Our Time

Yesterday Franz Liszt performed his piano concert very successfully in Vienna. (A)<u>This concert was different from others.</u> The side of the piano faced the audience. They could see Liszt better this way. He didn't have any sheet music and played from memory. His music was so powerful and rich. When the concert ended, the concert hall went wild.

(A) Unlike _____

_____.

[01~03] 다음 대화를 읽고, 물음에 답하시오.

Mina: Good afternoon, friends. I'm Mina with the school radio show. Today Mr. Smith, our English teacher, is here with us. Hi, Mr. Smith.

Mr. Smith: Hello, everyone. I'm happy to be here with you.

Mina: Let's talk about music. Mr. Smith, what's your favorite band?

Mr. Smith: _____(A)_____ The Beatles.

Mina: Oh, I like them, too. (B)어느 노래를 가장 좋아하시나요? (which)

Mr. Smith: I like most of their songs, but I like *Hey Jude* best.

Mina: Why do you like it?

Mr. Smith: Because the song makes me feel better when I'm down.

Mina: That's great! Let's listen to the song.

01 위 대화의 빈칸 (A)에 다음 영영풀이에 해당하는 단어를 쓰시오. (D로 시작할 것)

a way of emphasizing that something is true and that there is no doubt about it

➡ _____

02 Which song are they going to listen to together?

➡ _____

03 위 대화의 우리말 (B)를 주어진 단어를 사용하여 영어로 쓰시오.

➡ _____

04 다음 문장을 수동태로 각각 쓰시오.

• She made some mistakes.
• My friend made me lots of cookies.
• Jason always makes me laugh.

➡ _____
_____
_____

05 다음 괄호 안에 주어진 동사를 어법에 맞게 쓰시오.

A: I think I left my textbook at your house. Have you seen it?
B: No, but if I (find) it, I (tell) you.

➡ _____

06 괄호 안에 주어진 어휘를 이용하여 어법에 맞게 쓰시오.

A: Do you have time to go to a movie?
B: I don't know yet if there will be homework to do. If I (not / have / any homework / do), I (go / to) with you.

➡ _____

07 다음 우리말 뜻에 맞도록 주어진 단어를 이용하여 빈칸을 채우시오.

• If _____, _____ a n apple pie this afternoon. (enough, bake) (내가 충분한 사과를 가지고 있다면 나는 오늘 오후에 사과파이를 구을 거야.)
• Vietnam _____ in Southeast Asia. (locate) (베트남은 동남아시아에 위치해 있다.)

08 다음 두 문장이 같은 의미가 되도록 빈칸에 알맞은 말을 쓰시오.

> The teacher didn't write the letters on the table.
> = The letters on the table _____ the teacher.

➡ _____

10 위 글의 밑줄 친 문장 (B)를 수동태로 전환하시오.

➡ _____

11 위 글의 밑줄 친 문장 (C)에서 어법상 바르지 않은 것을 바르게 고치시오.

_____ ➡ _____

[09~11] 다음 글을 읽고, 물음에 답하시오.

The audience pays attention to his every little body movement. His long beautiful hair flies everywhere. (A)이것은 마치 피아노와 발레 공연을 동시에 보는 것 같다. Time flies and the concert ends. People scream and throw flowers and pieces of clothing onto the stage. The concert hall goes wild!

Who was this amazing star? His name was Franz Liszt and he was born in 1811 in Hungary. He first started playing the piano when he was seven. Liszt later became a great pianist, composer and teacher. But (B) many people think of him as the first idol. Why don't you give his music a listen? (C)If you will like today's idols, you will love the original idol.

[12~13] 다음 글을 읽고, 물음에 답하시오.

The Star of Our Time

Yesterday Franz Liszt performed his piano concert very successfully in Vienna. This concert was different from ⓐothers. The side of the piano faced the audience. ⓑThey could see Liszt better this way. He didn't have any sheet music and played from memory. His music was so powerful and rich. When the concert ended, the concert hall went wild.

12 위 글의 밑줄 친 ⓐ를 두 개의 단어로 쓰시오.

➡ _____

09 위 글의 주어진 단어를 활용하여 밑줄 친 우리말 (A)를 영어로 쓰시오.

> (like / performance)

➡ _____

13 다음은 밑줄 친 ⓑ와 같은 의미의 문장이다. 빈칸을 알맞게 채우시오.

> This way, Liszt could _____.

➡ _____

01 다음 대화의 내용과 일치하도록 Tom의 어머니의 담화에 있는 빈칸을 알맞은 말로 채우시오.

> **Sujin:** Tom, why do you have so many paper flowers?
>
> **Tom:** They're for my mom's birthday.
>
> **Sujin:** They're so beautiful. Where did you get them?
>
> **Tom:** I made them.
>
> **Sujin:** Wow, you're really good.
>
> **Tom:** Thanks. I'm taking a paper folding class these days.
>
> **Sujin:** They are going to be the perfect gift for your mom.
>
> **Tom:** I hope so, too.

> Tom's mother:
>
> Today, I was so happy when I got Tom's present. He made (1)_____ for me.
> It looked so (2)_____. These days he was taking (3)_____. He
> seemed to learn (4)_____ to make them in that class. I was proud of him so much.

02 다음 주어진 동사를 이용하여 수동태 문장을 만드시오.

> ┌ 보기 ┐
>
> bake   read   draw   pass   make

(1) _____

(2) _____

(3) _____

(4) _____

(5) _____

03 다음 단어를 이용하여 〈보기〉와 같이 내일 계획을 써 보시오.

> ┌ 보기 ┐
>
> sunny   windy   rain   hot
>
> ➡ If it is cloudy tomorrow, I will cancel my appointment.

(1) _____

(2) _____

(3) _____

(4) _____

단원별 모의고사

01 다음 대화의 밑줄 친 우리말을 영어로 쓰시오.

> A: 너는 어느 나라를 방문하고 싶니?
> B: I want to visit China because I want to see the Great Wall of China.

➡ _____

02 다음 우리말을 주어진 단어를 배열하여 문장을 완성하시오.

(1) 어느 소설이 가장 인기가 있나요?
(popular / novel / is / the / most / which)

➡ _____

(2) 어떻게 당신의 역할을 준비하였나요?
(you / did / prepare / role / your / how / for)

➡ _____

(3) 왜 세종대왕은 한글을 창조하셨나요?
(Hangeul / why / King Sejong / did / invent)

➡ _____

03 다음 문장의 빈칸에 들어갈 말을 〈보기〉에서 골라 쓰시오. (필요하면 어형을 바꿀 것)

> ┤ 보기 ├
> throw / performance / invent / face

(1) The students were _____ with difficult problems.
(2) I enjoyed ballet _____, *The Nutcracker*.
(3) Don't _____ stones at the animals.
(4) Who _____ the first bicycle?

04 다음 대화의 빈칸 (A)와 (B)에 들어갈 말이 바르게 짝지어진 것은?

> A: (A)_____ country do you want to visit for your dream vacation?
> B: I want to visit Canada.
> A: (B)_____ do you want to visit Canada?
> B: Because I want to see Niagara Falls.

	(A)	(B)
①	Which	When
②	Which	Why
③	Where	Why
④	Where	Which
⑤	Why	Which

05 주어진 문장에 이어지는 대화가 자연스럽게 이어지도록 순서대로 배열하시오.

> Which singer do you like best?
> (A) I like *Imagine* best. It cheers me up.
> (B) Why do you like him?
> (C) Which song do you like best?
> (D) I like John Lennon best.
> (E) Because he is a great singer.

➡ _____

06 다음 〈보기〉의 주어진 단어를 모두 배열하여 빈칸을 완성하시오.

> A: _____
> B: Because I want to see Niagara Falls.

> ┤ 보기 ├
> visit / do / why / to / Canada / you / want

➡ _____

[07~08] 다음 대화를 읽고, 물음에 답하시오.

> Sujin: Tom, why do you have ⓐso many paper flowers?
> Tom: They're ⓑfor my mom's birthday.
> Sujin: They're so beautiful. Where did you get them?
> Tom: I made them.
> Sujin: Wow, you're really ⓒgood.
> Tom: Thanks. I'm taking a paper folding class ⓓthose days.
> Sujin: They are going to be the perfect (A)gift for your mom.
> Tom: I hope ⓔso, too.

07 위 대화의 밑줄 친 ⓐ~ⓔ 중 어색한 것을 골라 바르게 고치시오.

➡ _____

08 위 대화의 밑줄 친 (A)와 의미가 <u>다른</u> 것은?

① I was given a special <u>gift</u> at the event.
② My sister was wrapping a <u>gift</u> in her room.
③ She has a great <u>gift</u> for art.
④ A small <u>gift</u> moved his heart.
⑤ His baseball was the best <u>gift</u> for me.

[09~10] 다음 대화를 읽고, 물음에 답하시오.

Amy: Jiho, what are you going to do this Saturday?
Jiho: I'm going to Blue Sky's fan meeting with my friends.
Amy: Wow, I'm also a big fan of the band.
Jiho: Really? (A)너는 어느 멤버를 가장 좋아하니? (like, which)
Amy: I like Lucy best. She sings really well.
Jiho: I like the drummer, Mike, best. He's fantastic! Do you want to join us?
Amy: Sure, I'd love to. I can't wait!

09 위 대화의 밑줄 친 (A)의 우리말을 주어진 단어를 사용하여 영어로 쓰시오.

➡ _____

10 위 대화의 내용과 일치하지 <u>않는</u> 것은?

① Lucy and Mike are the members of Blue Sky.
② Jiho is planning to go to Blue Sky's fan meeting.
③ Amy's favorite member is Lucy.
④ Mike is the drummer of Blue Sky.
⑤ Amy cannot go with Jiho this Saturday.

11 다음 대화가 자연스럽게 이어지도록 순서대로 배열하시오.

(A) Okay.
(B) Why do you have all those old clothes?
(C) Really? I have some old clothes, too.
(D) I'm going to sell them at the flea market.
(E) Then why don't you join me this Saturday?

➡ _____

[12~13] 다음 대화를 읽고, 물음에 답하시오.

Jack: Hi, Sumin. How's the book club going?
Sumin: It's fun. I read lots of (A)_____ books.
Jack: (B)Which book do you like best?
Sumin: I like *Charlotte's Web* best.

12 위 대화의 빈칸 (A)에 들어갈 말로 어색한 것은?

① useful   ② impressive
③ fascinating   ④ boring
⑤ interesting

13 위 대화의 밑줄 친 (B)와 바꾸어 쓸 수 있는 것은?

① What is your favorite book?
② Why do you like that book?
③ What kind of book do you like?
④ Why don't you read the book?
⑤ Do you like reading books?

14 다음 중 어법상 바르지 <u>않은</u> 것은?

① The blouse is made of cotton.
② We can leave now because the class has just ended.
③ By whom was the door shut?
④ The keys to the house is lost.
⑤ If you are done with your work, you can go out.

15 다음 주어진 단어를 이용하여 대화를 문맥에 맞게 완성하시오.

> back / pay

> A: I don't have enough money to buy the ear phone. If _____ _____ _____ ten dollars, _____ _____ _____ you _____ tomorrow.
>
> B: Sure. I can lend you more than that.

➡ _____, _____, _____

16 다음 중 빈칸에 들어갈 말이 다른 하나는?

① Every little movement is paid attention _____ by the audience.
② Jane is married _____ Jack.
③ The star's life is exposed _____ all the people.
④ My grandparents are accustomed _____ reading books with glasses.
⑤ Water is composed _____ oxygen and hydrogen.

17 두 문장이 같은 의미가 되도록 빈칸에 알맞은 말을 쓰시오.

> We saw the car stop.
> = The car _____.

➡ _____

18 다음 중 문장 전환이 올바르지 <u>않은</u> 것은?

① He laughed at me.
　→ I was laughed at by him.
② John could see Jane in the mirror.
　→ Jane could be seen in the mirror by John.
③ Jina gave Tom some good advice about studying English.
　→ Tom was given to some good advice about studying English.
④ If you have a problem, we will discuss it later.
　→ If you have a problem, it will be discussed later by us.
⑤ They let me enter the church.
　→ I was allowed to enter the church.

[19~21] 다음 글을 읽고, 물음에 답하시오.

Are idols a recent creation? ⓐNo way! Did idols begin with The Beatles in the 1960's? They were loved by many, but they were not the first. How about Elvis Presley in the 1950's? Not even close. ⓑTo find the answer, ⓒlet's take a time machine to a concert hall in Vienna in 1845.

ⓓAll the seats are filled. ① Unlike other concerts, the side of the piano faces the audience. ② He doesn't have any sheet music with him. He begins to play from memory. ③ He starts slowly by softly touching the keys. ④ All the people hold their breath because they don't want to miss a single note. ⑤ He builds up speed, and his long fingers press down on many keys ⓔat once. This makes the music very powerful and rich.

19 주어진 문장이 들어가기에 가장 적절한 곳은?

> This way, the audience can see the handsome 185cm pianist better.

①　　　②　　　③　　　④　　　⑤

20 ⓐ~ⓔ에 관한 설명으로 바르지 <u>않은</u> 것은?

① ⓐ: 'Not at all!'로 바꾸어 쓸 수 있다.

② ⓑ: 'In order to find'의 의미로 쓰였다.

③ ⓒ: 'shall we take a time machine to a concert hall in Vienna in 1845?'와 같은 의미이다.

④ ⓓ: 'All the seats are filled with the audience.'로 바꾸어 쓸 수 있다.

⑤ ⓔ: 'one at a time'과 같은 의미이다.

21 위 글을 참고하여 대화의 빈칸에 알맞은 말을 쓰시오.

> A: I don't want to miss a single note of his play. What should I do?
> B: If _____.

➡ _____

[22~25] 다음 글을 읽고, 물음에 답하시오.

The audience ⓐpay attention to his every little body movement. His long beautiful hair flies everywhere. It's like watching a piano and ballet performance ⓑonce. Time ⓒis flown and the concert ends. People scream and throw flowers and pieces of clothing onto the stage. The concert hall goes wild!

Who was this ⓓamazed star? His name was Franz Liszt and he was born in 1811 in Hungary. He first started playing the piano when he was seven. Liszt later became a great pianist, composer and teacher. But many people think of him ⓔto be the first idol. (A) 그의 음악을 한 번 들어 보는 것이 어때? If you like today's idols, you will love the original idol.

22 콘서트가 끝난 후 사람들의 반응으로 가장 적절한 것은?

① sad   ② embarrassed

③ upset   ④ excited

⑤ annoyed

23 밑줄 친 ⓐ~ⓔ를 바르게 고치지 <u>않은</u> 것은?

① ⓐ → pays attention to

② ⓑ → at once

③ ⓒ → flies

④ ⓓ → amazing

⑤ ⓔ → about

24 위 글의 내용과 일치하지 <u>않는</u> 것은?

① Franz Liszt's body movement is paid attention to by the audience.

② The audience seems to be satisfied with the concert.

③ Franz Liszt was born in Hungary.

④ Franz Liszt started to play the piano at the age of seven.

⑤ The writer thinks Franz Liszt isn't the original idol.

25 주어진 단어를 활용하여 밑줄 친 우리말 (A)를 영어로 쓰시오.

> why / give / listen

➡ _____

26 다음 빈칸에 알맞은 기사 제목으로 가장 적절한 것은?

> _____
>
> Yesterday Franz Liszt performed his piano concert very successfully in Vienna. This concert was different from others. The side of the piano faced the audience. They could see Liszt better this way. He didn't have any sheet music and played from memory. His music was so powerful and rich. When the concert ended, the concert hall went wild.

① The Worst Piano Concert

② The Star of Our Time

③ Franz Liszt: Who Is He?

④ What You Should Know about Music

⑤ The Most Famous Concert Hall in Vienna

Lesson 4

Go for It!

 의사소통 기능

- 여가 활동 말하기
  A: What do you do in your free time?
  B: I often play table tennis.

- 경험 말하기
  A: Have you ever ridden a horse?
  B: Yes, I have.

 언어 형식

- 최상급
  The Atacama Desert is **the driest** desert in the world.

- 관계대명사
  They are the people **who** take part in the 4 Deserts Race.

Words & Expressions

교과서

Key Words

- □ **amazing**[əméiziŋ] 형 놀라운
- □ **Antarctica**[æntάːrktikə] 명 남극대륙
- □ **athlete**[ǽθliːt] 명 선수, 육상 경기 선수
- □ **backpack**[bǽkpæk] 명 배낭
- □ **bake**[beik] 동 굽다
- □ **bat**[bæt] 명 배트, 막대기, 박쥐
- □ **boiling**[bɔ́iliŋ] 형 끓는, 끓어오르는
- □ **burn**[bəːrn] 동 태우다, 타다
- □ **desert**[dézərt] 명 사막
- □ **direction**[dirékʃən] 명 방향
- □ **dry**[drai] 형 마른, 건조한
- □ **equipment**[ikwípmənt] 명 장비, 설비
- □ **expect**[ikspékt] 동 기대하다
- □ **field**[fiːld] 명 들(판), 경기장
- □ **finish line** 결승선
- □ **freeze**[friːz] 동 얼다, 얼어붙다
- □ **giant**[dʒáiənt] 형 거대한
- □ **gym**[dʒim] 명 체육관
- □ **hang**[hæŋ] 동 매달다
- □ **hit**[hit] 동 치다, 때리다
- □ **imagine**[imǽdʒin] 동 상상하다
- □ **jump rope** 줄넘기
- □ **kick**[kik] 동 차다
- □ **librarian**[laibrɛ́əriən] 명 사서
- □ **limit**[límit] 명 한계, 제한 동 제한하다

- □ **marathon**[mǽrəθὰn] 명 마라톤
- □ **mean**[miːn] 동 의미하다
- □ **ordinary**[ɔ́ːrdənèri] 형 보통의, 평범한
- □ **participant**[pɑːrtísəpənt] 명 참가자
- □ **planet**[plǽnit] 명 행성
- □ **protect**[prətékt] 동 보호하다
- □ **punch**[pʌntʃ] 명 타격, 펀치
- □ **race**[reis] 명 경주, 경쟁
- □ **reach**[riːtʃ] 동 도달하다, ~에 이르다
- □ **relay**[ríːlei] 명 계주, 릴레이 경주
- □ **request**[rikwést] 동 요청하다 명 요구, 요청
- □ **ride**[raid] 동 타다
- □ **rock climbing** 암벽 등반
- □ **sand**[sænd] 명 모래
- □ **scared**[skɛərd] 형 무서워하는
- □ **scary**[skɛ́əri] 형 무서운, 두려운
- □ **temperature**[témpərətʃər] 명 온도
- □ **throat**[θrout] 명 목구멍
- □ **throw**[θrou] 동 던지다
- □ **tough**[tʌf] 형 힘든, 어려운
- □ **traditional**[trədíʃənl] 형 전통적인
- □ **train**[trein] 동 훈련하다 명 기차
- □ **uniform**[júːnəfɔ̀ːrm] 명 제복, 유니폼
- □ **wet**[wet] 형 젖은, 축축한
- □ **windy**[wíndi] 형 바람이 (많이) 부는

Key Expressions

- □ **a series of** 일련의
- □ **be out of** ~가 떨어지다, 바닥나다
- □ **for a living** 생계를 위해
- □ **go on** 계속되다
- □ **in fact** 사실은, 실제로

- □ **in the middle of** ~의 한가운데에
- □ **take care of** ~을 돌보다
- □ **take part in** ~에 참가하다
- □ **take place** 일어나다, 개최되다
- □ **up to** ~까지

Word Power

※ 서로 반대되는 뜻을 가진 어휘

□ **dry** 건조한 ↔ **wet** 젖은, 축축한

□ **thin** 마른 ↔ **fat** 살찐

□ **ordinary** 보통의, 평범한 ↔ **extraordinary** 대단한, 보통이아닌

□ **giant** 거인 ↔ **dwarf** 난쟁이

□ **careful** 주의깊은 ↔ **careless** 부주의한

□ **ancient** 고대의 ↔ **modern** 현대의

□ **get on** ~에 타다 ↔ **get off** ~에서 내리다

□ **freeze** 얼다, 얼어붙다 ↔ **melt** 녹다

□ **limited** 한정된, 제한된 ↔ **limitless, unlimited** 무한의, 무제한의

□ **arrive** 도착하다 ↔ **depart** 출발하다

□ **throw** 던지다 ↔ **catch** 잡다

□ **high** 높은 ↔ **low** 낮은

English Dictionary

□ **Antarctica** 남극대륙
→ the continent around the South Pole
남쪽 극지방 주위의 대륙

□ **athlete** (운동) 선수
→ a person who competes in sports
스포츠에서 경쟁하는 사람

□ **backpack** 배낭
→ a piece of equipment that is carried on the back
등으로 나르는 장비의 하나

□ **boil** 끓다
→ to be heated to the point where it forms bubbles and turns to steam or vapour
공기 방울이 형성되거나 수증기 또는 기체로 변하는 지점까지 열을 받다

□ **desert** 사막
→ a large area of land that has very little water and very few plants growing on it
물이 거의 없고 이곳에서 자라는 식물도 거의 없는 넓은 땅

□ **freeze** 얼다, 얼어붙다
→ to become hard, and often turn to ice, as a result of extreme cold
극도의 추위로 딱딱해지거나 얼음으로 변하다

□ **gym** 체육관
→ a room or hall with equipment for doing physical exercise
신체 운동을 하기 위해 장비가 있는 공간 또는 회관

□ **librarian** 사서
→ a person who is in charge of or works in a library
도서관을 담당하거나 도서관에서 일을 하는 사람

□ **marathon** 마라톤
→ a race in which people run a distance of 26 miles, which is about 42 km
26마일, 즉 약 42km의 거리를 달리는 경주

□ **participant** 참가자
→ a person who is taking part in an activity or event
활동 또는 행사에 참가하는 사람

□ **protect** 보호하다
→ to make sure that somebody/something is not harmed, injured, damaged
여러 사람 또는 어떤 것이 손상이나 부상 또는 해를 입지 않도록 하다

□ **race** 경주
→ a competition between people, animals, vehicles, etc. to see which one is faster or the fastest
누가 더 빠르거나 가장 빠른지 보기 위한 사람, 동물, 수송수단 간의 경쟁

□ **temperature** 온도
→ the measurement in degrees of how hot or cold a thing or place is
어떤 물건이나 장소가 얼마나 뜨거운지 또는 차가운지 그 정도의 측정

□ **traditional** 전통적인
→ being part of the beliefs, customs or way of life of a particular group of people, that have not changed for a long time
오랫동안 변하지 않은 특정 그룹의 사람들의 삶의 양식, 믿음, 관습의

서답형

01 다음 짝지어진 단어의 관계가 같도록 빈칸에 알맞은 말을 쓰시오.

heavy : light = _____ : wet

서답형

[02~03] 다음 영영풀이에 해당하는 단어를 쓰시오.

02

a person who is taking part in an activity or event

➡ _____

03

a person who is in charge of or works in a library

➡ _____

04 다음 중 밑줄 친 부분의 뜻풀이가 바르지 <u>않은</u> 것은?

① He felt so thirsty in the middle of the <u>desert</u>. 사막
② She always smiled when she was dealing with a <u>tough</u> work. 힘든
③ They went through the desert on a <u>windy</u> day. 바람이 (많이) 부는
④ We attended an <u>ordinary</u> meeting to discuss the issue. 여느 때와 다른
⑤ Tom was an active <u>participant</u> in the discussion. 참가자

05 다음 문장의 밑줄 친 단어와 같은 의미로 쓰인 것은?

The baseball is played with a <u>bat</u> and a ball.

① The <u>bat</u> was flying in the cave.
② There are lots of different <u>bat</u> species in the world.
③ Would you put the <u>bat</u> down and help me, please?
④ He is as blind as a <u>bat</u> without glasses.
⑤ Do you know how the <u>bat</u> avoids obstacles?

서답형

06 다음 문장의 빈칸에 들어갈 말을 〈보기〉에서 골라 쓰시오.

┌─ 보기 ─┐
tough / burn / frozen / giant

(1) Don't worry. I won't _____ the bread.
(2) I don't know how to deal with this _____ situation.
(3) Minsu slipped on the _____ path.
(4) This balloon looks like a _____ ball.

07 다음 문장의 빈칸에 공통으로 들어갈 말로 적절한 것은?

• Emma is famous in the _____ of education.
• John is working on the _____ of wheat.
• The gold _____ was found in the woods.

① region ② area
③ garden ④ field
⑤ land

01 다음 짝지어진 단어의 관계가 같도록 빈칸에 알맞은 말을 쓰시오.

> dark : bright = freeze : _____

[02~03] 다음 영영풀이에 해당하는 단어를 쓰시오.

02
> being part of the beliefs, customs or way of life of a particular group of people, that have not changed for a long time

➡ _____

03
> a large area of land that has very little water and very few plants growing on it

➡ _____

04 다음 문장의 빈칸에 들어갈 말을 순서대로 쓰시오.

> • (A)_____ fact, today was the busiest day for me.
> • I'm so worried because I'm almost (B)_____ of water.
> • She practiced a lot before taking part (C)_____ the dance contest.

(A) _____ (B) _____ (C) _____

05 다음 문장의 빈칸에 들어갈 말을 〈보기〉에서 골라 알맞은 형태로 쓰시오.

> ┤ 보기 ├
> take place / be out of / go on / in the middle of

(1) I woke up _____ the night.
(2) The fashion show _____ every year.
(3) The event will _____ for a week.
(4) Because we _____ sugar, I have to go to the grocery store.

06 다음 대화의 밑줄 친 우리말을 영어로 쓰시오.

> A: Have you ever been to Busan?
> B: 아니요, 그곳에 가본 적이 없어요.

➡ _____

07 다음 우리말을 주어진 단어를 모두 배열하여 문장을 완성하시오.

(1) 너는 요가를 해 본 적이 있니?
(yoga / you / tried / ever / have)
➡ _____

(2) 사실, 우리는 소금이 다 떨어졌어.
(of / salt / out / in / we / fact / are)
➡ _____

(3) 나는 암벽 등반 대회에 참가하고 싶어.
(contest / to / rock / in / the / part / I / take / want / climbing)
➡ _____

Conversation

① 여가 활동 말하기

> **A** What do you do in your free time? 너는 여가 시간에 무엇을 하니?
> **B** I often play table tennis. 나는 종종 탁구를 쳐.

■ What do you do in your free time? 또는 What's your favorite free time activity?를 통해 상대방이 여가 시간을 어떻게 보내는지 물어볼 수 있다. free time은 '여가 시간'을 의미하며 leisure time 또는 spare time으로 바꾸어 쓸 수 있다.

여가 활동 묻기

- What's your hobby? 너의 취미가 무엇이니?
- What do you do in your leisure[spare] time? 너는 여가 시간에 무엇을 하니?
- How do you spend your leisure time? 너는 여가 시간을 어떻게 보내니?
- What's your favorite free time activity? 네가 가장 좋아하는 여가 시간 활동은 무엇이니?
- What do you like doing for fun? 너는 재미로 무엇을 하는 것을 좋아하니?

핵심 Check

1. 다음 우리말과 일치하도록 빈칸에 알맞은 말을 쓰시오.

(1) A: _____ _____ _____ _____ _____ _____ _____?
   (너는 여가 시간에 무엇을 하니?)

   B: I usually play baseball. (나는 보통 야구를 해.)

(2) A: What's your _____ _____ _____ _____?
   (당신이 가장 좋아하는 여가 활동은 무엇인가요?)

   B: I love _____ _____. (나는 요가하는 것을 매우 좋아해요.)

(3) A: What do you do in your free time? (너는 여가 시간에 무엇을 하니?)

   B: _____ _____ _____ _____. (나는 종종 쿠키를 구워.)

② 경험 말하기

> **A** Have you ever ridden a horse? 너는 말을 타본 적이 있니?
>
> **B** Yes, I have. 응, 있어.

- 'Have you ever+과거분사 ～?'는 경험을 묻는 표현으로 이에 대한 대답으로 긍정일 때는 'Yes, I have.', 부정일 때는 'No, I haven't.'로 대답한다. Have you?는 상대방에게 받은 질문을 다시 상대방에게 묻는 표현으로 반복된 부분은 생략한다.

- 현재까지의 경험을 물을 때 현재완료 시제를 사용하므로 'Have you ever+과거분사～?' 형태에 유의한다.

- 경험하지 못한 것으로 '전혀 ～해 본 적이 없다.'라고 강조하기 위해 'No, I've never ～'로 대답할 수 있다.

- 과거의 경험은 과거시제를 이용한다.

  ex) • Did you ever play table tennis? 과거에 탁구를 친 적이 있는지 묻는 표현
  • Have you ever played table tennis? 과거부터 현재까지 탁구를 친 적이 있는지 묻는 표현

핵심 Check

2. 다음 우리말과 일치하도록 빈칸에 알맞은 말을 쓰시오.

(1) **A:** _____ _____ _____ _____ a marathon? (마라톤을 해 본 적이 있나요?)

　　B: No, I haven't. (아니요, 해 본 적이 없어요.)

(2) **A:** Have you ever _____ _____? (캐나다에 가 본 적이 있나요?)

　　B: _____, _____ _____. _____ _____?

　　(예, 가 보았어요. 당신은 가 본 적이 있나요?)

(3) **A:** Have you ever _____ a paper flower? (종이꽃을 만들어 본 적이 있나요?)

　　B: No, I've _____ done it. (아니요, 전혀 해 보지 않았어요.)

A. Listen and Speak 1-A

Tony: Bomi, ❶what do you do in your free time?

Bomi: ❷I often bake cookies. ❸How about you, Tony?

Tony: I usually watch movies.

> Tony: 보미야, 너는 한가할 때 무엇을 하니?
> Bomi: 나는 종종 쿠키를 구워. 너는 어때, Tony?
> Tony: 나는 보통 영화를 봐.

❶ what do you do in your free time?은 '너는 여가 시간에 무엇을 하니?'라는 뜻으로 여가 활동에 관해 묻는 표현이다.

❷ 자신의 여가 활동에 대해 말할 때는 'I often/usually ~'의 표현을 사용하여 말할 수 있다.

❸ 'How about you?'는 '너는 어때?'라고 상대방에게 같은 질문을 할 때 사용할 수 있으며 'What about you?'로 바꾸어 쓸 수 있다.

Check(√) True or False

(1) Bomi has never baked cookies.　　　　　　　　　　T ☐　F ☐

(2) Tony usually watches movies in his free time.　　　T ☐　F ☐

A. Listen and Speak 1-B

Jean: I'm so happy. It's Friday!

Tom: ❶What are you going to do on the weekend, Jean?

Jean: ❷I'm going to play badminton.

Tom: Do you play badminton often?

Jean: Yes, it's my favorite ❸free time activity.

Tom: Who do you usually play with?

Jean: ❹My dad. What do you do in your free time?

Tom: I often go to the Han River and ❺ride my bike.

> Jean: 정말 기뻐. 금요일이야!
> Tom: 주말에 무엇을 할 거니, Jean?
> Jean: 나는 배드민턴을 칠 거야.
> Tom: 배드민턴을 자주 치니?
> Jean: 응, 그건 내가 가장 좋아하는 여가 활동이야.
> Tom: 보통 누구랑 치니?
> Jean: 우리 아빠랑. 너는 여가 시간에 무엇을 하니?
> Tom: 나는 종종 한강에 가서 자전거를 타.

❶ What are you going to do on the weekend?는 '주말에 무엇을 할 거니?'라는 뜻으로 계획을 묻는 표현이다. 이와 같은 표현으로 'What's your plan for the weekend?'가 있다.

❷ be going to ~: ~할 것이다

❸ free time activity: 여가 활동

❹ 'I usually play with my dad.'를 줄인 표현이다.

❺ ride a bike: 자전거를 타다

Check(√) True or False

(3) Jean loves playing badminton in her free time.　　　　　　　　　　T ☐　F ☐

(4) Tom often goes to the Han River to play badminton with his dad.　　T ☐　F ☐

Listen and Speak 1-C

Minsu: Ms. Allen, ❶what do you do for a living?

Allen: I'm a doctor.

Minsu: ❷What do you do in your free time?

Allen: I often play table tennis.

❶ what do you do for a living?는 직업이 무엇인지 묻는 표현이다.
❷ 여가 활동에 관한 질문으로 대답은 often 또는 usually를 이용하여 대답할 수 있다.

Listen and Speak 2-A

Mina: Tom, ❶have you ever been to Jeju-do?

Tom: ❷Yes, I have. I went there last winter vacation. What about you?

Mina: I've never been there, but I'm going there this summer.

Tom: That's great! ❸I'm sure you'll like it a lot.

❶ have you (ever) ~?는 '~해 본 적이 있니?'라는 뜻으로 상대방의 경험 유무를 묻는다.
❷ 경험을 한 경우 'Yes, I have.'로, 경험하지 않은 경우는 'No, I haven't.'로 대답한다.
❸ 'I'm sure ~'는 '~을 확신하다'는 표현으로 확실성을 나타낸다.

Listen and Speak 2-B

Suji: Mike, ❶have you ever heard of flying yoga?

Mike: Yeah! I've seen it on TV. People were ❷ hanging in the air!

Suji: Guess what? I'm learning it these days.

Mike: Really? It looked so ❸scary. Do you like it, Suji?

Suji: ❹At first, I was a little scared, but now I'm enjoying it.

Mike: Sounds great! I think I should exercise ❺ more, too.

Suji: Do you want to join my yoga class?

Mike: No, that's too scary for me. I'll ❻just play basketball.

❶ 'have you (ever) ~?'는 '~해 본 적이 있니?'라는 뜻으로 상대방의 경험 유무를 묻는다.
❷ hang: 매달리다 / in the air: 공중에
❸ scary: 무서운, 두려운
❹ at first: 처음에는
❺ more: 더 (much의 비교급)
❻ just: 그저, 단지

Listen and Speak 2-C

A: Have you ever ❶ridden a horse?

B: ❷Yes, I have.

A: When did you ride a horse?

B: Last summer.

❶ ride a horse: 말을 타다
❷ 경험을 한 경우 'Yes, I have.'로, 경험하지 않은 경우는 'No, I haven't.'로 대답한다.

Real Life Talk

Hojin: Judy, what do you do in your free time?

Judy: I often go ❶rock climbing with my dad.

Hojin: What mountain do you go to?

Judy: No, Hojin. I usually do it at a gym near my house.

Hojin: ❷I see. Have you ever done it on a real mountain?

Judy: ❸Not yet. But I hope to do it someday.

Hojin: That's really cool. Can I come and join you next time?

Judy: Sure. I'm going ❹this Saturday.

Hojin: That sounds great.

Judy: You're going to love it.

❶ rock climbing: 암벽등반
❷ I see.: '알겠어.' 또는 '그렇구나.'를 뜻한다.
❸ Not yet: 아직 없어.
❹ 이번 토요일에

● 다음 우리말과 일치하도록 빈칸에 알맞은 말을 쓰시오.

Listen & Speak 1 A

Tony: Bomi, what do you do _____ _____ _____ _____?

Bomi: I _____ bake cookies. How about you, Tony?

Tony: I _____ _____ _____.

Tony: 보미야, 너는 여가 시간에 무엇을 하니?
Bomi: 나는 종종 쿠키를 구워. 너는 어때, Tony?
Tony: 나는 보통 영화를 봐.

Listen & Speak 1 B

Jean: I'm so happy. It's Friday!

Tom: _____ _____ _____ _____ _____ _____ on the weekend, Jean?

Jean: I'm going to _____ _____.

Tom: Do you play badminton often?

Jean: Yes, it's _____ _____ _____ _____ _____.

Tom: _____ do you usually play with?

Jean: My dad. _____ _____ _____ _____ _____ _____ _____ _____?

Tom: I often go to the Han River and _____ _____ _____.

Jean: 정말 기뻐. 금요일이야!
Tom: 주말에 무엇을 할 거니, Jean?
Jean: 나는 배드민턴을 칠 거야.
Tom: 배드민턴을 자주 치니?
Jean: 응, 그건 내가 가장 좋아하는 여가 활동이야.
Tom: 보통 누구랑 치니?
Jean: 우리 아빠랑. 너는 여가 시간에 무엇을 하니?
Tom: 나는 종종 한강에 가서 자전거를 타.

Listen & Speak 1 C

Minsu: Ms. Allen, what do you do _____ _____ _____?

Allen: I'm a doctor.

Minsu: What do you do in your free time?

Allen: _____ _____ _____ _____ _____ _____.

Minsu: Ms. Allen, 직업이 무언가요?
Allen: 의사입니다.
Minsu: 여가 시간에 무엇을 하나요?
Allen: 나는 종종 탁구를 칩니다.

Listen & Speak 2 A

Mina: Tom, _____ _____ _____ _____ _____ Jeju-do?

Tom: Yes, _____ _____. I went there last winter vacation. What about you?

Mina: _____ _____ _____ _____, but I'm going there this summer.

Tom: That's great! I'm sure you'll like it a lot.

Mina: Tom, 너는 제주도에 가 본 적이 있니?
Tom: 응, 가 봤어. 지난 겨울 방학에 거기에 갔어. 너는?
Mina: 나는 거기에 가 본 적이 없는데, 이번 여름에 갈 거야.
Tom: 잘됐네! 네가 아주 좋아할 거라고 확신해.

Listen & Speak 2 B

Suji: Mike, _____ _____ _____ _____ _____ flying yoga?

Mike: Yeah! _____ _____ it on TV. People were hanging in the air!

Suji: Guess what? I'm learning it _____ _____.

Mike: Really? It looked so _____. Do you like it, Suji?

Suji: At first, I was a little _____, but now I'm enjoying it.

Mike: Sounds great! I think I should _____ more, too.

Suji: Do you want to _____ my yoga class?

Mike: No, that's too _____ for me. I'll just _____ _____.

Listen & Speak 1 C

A: _____ _____ _____ _____ a horse?

B: Yes, I have.

A: _____ did you ride a horse?

B: Last summer.

Real Life Talk

Hojin: Judy, what do you do in your free time?

Judy: I _____ _____ _____ _____ with my dad.

Hojin: _____ _____ do you go to?

Judy: No, Hojin. I usually do it at a _____ near my house.

Hojin: I see. _____ _____ _____ _____ it on a real mountain?

Judy: _____ _____. But I hope to do it someday.

Hojin: That's really cool. Can I _____ _____ _____ you next time?

Judy: Sure. I'm going _____ _____.

Hojin: That _____ great.

Judy: You're _____ _____ love it.

해석

Suji: Mike, 너는 플라잉 요가를 들어본 적이 있니?
Mike: 응! TV에서 본 적이 있어. 사람들이 공중에 매달려 있었어!
Suji: 그거 알아? 내가 요즘 그걸 배우고 있어.
Mike: 정말? 아주 무서워 보였는데. 그걸 좋아하니, 수지야?
Suji: 처음엔 조금 무서웠는데, 지금은 즐기고 있어.
Mike: 좋구나! 나도 운동을 더 해야 할 것 같아.
Suji: 우리 요가 수업을 함께 할래?
Mike: 아니, 그건 내게 너무 무서워. 나는 그냥 농구를 할게.

A: 너는 말을 타 본 적이 있니?
B: 응. 있어.
A: 언제 말을 타 보았니?
B: 지난 여름에.

Hojin: Judy, 너는 여가 시간에 무엇을 하니?
Judy: 나는 종종 아빠와 암벽 등반을 하러 가.
Hojin: 어떤 산에 가니?
Judy: 아니야, 호진아. 나는 보통 집 근처에 있는 체육관에서 그걸 해.
Hojin: 그렇구나. 실제 산에서 해 본 적이 있니?
Judy: 아직 없어. 하지만 언젠가 해 보기를 바라.
Hojin: 그거 정말 멋지다. 다음번에 내가 가서 함께 해도 될까?
Judy: 물론이야. 이번 주 토요일에 갈 거야.
Hojin: 잘됐네.
Judy: 너는 그걸 정말 좋아할 거야.

01 다음 대화의 빈칸에 들어갈 말을 주어진 단어를 모두 배열하여 완성하시오.

> A: Ms. Allen, _____?
>   (do / for / you / a / what / living / do)
> B: I'm a doctor.

➡ _____

02 다음 대화의 우리말을 영작하시오.

> A: 너는 말을 타 본 적이 있니?
> B: Yes, I have.

➡ _____

03 다음 빈칸에 들어갈 말로 어색한 것은?

> Tony: Bomi, what do you do in your free time?
> Bomi: I often bake cookies. How about you, Tony?
> Tony: _____

① I usually watch movies.   ② I read books.
③ I am a fire fighter.   ④ I listen to music.
⑤ I draw pictures.

04 다음 대화가 자연스럽게 이어지도록 순서대로 배열하시오.

> (A) That's great! I'm sure you'll like it a lot.
> (B) Have you ever been to Jeju-do?
> (C) I've never been there, but I'm going there this summer.
> (D) Yes, I have. I went there last winter vacation. What about you?

➡ _____

01 다음 빈칸에 들어갈 말로 어색한 것은?

> A: _____
>
> B: I'm a teacher.

① What kind of job do you have?
② What do you do?
③ What do you do for a living?
④ What is your occupation?
⑤ What are you going to do?

[02~03] 다음 대화를 읽고, 물음에 답하시오.

> Tony: Bomi, _____ do you do in your free time?
> Bomi: I often bake cookies. _____ about you, Tony?
> Tony: 나는 보통 영화를 봐.

02 위 대화의 빈칸에 공통으로 들어갈 말로 적절한 것은? (대·소문자 무시)

① why ② what ③ how
④ where ⑤ who

서답형

03 위 대화의 밑줄 친 우리말을 4단어를 사용하여 영작하시오.

➡ _____

[04~05] 다음 대화를 읽고, 물음에 답하시오.

> Jean: I'm so happy. It's Friday!
> Tom: _____
> Jean: I'm going to play badminton. (A)
> Tom: Do you play badminton often? (B)
> Jean: Yes, it's my favorite free time activity. (C)
> Tom: Who do you usually play with? (D)

Jean: My dad. (E)
Tom: I often go to the Han River and ride my bike.

04 위 대화의 빈칸에 들어갈 말로 어색한 것은?

① What are you going to do on the weekend?
② What are you planning to do on the weekend?
③ What's your plan for the weekend?
④ What will you do on the weekend?
⑤ What do you do for a living?

05 위 대화의 (A)~(E) 중 주어진 문장이 들어가기에 적절한 곳은?

> What do you do in your free time?

① (A) ② (B) ③ (C) ④ (D) ⑤ (E)

06 다음 대화가 자연스럽게 이어지도록 순서대로 배열하시오.

> Mike, have you ever heard of flying yoga?

> (A) Guess what? I'm learning it these days.
> (B) At first, I was a little scared, but now I'm enjoying it.
> (C) Really? It looked so scary. Do you like it, Suji?
> (D) Sounds great! I think I should exercise more, too.
> (E) Yeah! I've seen it on TV. People were hanging in the air!

➡ _____

[07~08] 다음 대화를 읽고 물음에 답하시오.

Suji: Mike, have you ever heard of flying yoga?

Mike: Yeah! I've seen it on TV. People were hanging in the air!

Suji: Guess what? I'm learning it these days.

Mike: Really? It looked so scary. Do you like it, Suji?

Suji: At first, I was a little scared, but now I'm enjoying it.

Mike: Sounds great! I think I should exercise more, too.

Suji: Do you want to join my yoga class?

Mike: No, that's too scary for me. I'll just play basketball.

서답형

07 What does Mike think about flying yoga?

➡ _____

서답형

08 What is Mike going to do instead of joining the yoga class?

➡ _____

09 다음 대화의 내용과 일치하도록 Hojin의 일기를 완성하시오.

Hojin: Judy, what do you do in your free time?

Judy: I often go rock climbing with my dad.

Hojin: What mountain do you go to?

Judy: No, Hojin. I usually do it at a gym near my house.

Hojin: I see. Have you ever done it on a real mountain?

Judy: Not yet. But I hope to do it someday.

Hojin: That's really cool. Can I come and join you next time?

Judy: Sure. I'm going this Saturday.

Hojin: That sounds great.

Judy: You're going to love it.

Mon, June 3th, 2019
Today, I talked about free time activity with Judy. She said (1)_____ in her free time. She usually does it at (2)_____. However, (3)_____ on a real mountain and she hopes to do it someday. I was interested in rock climbing so I asked if (4)_____. We are going to do it this Saturday. I'm really looking forward to it.

(1) _____
(2) _____
(3) _____
(4) _____

서답형

10 다음 대화가 자연스럽게 이어지도록 순서대로 배열하시오.

(A) Last summer.
(B) Yes, I have.
(C) When did you ride a horse?
(D) Have you ever ridden a horse?

➡ _____

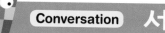
01 다음 대화의 밑줄 친 우리말을 주어진 어구를 이용하여 영작하시오.

> Tony: Bomi, 너는 여가 시간에 무엇을 하니? (free time)
> Bomi: I often bake cookies. How about you, Tony?
> Tony: I usually watch movies.

➡ _____

[02~04] 다음 대화를 읽고, 물음에 답하시오.

> Jean: I'm so happy. It's Friday!
> Tom: What are you going to do on the weekend, Jean?
> Jean: I'm going to play badminton.
> Tom: Do you play badminton often?
> Jean: Yes, it's my favorite free time activity.
> Tom: Who do you usually play with?
> Jean: ___(A)___ (my dad). What do you do in your free time?
> Tom: I often go to the Han River and ride my bike.

02 위 대화의 빈칸 (A)에 들어갈 대답을 주어진 단어를 사용하여 완전한 문장으로 쓰시오.

➡ _____

03 위 대화에서 다음 영영풀이가 나타내는 말을 찾아 쓰시오.

> liked more than others of the same kind

➡ _____

04 위 대화의 내용과 일치하도록 빈칸을 완성하시오.

> In her free time, Jean (1)_____ with her dad, while Tom often (2)_____ _____ and (3)_____.

[05~07] 다음 대화를 읽고, 물음에 답하시오.

> Hojin: Judy, what do you do in your free time?
> Judy: (A)나는 종종 아빠와 함께 암벽 등반을 하러 가.
> Hojin: What mountain do you go to?
> Judy: No, Hojin. I usually do it at a gym near my house.
> Hojin: I see. Have you ever done it on a real mountain?
> Judy: Not yet. But I hope to do it someday.
> Hojin: That's really cool. Can I come and join you next time?
> Judy: Sure. I'm going this Saturday.
> Hojin: That sounds great.
> Judy: You're going to love it.

05 위 대화의 밑줄 친 (A)의 우리말을 8단어를 사용하여 영작하시오.

➡ _____

06 Where does Judy usually do rock climbing?

➡ _____

07 What are Judy and Hojin going to do this Saturday?

➡ _____

Grammar

① 최상급

- She is **the smartest** girl in our class. 그녀는 우리 반에서 가장 똑똑한 소녀이다.
- Seoul is **the biggest** city in Korea. 서울은 한국에서 가장 큰 도시이다.

■ 최상급은 셋 이상의 것 중에서 양, 정도, 수에 있어서 가장 많거나 가장 정도가 높은 것을 나타낼 때 쓰는 표현이다. 형용사의 최상급은 정관사 the를 사용하지만, 부사의 최상급에서는 정관사 the를 생략하는 것이 일반적이다. 최상급의 범위를 나타낼 때에는 'of+기간' 혹은 'in+장소, 조직, 사람들의 무리'를 사용하여 '~ 중에서'라는 의미로 쓸 수 있다.

- James is **the busiest** man in the company. James는 그 회사에서 가장 바쁜 사람이다.
- Yesterday was **the hottest** day of the year. 어제는 1년 중 가장 더운 날이었다.

■ 최상급은 형용사 어미에 '-est'를 붙여서 만든다. 단, 3음절 이상의 단어와 -ous, -ful, -ive, -less, -ant, -ing 등으로 끝나는 2음절의 단어는 'the most'를 사용하여 최상급을 만든다.

- It is **the most difficult** problem. 그것은 가장 어려운 문제이다.
- BTS is **the most famous** K-pop star in America. BTS는 미국에서 가장 유명한 K-pop 스타이다.

■ 불규칙으로 변하는 최상급

- good, well − best   many, much − most
- bad, ill − worst   little − least
- I like math **(the) best of** all subjects. 나는 모든 과목 중에서 수학을 가장 좋아한다.

■ 비교급과 원급을 이용하여 최상급의 의미를 표현할 수 있다.

- Chris is **the strongest** boy in his class. Chris는 그의 반에서 가장 힘이 센 소년이다.
  = Chris is **stronger than any other** boy in his class. [비교급+than any other+단수명사]
    Chris는 그의 반에서 다른 어떤 소년보다 더 힘이 세다.
  = Chris is **stronger than all the other** boys in his class. [비교급+than all the other+복수명사]
    Chris는 그의 반에서 다른 모든 소년들보다 더 힘이 세다.
  = **No other** boy in his class is **as strong as** Chris. [부정주어+so[as] 원급 as]
    그의 반에서 다른 어떤 소년도 Chris만큼 힘이 세지 않다.
  = **No other** boy in his class is **stronger than** Chris. [부정주어+비교급+than]
    그의 반에서 다른 어떤 소년도 Chris보다 더 힘이 세지 않다.

핵심 Check

1. 다음 우리말과 같도록 빈칸에 알맞은 말을 쓰시오.

   (1) 그것은 모든 펜 중에서 가장 싼 펜이다.

   ➡ It is _____ _____ pen of _____.

   (2) 이것은 일곱 권 중 가장 흥미로운 책이다.

   ➡ This is _____ _____ _____ book of the seven books.

2 관계대명사

> • I have a friend **who** makes pumpkin pies well. 내게는 호박파이를 잘 만드는 친구가 있다.
> • The book **whose** cover is red is mine. 표지가 빨간색인 그 책은 내 것이다.

■ 관계대명사는 두 개의 문장을 하나로 이어주는 접속사 역할을 하면서 동시에 대명사 역할을 한다. 본래 문장에서 주격으로 쓰인 명사는 주격 관계대명사로, 소유격으로 쓰인 명사는 소유격 관계대명사로, 목적격으로 쓰인 명사는 목적격 관계대명사로 바꾸어 준다.

- I thanked the woman. She helped me.
  = I thanked the woman **who** helped me.

- The sunglasses were under the sofa. I was looking for them.
  = The sunglasses **which** I was looking for were under the sofa.

■ 선행사에 따라서 사용되는 관계대명사의 종류는 다음과 같으며, 목적격 관계대명사는 생략 가능하다.

	주격	소유격	목적격
사람	who	whose	whom[who]
사물	which	whose / of which	which

- Tell me about the people **who[whom]** you visited when you were in Harvard.
  네가 Harvard에 있을 때 방문했던 사람들에 대해 말해 줘.

- I know a doctor **whose** last name is Peterson. 나는 성이 Peterson인 의사를 안다.

- The movie **which** we saw last night was not so good. 우리가 어젯밤에 본 영화는 그리 좋지 않았다.

■ 관계대명사 that은 who와 which를 대신하여 사용될 수 있으며 소유격은 쓰이지 않는다. 또, 선행사가 '사람+사물[동물]'인 경우에는 반드시 that을 쓰며, 선행사가 'the+최상급', 'the+서수', 'the only', 'the very', 'the same'의 수식을 받거나, 선행사가 '-thing', '-body', '-one'으로 끝나는 경우에는 that을 쓰는 경우가 많다.

- The woman **that[who]** I met yesterday was kind. 내가 어제 만난 여자는 친절했다.

- Jina is the only friend **that[whom]** I can rely on. Jina는 내가 의지할 수 있는 유일한 친구이다.

핵심 Check

2. 다음 우리말과 같도록 빈칸에 알맞은 말을 쓰시오.

(1) 경주에서 이긴 그 소녀는 행복했다.
  ➡ The girl _____ won the race was happy.

(2) 나는 자전거를 도난당한 남자를 안다.
  ➡ I know the man _____ _____ was stolen.

01 관계대명사를 이용하여 다음 두 문장을 하나의 문장으로 만드시오. (that은 쓰지 말 것)

(1) I have a friend. She studies abroad.

➡ _____

(2) We stayed in the hotel. It had a beautiful lounge.

➡ _____

(3) Do you want to see the pictures? The photographer took them.

➡ _____

(4) Jenny took care of the dog. Its leg was hurt. (whose를 이용할 것)

➡ _____

02 주어진 단어를 어법에 맞게 빈칸에 쓰시오.

(1) Summer is _____ _____ season of the year. (hot)
(2) No other boy in the club is _____ _____ Jimmy. (tall)
(3) Look at the girl who _____ playing the violin on the stage. (be)
(4) Parker is _____ _____ _____ boy in his school. (diligent)

03 다음 우리말에 맞게 주어진 단어를 바르게 배열하시오. (필요하면 어형을 바꿀 것)

(1) 내가 너에게 빌려준 책을 읽었니?

(the book / did / to / you / you / read / that / I / lend)

➡ _____

(2) 묻고 싶은 것이 있나요?

(ask / there / to / is / you / anything / that / want)

➡ _____

(3) 세계에서 제일 긴 강을 아니?

(in / do / you / the / long / the / know / world / river)

➡ _____

(4) 시간은 모든 것 중에서 가장 귀중하다.

(all / time / precious / of / the / is / most)

➡ _____

01 다음 중 최상급의 형태가 다른 하나는?

① healthy   ② tired   ③ afraid

④ foolish   ⑤ helpful

02 다음 빈칸에 들어갈 말이 다른 하나는?

① He is the man _____ you can trust.

② You can see many people _____ live and work nearby.

③ There lived a girl _____ fell in love with a king.

④ I know the boy _____ hobby is jumping rope.

⑤ The man _____ invented the telephone was Bell.

03 다음 중 어법상 바르지 않은 것은?

A: Did you ①see the movie ②that I told you about?

B: Yes, I ③did. I think that's ④more boring movie ⑤that I've ever seen.

① ② ③ ④ ⑤

04 적절한 관계사를 이용하여 다음 두 문장을 하나의 문장으로 쓰시오.

• Where is the cheese?
• It was in the refrigerator.

➡ _____

_____

05 다음 빈칸에 알맞은 말이 바르게 짝지어진 것은?

No other hotel room in the world is bigger than this room.

= This room is _____ than any other hotel room in the world.

= This room is _____ hotel room in the world.

= No other hotel room is as _____ as this room.

① bigger – bigger – big

② bigger – the big – bigger

③ bigger – the biggest – big

④ the biggest – the biggest – big

⑤ the biggest – the biggest – bigger

06 다음 빈칸에 적절한 것을 모두 고르시오.

The people _____ I call most often on my cell phone are my mother and my sisters.

① which   ② who   ③ that
④ whose   ⑤ whom

07 다음 빈칸에 알맞지 않은 것은?

돌고래는 세계에서 가장 영리한 동물이다.

= A dolphin is _____ in the world.

① the smartest animal

② smarter than any other animal

③ the smartest of all the animals

④ smarter than all the other animals

⑤ as smart as all the other animals

서답형

08 주어진 문장의 밑줄 친 부분과 같은 의미가 되도록 빈칸에 알맞은 말을 쓰시오.

> I prefer this chair to the others. It's <u>the most comfortable.</u>
>
> = This chair is _____ _____ _____ all the other chairs.

09 다음 중 어법상 바르지 <u>않은</u> 것은?

> Bill Gates ①who ②was born in 1955 is the man ③who established a company ④named Microsoft. He is one of the richest ⑤man in the world.

① ② ③ ④ ⑤

10 다음 중 의미가 <u>다른</u> 하나는?

① This is the most valuable painting in the gallery.
② No other painting in the gallery is more valuable than this.
③ This is more valuable than any other painting in the gallery.
④ This is more valuable than all the other paintings in the gallery.
⑤ This is as valuable as all the other paintings in the gallery.

서답형

11 다음 질문에 어법에 맞게 답하시오.

> A: What is the tallest building in the world?
> B: Burj Khalifa _____ is in Dubai is _____ any other building in the world.

➡ _____

12 다음 중 어법상 바르지 <u>않은</u> 것은?

① He is the best guitarist that I have ever known.
② Yesterday I ran into an old friend whom I hadn't seen for years.
③ Family is the most important than all the other things.
④ No other singer is as popular as Adele.
⑤ Kyle has a sister whose job is taking care of the elderly.

중요

13 다음 중 어법상 옳은 것을 바르게 묶은 것은?

> ⓐ In our town, there are people don't have a car.
> ⓑ The dress she is wearing is new.
> ⓒ The music that I listened to last night was good.
> ⓓ Helen actually enjoyed the book I told her to read it.
> ⓔ Mr. Kim teaches a subject which I am not interested in.

① ⓐ, ⓑ, ⓓ　　　　② ⓑ, ⓒ, ⓓ
③ ⓑ, ⓒ, ⓔ　　　　④ ⓒ, ⓓ, ⓔ
⑤ ⓐ, ⓓ, ⓔ

서답형

14 다음 빈칸에 적절한 관계대명사를 쓰시오.

> • The story _____ he told us was hard to believe.
> • I know the girl _____ eyes are brown.
> • Is this the watch _____ Kevin bought last month?

15 주어진 단어를 활용하여 다음 우리말을 영어로 쓰시오.

> 나와 함께 대화를 나눈 그 여자는 내게 좋은 조언을 해 주었다.
> (speak to / give / advice)

➡ _____

_____

16 주어진 단어를 활용하여 다음 우리말을 영어로 쓰시오.

> 너희 나라에서 가장 인기 있는 스포츠는 무엇이니? (popular)

➡ _____

17 다음 중 밑줄 친 부분의 쓰임이 <u>다른</u> 하나는?

① Jason will buy a robot <u>that</u> cleans the house.

② Don't you have a dog <u>that</u> has a cute tail?

③ This is the purse <u>that</u> Kelly lost on the street.

④ He knew <u>that</u> he had to do the work.

⑤ I didn't call the man <u>that</u> gave me his phone number.

18 다음 빈칸에 공통으로 들어갈 말은?

> • What is the name of the man _____ car you borrowed?
> • This school is only for children _____ first language is not Korean.

① who   ② that   ③ which
④ whose   ⑤ whom

19 주어진 단어를 이용하여 빈칸에 알맞은 말을 쓰시오.

> Mr. and Mrs. Brown have three daughters.
> _____ of their three daughters is 15 years old. (old)

➡ _____

20 적절한 관계대명사를 이용하여 다음 두 문장을 하나의 문장으로 쓰시오.

> • I liked the woman.
> • I met her at the party last night.

➡ _____

21 다음 문장을 바르게 영작한 것은?

> 그건 내가 저지른 것 중 최악의 실수야.

① It's a bad mistake that I made.

② It's the baddest mistake that I had.

③ It's the worst mistake that I've ever made.

④ It's worse mistake than any other mistakes.

⑤ It's the bad mistake that I've ever done.

22 다음 중 어법상 바르지 <u>않은</u> 것은?

① Did you check everything that you needed?

② It is the most prettiest cat I've ever had.

③ I know the boy whose hands are so cold.

④ Kelly kept the secret that I told her.

⑤ No other flowers are more beautiful than roses.

01 다음 빈칸에 적절한 말을 어법에 맞게 쓰시오.

> • Everest is _____ mountain in the world.
> • Everest is _____ any other mountain in the world.

➡ _____

02 〈보기〉의 문장과 관계대명사를 이용하여 빈칸을 알맞게 채우시오.

> ┤ 보기 ├
> • They were on the wall.
> • They are never on time.
> • It cannot be explained.

(1) A mystery is something _____
_____ .

(2) What happened to the pictures _____
_____?

(3) I don't like people _____ .

03 다음 주어진 단어를 이용하여 우리말을 영어로 쓰시오.

> 아픈 아이들을 진찰한 그 남자는 이 병원에서 가장 친절한 의사이다.
> (examine / the / kind / in)

➡ _____
_____

04 다음 중 알맞은 것을 골라 최상급을 이용하여 빈칸에 알맞은 말을 쓰시오.

> • Sydney • Jupiter • The Nile

> • long   • large

(1) _____ city in Australia.
(2) _____ any other planet in the solar system.
(3) _____ in the world.

05 주어진 단어를 바르게 배열하여 다음 우리말을 영어로 쓰시오.

> 그는 내가 만나 본 사람 중 가장 지루한 사람이야.
> (the / most / ever / he / have / is / person / met / boring / that / I)

➡ _____

06 다음은 Rope A, B, C, D에 대한 설명이다. 빈칸에 알맞은 말을 쓰시오.

> Rope A _____
> Rope B _____
> Rope C _____
> Rope D _____

(1) Rope B is _____ Rope A.
(2) Rope D is _____ the other ropes.
(3) Rope A is _____ of all.
(4) No other rope is _____ Rope A.

07 다음 중 서로 관련 있는 문장을 연결하여 하나의 문장으로 쓰시오.

> • A customer is someone.
> • The boy is now in the hospital.
> • The bus runs every half hour.
> • A dictionary is a book.
> • I met somebody.

> • It gives you the meanings of words.
> • Her mother is a famous writer.
> • He was injured in the accident.
> • It goes to the airport.
> • The person buys something from a store.

➡ _____

➡ _____

➡ _____

➡ _____

➡ _____

08 우리말과 같은 뜻이 되도록 빈칸에 알맞은 말을 쓰시오.

(1) 나는 나와 함께 일하는 그 사람들을 좋아해.
  ➡ I like _____ _____ _____ I work with.

(2) 그들은 그들의 아이들에게 원하는 모든 것을 준다.
  ➡ They give _____ _____ _____ _____ they want.

(3) 나는 메뉴가 매우 단순한 식당을 안다.
  ➡ I know a restaurant _____ _____ is very simple.

09 다음 상황을 읽고 빈칸에 알맞은 말을 쓰시오.

> Jason is talking to his friend about Kelly. Kelly is very patient. He has never met a person like Kelly. So Jason tells his friend about Kelly like this.
> **Jason:** She is _____.

➡ _____

10 〈보기〉와 같이 하나의 문장을 두 개의 문장으로 쓰시오.

> ┤ 보기 ├
> The people who live upstairs talk very loudly in the morning.
> ➡ The people talk very loudly in the morning.
> ➡ They live upstairs.

(1) I know the boy whose bicycle was stolen.
  ➡ _____
  ➡ _____

(2) Daisy lectured on a topic which she knew very little about.
  ➡ _____
  ➡ _____

11 다음은 주어진 문장과 같은 의미의 문장이다. 빈칸에 알맞은 말을 쓰시오.

> The Mississippi River is longer than any other river in the United States.

(1) _____ _____ _____ in the United States is _____ _____ the Mississippi River.

(2) The Mississippi River is _____ _____ _____ the United States.

Reading

Too Hot to Run

Imagine you are in the middle of a great desert. The sands go on and
on in every direction. The sun feels like a giant ball of fire. The hot
wind burns your face and throat. You open your backpack to drink
some water. Oh, no! You're almost out of water. You wet your throat
with a drop of water and keep going.

Sounds like a bad dream? Well, this is not a dream for the people who
take part in the 4 Deserts Race. The 4 Deserts Race is a series of four
races across the world's toughest deserts. Each race is 250 kilometers
long and takes seven days.

The first race takes place in the Atacama Desert in Chile. It is the
driest desert in the world. In fact, it hasn't rained in some parts of the
Atacama Desert for 400 years! The next race goes to the Gobi Desert
in China. It is the windiest desert on earth.

imagine 상상하다
desert 사막
in the middle of ~의 한 가운데에
go on 계속되다
burn 태우다
throat 목구멍
be out of 떨어지다, 바닥나다
wet 적시다
keep Ving 계속해서 V하다
take part in ~에 참가하다
(= participate in)
a series of 일련의, 연속된
each 각각의
take ~의 시간이 걸리다
take place 개최되다, 일어나다
dry 건조한
in fact 사실은, 실제로
for+기간 ~ 동안
windy 바람이 (많이) 부는

확인문제

● 다음 문장이 본문의 내용과 일치하면 T, 일치하지 않으면 F를 쓰시오.

1 The sun makes you feel thirsty. ☐

2 Your water is in your backpack. ☐

3 There is enough water to drink. ☐

4 The 4 Deserts Race takes place in the world's toughest deserts. ☐

5 The Gobi Desert is drier than any other place in the world. ☐

The third race heads to the Sahara Desert in Egypt. It is the hottest of
the four deserts. Temperatures can reach up to 50°C. Finally, the race
travels to the coldest desert on earth, Antarctica. If you throw boiling
water into the air here, it freezes!

Only the greatest runners on the planet can take part in 4 Deserts Race,
right? Not exactly. Many of the participants are ordinary people like
you and me. So why do they do it? Adrianna, a librarian from France,
says, "It's a chance to test your limits and make your own history.
Anyone who crosses the finish line can do anything."

---

head to ~로 향하다

temperature 온도

reach up ~에 도달하다

boil 끓다, 끓어오르다

freeze 얼다, 얼어붙다

planet 행성

exactly 정확하게

participant 참가자

ordinary 평범한, 보통의

like ~처럼

librarian 사서

chance 기회

limit 한계

cross 가로지르다

finish line 결승선

확인문제

● 다음 문장이 본문의 내용과 일치하면 T, 일치하지 않으면 F를 쓰시오.

1 The Sahara Desert is the last race. ☐

2 We can see the Sahara Desert in Egypt. ☐

3 The temperature of the Sahara Desert is higher than 50°C. ☐

4 The final race takes place in Antarctica. ☐

5 Only expert runners take part in the 4 Deserts Race. ☐

6 Anyone who wants to test his or her limits can take part in the race. ☐

● 우리말을 참고하여 빈칸에 알맞은 말을 쓰시오.

1 _____ you are _____ _____ _____ _____ a great desert.

2 The sands _____ _____ _____ _____ in every direction.

3 The sun _____ _____ a giant ball of _____ .

4 The hot wind _____ _____ _____ and _____ .

5 You open _____ _____ _____ _____ some water.

6 Oh, no! You're almost _____ _____ _____ .

7 You _____ your throat _____ _____ _____ _____ water and _____ _____ .

8 _____ _____ a bad dream?

9 Well, this is not a dream for the people _____ _____ _____ _____ the 4 Deserts Race.

10 The 4 Deserts Race is _____ _____ _____ _____ across the world's _____ _____ .

11 _____ _____ _____ 250 kilometers long and _____ seven days.

12 The first race _____ _____ in the Atacama Desert _____ Chile.

13 It is _____ _____ _____ in the world.

14 In fact, it _____ _____ in some parts of the Atacama Desert _____ 400 years!

15 The next race _____ _____ the Gobi Desert _____ China.

16 It is _____ _____ _____ on earth.

1 당신이 아주 큰 사막의 한 가운데에 있다고 상상해 봐라.

2 모래 벌판이 사면팔방으로 계속 이어진다.

3 태양은 거대한 불덩이 같다.

4 뜨거운 바람이 당신의 얼굴과 목구멍을 태운다.

5 당신은 물을 좀 마시려고 배낭을 연다.

6 오, 이런! 물이 거의 떨어져 간다.

7 당신은 물 한 방울로 목을 적시고 계속 간다.

8 나쁜 꿈인 것 같은가?

9 글쎄, '4 Deserts Race'에 참가하는 사람들에게 이것은 꿈이 아니다.

10 '4 Deserts Race'는 세계에서 가장 험한 사막들을 가로지르는 연속된 4개의 경주이다.

11 각 경주는 250킬로미터이고 7일이 걸린다.

12 첫 번째 경주는 칠레에 있는 아타카마 사막에서 열린다.

13 그곳은 세계에서 가장 건조한 사막이다.

14 실제로 아타카마 사막의 어떤 곳에는 400년간 비가 내리지 않았다!

15 다음 경주는 중국에 있는 고비 사막으로 이어진다.

16 그곳은 세상에서 가장 바람이 많이 부는 사막이다.

17 The third race _____ _____ the Sahara Desert in Egypt.

18 It is _____ _____ of the four deserts.

19 Temperatures can _____ _____ _____ 50℃.

20 Finally, the race _____ _____ _____ _____ _____ on earth, Antarctica.

21 If you throw _____ _____ into the air here, it _____!

22 Only _____ _____ _____ on the planet can _____ _____ _____ 4 Deserts Race, right?

23 Not _____.

24 Many of _____ _____ _____ _____ people like you and me.

25 So why do they _____ _____?

26 Adrianna, _____ _____ _____ France, says,

27 "It's _____ _____ _____ _____ your limits and _____ your own history.

28 Anyone _____ _____ the finish line _____ _____ _____."

17 세 번째 경주는 이집트에 있는 사하라 사막으로 향한다.

18 그곳은 네 개의 사막 중 가장 뜨겁다.

19 온도가 섭씨 50도까지 올라갈 수 있다.

20 마지막으로 경주는 세상에서 가장 추운 사막인 남극 대륙으로 향한다.

21 이곳에서 끓는 물을 공중에 던지면, 그것은 얼어버린다!

22 세상에서 가장 훌륭한 달리기 주자들만 '4 Deserts Race'에 참가할 수 있다. 맞는가?

23 꼭 그렇진 않다.

24 많은 참가자들은 당신과 나와 같은 평범한 사람들이다.

25 그러면 그들은 왜 그것을 하는가?

26 프랑스 출신의 사서인 Adrianna는 말한다.

27 "그것은 당신의 한계를 시험하고 당신만의 역사를 만들 기회예요.

28 결승선을 넘는 사람은 어떤 것이든 할 수 있어요."

● 우리말을 참고하여 본문을 영작하시오.

1 당신이 아주 큰 사막의 한 가운데에 있다고 상상해 봐라.

➡ _____

2 모래 벌판이 사면팔방으로 계속 이어진다.

➡ _____

3 태양은 거대한 불덩이 같다.

➡ _____

4 뜨거운 바람이 당신의 얼굴과 목구멍을 태운다.

➡ _____

5 당신은 물을 좀 마시려고 배낭을 연다.

➡ _____

6 오, 이런! 물이 거의 떨어져 간다.

➡ _____

7 당신은 물 한 방울로 목을 적시고 계속 간다.

➡ _____

8 나쁜 꿈인 것 같은가?

➡ _____

9 글쎄, '4 Deserts Race'에 참가하는 사람들에게 이것은 꿈이 아니다.

➡ _____

10 '4 Deserts Race'는 세계에서 가장 험한 사막들을 가로지르는 연속된 4개의 경주이다.

➡ _____

11 각 경주는 250킬로미터이고 7일이 걸린다.

➡ _____

12 첫 번째 경주는 칠레에 있는 아타카마 사막에서 열린다.

➡ _____

13 그곳은 세계에서 가장 건조한 사막이다.

➡ _____

14 실제로 아타카마 사막의 어떤 곳에는 400년간 비가 내리지 않았다!

➡ _____

15 다음 경주는 중국에 있는 고비 사막으로 이어진다.

➡ _____

16 그곳은 세상에서 가장 바람이 많이 부는 사막이다.

➡ _____

17 세 번째 경주는 이집트에 있는 사하라 사막으로 향한다.

➡ _____

18 그곳은 네 개의 사막 중 가장 뜨겁다.

➡ _____

19 온도가 섭씨 50도까지 올라갈 수 있다.

➡ _____

20 마지막으로 경주는 세상에서 가장 추운 사막인 남극 대륙으로 향한다.

➡ _____

21 이곳에서 끓는 물을 공중에 던지면, 그것은 얼어버린다!

➡ _____

22 세상에서 가장 훌륭한 달리기 주자들만 '4 Deserts Race'에 참가할 수 있다. 맞는가?

➡ _____

23 꼭 그렇진 않다.

➡ _____

24 많은 참가자들은 당신과 나와 같은 평범한 사람들이다.

➡ _____

25 그러면 그들은 왜 그것을 하는가?

➡ _____

26 프랑스 출신의 사서인 Adrianna는 말한다.

➡ _____

27 "그것은 당신의 한계를 시험하고 당신만의 역사를 만들 기회예요.

➡ _____

28 결승선을 넘는 사람은 어떤 것이든 할 수 있어요."

➡ _____

[01~04] 다음 글을 읽고, 물음에 답하시오.

⎯⎯ ⓐ you are in the middle of a great desert. The sands go on and on in every direction. The sun feels like a ⓑgiant ball of fire. The hot wind burns your face and throat. You open your backpack ⎯ⓒ⎯ some water. Oh, no! You're almost out of water. You wet your throat with a drop of water and keep ⎯ⓓ⎯.

01 다음과 같이 풀이되는 단어를 빈칸 ⓐ에 쓰시오.

> This word is used when you think about something and your mind forms a picture or idea of it.

➡ _____

02 위 글을 읽고 떠올릴 수 없는 것은?

① a person who is standing in the middle of a desert
② a desert which stretches endlessly
③ a burning throat with the hot wind
④ a full bottle of water
⑤ a person who has a backpack

03 위 글의 밑줄 친 ⓑ를 대신하여 쓸 수 있는 것은?

① tiny　　② small　　③ huge
④ round　　⑤ rolling

04 위 글의 빈칸 ⓒ와 ⓓ에 들어갈 말이 적절하게 짝지어진 것은?

① drinking – go　　② drinking – going
③ to drink – to go　　④ drinking – to go
⑤ to drink – going

[05~09] 다음 글을 읽고, 물음에 답하시오.

Imagine you are ⓐin the middle of a great desert. The sands go ⓑon and on in every direction. The sun feels like (A)a giant ball of fire. The hot wind burns your face and throat. You open your backpack (B)to drink some water. Oh, no! You're almost out of water. You wet your throat with a drop of water and keep going.

Sounds like a ⓒbad dream? Well, this is not a dream for (C)'4 Deserts Race'에 참가한 사람들. The 4 Deserts Race is ⓓa series of four races across the world's toughest deserts. Each race is 250 kilometers long and takes seven days.

05 다음 중 밑줄 친 ⓐ~ⓓ를 대신할 수 없는 것은?

① continuously　　② in the heart of
③ a chain of　　④ carry on
⑤ terrible

06 위 글의 밑줄 친 (A)와 같이 표현한 이유로 가장 적절한 것은?

① It's because the sun looks like a ball.
② It's because the sun makes fire.
③ It's because the sun is huge.
④ It's because the sun is too hot.
⑤ It's because the sun is like a monster.

07 위 글의 밑줄 친 (B)와 쓰임이 같은 것은?

① She wants us to become friends.
② Kyle went to the library to study hard.
③ Do you want something to drink?
④ I would like to have some cookies.
⑤ It is good to see you again.

서답형

08 위 글의 밑줄 친 우리말 (C)를 주어진 단어를 이용하여 영어로 쓰시오.

> (take / the 4 Deserts Race)

➡ _____

서답형

09 위 글의 내용에 맞도록 다음 물음에 답하시오.

> A: How long is each of the deserts race?
> B: _____

[10~14] 다음 글을 읽고, 물음에 답하시오.

The first race takes place in the Atacama Desert in Chile. It is the driest desert in the world. ⓐ , it hasn't rained in some parts of the Atacama Desert for 400 years! The next race goes to the Gobi Desert in China. ⓑ그곳은 세상에서 가장 바람이 많이 부는 사막이다. The third race heads to the Sahara Desert in Egypt. It is the hottest of the four deserts. Temperatures can reach up to 50℃. Finally, the race travels to the coldest desert on earth, Antarctica. If you throw boiling water into the air here, ⓒit freezes!

10 위 글의 빈칸 ⓐ에 들어갈 말로 가장 적절한 것은?

① However   ② In fact
③ Thus   ④ For example
⑤ Then

11 '4 Deserts Race'에 관한 위 글을 읽고 답할 수 없는 것은?

① Where does the first race take place?
② What is the next race following the first race?
③ Where is the Atacama Desert?
④ Where is the smallest desert on earth?
⑤ Which desert is hotter than all the other deserts?

12 위 글을 밑줄 친 우리말 ⓑ를 영어로 바르게 옮기지 않은 것은?

① It is windier than any other desert on earth.
② No other desert on earth is windier than it.
③ It is the windiest desert on earth.
④ No other desert on earth is as windy as it.
⑤ It is not windier than all the other deserts on earth.

중요

13 위 글의 밑줄 친 ⓒ가 가리키는 것을 영어로 쓰시오.

➡ _____

중요

14 위 글의 내용에 맞도록 다음 빈칸에 알맞은 말을 쓰시오.

> A: Where is the final destination of the desert race?
> B: It is in _____ which _____.

➡ _____

[15~19] 다음 글을 읽고, 물음에 답하시오.

Only the greatest runners on the planet can take part in 4 Deserts Race, right? Not exactly. Many of the participants are _____ⓐ_____ people like you and me. So why do they ⓑdo it? Adrianna, a librarian from France, says, "It's a chance to test your limits and make your own history. Anyone _____ⓒ_____ crosses the finish line can do anything."

서답형

15 다음과 같이 풀이되는 단어를 위 글에서 찾아 쓰시오.

the greatest amount, extent, or degree of something that is possible

➡ _____

16 위 글의 문맥상 빈칸 ⓐ에 들어갈 말로 가장 적절한 것은?

① special   ② traditional
③ ordinary   ④ certain
⑤ unusual

서답형

17 위 글의 밑줄 친 ⓑ가 의미하는 것을 위 글에서 찾아 쓰시오.

➡ _____

18 위 글의 빈칸 ⓒ에 적합한 것을 <u>모두</u> 고르시오.

① whom   ② whose   ③ who
④ that   ⑤ which

19 위 글의 주제로 가장 적절한 것은?

① the difficulty of applying for the 4 Deserts Race
② the reason ordinary people participate in the 4 Deserts Race
③ an effort to run through all the deserts
④ the importance of testing one's limits
⑤ the importance of knowing one's history

[20~23] 다음 글을 읽고, 물음에 답하시오.

Reporter: _____(A)_____
Adrianna: I've run through four deserts. They were the Atacama Desert, the Gobi Desert, the Sahara Desert, and Antarctica.
Reporter: (B)Which desert was the toughest for you?
Adrianna: The Sahara Desert. Temperature often reached up to 50℃.
Reporter: What kind of people ran in the race?
Adrianna: Most of them were ordinary people like you and me. I became good friends with them.
Reporter: Why did you take part in the race?
Adrianna: I wanted to test my limits and make my own history. I thought, "If I can (C)finish the race, then I can do anything."

서답형

20 위 글의 빈칸 (A)에 알맞은 질문을 쓰시오.

➡ _____

서답형

21 위 글의 밑줄 친 (B)와 같은 의미의 문장이 되도록 빈칸에 알맞은 말을 쓰시오.

Which desert was _____ _____ all the other _____ for you?

➡ _____

22 위 글의 내용과 일치하지 <u>않는</u> 것은?

① Adrianna has run through the Atacama Desert.

② Adrianna thinks the Sahara Desert is the toughest.

③ Most of the participants were not special people.

④ It was hard for Adrianna to become friends with the participants.

⑤ There were two reasons why Adrianna took part in the race.

서답형

23 다음과 같이 풀이되는 말을 위 글에서 찾아 쓰시오.

a measure of how hot or cold something is

➡ _____

[24~27] 다음 글을 읽고, 물음에 답하시오.

Sounds like a bad dream? Well, this is not a dream for the people who take part in the 4 Deserts Race. The 4 Deserts Race is a series of four races across the world's toughest deserts. Each race is 250 kilometers long and takes seven days.

The first race takes place in the Atacama Desert in Chile. ⓐIt is the driest desert in the world. ① In fact, it hasn't rained in some parts of the Atacama Desert for 400 years! ② The next race goes to the Gobi Desert in China. It is the windiest desert on earth. ③ The third race heads to the Sahara Desert in Egypt. ④ It is the hottest of the four deserts. Temperatures can reach up to 50℃. ⑤ If you throw boiling water into the air here, it freezes!

서답형

24 다음 주어진 문장이 들어가기에 가장 적합한 곳은?

Finally, the race travels to the coldest desert on earth, Antarctica.

①   ②   ③   ④   ⑤

25 위 글을 읽고 답할 수 <u>없는</u> 것은?

① How long does it take to run through the Atacama Desert?

② What makes the Atacama Desert the driest place in the world?

③ Where is the Gobi Desert?

④ What makes the Gobi Desert windier than any other place?

⑤ What degrees does the temperature of the Sahara Desert reach up to?

26 위 글의 밑줄 친 ⓐ와 쓰임이 같은 것은?

① It is wise to accept the apology.

② Is it the invitation card from her?

③ It is warm outside.

④ I find it strange that he is not here.

⑤ It is a long time since they left.

서답형

27 위 글의 내용에 맞게 빈칸에 알맞은 말을 쓰시오.

The participants of the 4 Deserts Race run through four deserts _____ are the world's _____.

➡ _____

[01~03] 다음 글을 읽고 물음에 답하시오.

_____(A)_____ The sands go on and on in every direction. The sun feels like a giant ball of fire. The hot wind burns your face and throat. You open your backpack to drink some water. Oh, no! You're almost out of water. You wet your throat with a drop of water and keep going.

01 주어진 어구를 바르게 배열하여 빈칸 (A)에 들어갈 말을 쓰시오.

(a great desert / imagine / of / in / are / the middle / you / that)

➡ _____

02 What makes your face and throat burn? Answer in English with a full sentence.

➡ _____

03 위 글의 내용에 맞도록 빈칸에 알맞은 말을 쓰시오.

A: Aren't you thirsty? Why did you drink only a drop of water?
B: It's because _____.

➡ _____

[04~06] 다음 글을 읽고, 물음에 답하시오.

Imagine you are in the middle of a great desert. The sands go on and on in every direction. The sun feels like a giant ball of fire. The hot wind burns your face and throat. You open your backpack to drink some water. Oh, no! You're almost out of water. You wet your throat with a drop of water and keep going.

Sounds like a bad dream? _____(A)_____ The 4 Deserts Race is a series of four races across the world's __(B)__ deserts. Each race is 250 kilometers long and takes seven days.

04 위 글의 내용에 맞도록 빈칸에 알맞은 말을 6단어로 쓰시오.

A: Why do you open your backpack?
B: I open it _____.

➡ _____

05 관계대명사를 이용하여 다음 두 문장을 하나로 이어 빈칸 (A)에 쓰시오.

• Well, this is not a dream for the people.
• They take part in the 4 Deserts Race.

➡ _____

_____

06 위 글의 빈칸 (B)에 주어진 단어를 어법에 맞게 쓰시오.

(tough)

➡ _____

[07~10] 다음 글을 읽고, 물음에 답하시오.

The first race takes place in the Atacama Desert in Chile. It is the driest desert in the world. In fact, it hasn't rained in some parts of the Atacama Desert for 400 years! The next race goes to the Gobi Desert in China. It is the windiest desert on earth. The third race heads to the Sahara Desert in Egypt. It is the hottest of the four deserts. Temperatures can reach up to 50℃. Finally, the race travels to the coldest desert on earth, Antarctica. If you throw boiling water into the air here, it ___ⓐ___ !

07 다음과 같이 풀이되는 단어를 빈칸 ⓐ에 어법에 맞게 쓰시오.

This word is used when something becomes solid because of low temperatures.

➡ _____

08 위 글을 읽고 다음 조건에 맞도록 사하라 사막의 특징을 쓰시오.

• 비교급을 사용할 것
• 단어 all을 사용할 것

➡ _____
_____

09 다음 질문에 완전한 문장의 영어로 답하시오.

Where does the second race take place?

➡ _____
_____

10 위 글의 내용에 맞도록 빈칸에 알맞은 말을 쓰시오.

No other desert on earth is _____ Antarctica.

➡ _____

[11~12] 다음 글을 읽고, 물음에 답하시오.

Only the greatest runners on the planet can take part in 4 Deserts Race, right? Not exactly. Many of the participants are ordinary people like you and me. ⓐSo why do they do it? Adrianna, a librarian from France, says, "It's a chance to test your limits and make your own history. Anyone who crosses the finish line can do anything."

11 다음은 밑줄 친 ⓐ를 다시 쓴 것이다. 같은 의미가 되도록 빈칸에 알맞은 말을 쓰시오.

So why do the people _____ _____ _____ like us do it?

➡ _____

12 관계대명사를 이용하여 다음 빈칸에 알맞은 말을 쓰시오.

Adrianna is a woman _____
_____ .

➡ _____

Real Life Talk - Step 2

G: What do you do in your free time?
여가 시간에

B: I often play sports.

G: Have you ever played table tennis?
have + p.p.: 현재완료 (경험)

B: No, I haven't.
부정의 대답에 do가 아닌 have를 써서 답한다.

G: Have you ever played baseball?

B: Yes, I have.
긍정의 대답에 do 동사가 아닌 have를 써서 답한다.

G: Have you ever hit a home run?
홈런을 치다

B: Yes, I have.

구문해설 ・free time: 여가 시간 ・table tennis: 탁구 ・hit: 치다 ・home run: 홈런

G: 너는 여가 시간에 무엇을 하니?
B: 나는 종종 운동을 해.
G: 탁구를 쳐 본 적이 있니?
B: 아니, 없어.
G: 야구를 해 본 적이 있니?
B: 응, 있어.
G: 홈런을 쳐 본 적이 있니?
B: 응, 있어.

Think and Write

A Happy Day for Class 3

The school sports day was held on May 14th. It was very exciting. Students
특정 날짜 앞에 쓰는 전치사 ／ 감정을 유발할 때 현재분사형
played basketball and did group jump rope. They also ran a relay race and a
릴레이 경주를 했다
100m race. Class 2 won the group jump rope, and Class 1 won the relay race.
Class 3 won the basketball game and the 100m race. They got the highest
(점수를) 얻었다
score and became the overall winner. All the classes had great fun.
～이 되었다 ／ have fun 재미있게 놀다, 흥겨워하다

구문해설 ・hold: 개최하다 ・exciting: 신나는 ・group jump rope: 단체 줄넘기
・relay race: 릴레이 경주 ・overall: 전반적인

3반을 위한 행복한 날
학교 운동회는 5월 14일에 개최되었다. 그것은 매우 신났다. 학생들은 농구를 하고 단체 줄넘기를 했다. 그들은 또한 릴레이 경주를 했고 100미터 달리기도 했다. 2반은 단체 줄넘기에서 우승을 했고, 1반은 릴레이 경주에서 우승을 했다. 3반은 농구 경기와 100미터 경주에서 우승을 차지했다. 그들은 가장 높은 점수를 얻어서 전체 우승자가 되었다. 모든 반은 재미있는 시간을 보냈다.

Culture

Taekwondo is a Korean traditional sport that trains one's body and mind. It is
= which ／ 몸과 마음
one of the most popular sports in the world. People who do taekwondo wear
one of the 최상급+복수명사 ／ 주격 관계대명사
white uniforms. Taekwondo training includes jumping, punching, kicking and
shouting. It teaches you ways to protect yourself.
to부정사의 형용사 용법

구문해설 ・traditional: 전통적인 ・train: 단련시키다, 훈련하다 ・popular: 인기 있는, 대중적인
・wear: 입다 ・include: 포함하다 ・protect: 보호하다

태권도는 몸과 마음을 단련하는 한국의 전통 스포츠이다. 그것은 세계에서 가장 인기 있는 스포츠 중 하나이다. 태권도를 하는 사람들은 흰색 유니폼을 입는다. 태권도 훈련은 뛰기, 치기, 차기, 소리치기를 포함한다. 태권도는 너에게 스스로를 보호하는 방법을 가르쳐 준다.

01 다음 영영풀이가 나타내는 말을 쓰시오.

> a race in which people run a distance of 26 miles, which is about 42 km

➡ _____

02 다음 중 밑줄 친 부분의 뜻풀이가 바르지 않은 것은?

① I took part in the marathon to test my limits. 한계
② I got a punch on my chin during the boxing match. 타격
③ His work is to train dogs to obey their owners. 훈련시키다
④ We need to wear a hat to protect our skin from the sunlight. 보호하다
⑤ I have a sore throat because of the cold. ~을 통하여

03 다음 문장의 빈칸에 들어갈 말을 〈보기〉에서 골라 쓰시오.

> ┌ 보기 ┐
> take part in / a series of / for a living

(1) I'm reading _____ _____ magazines about science.
(2) They will _____ _____ the English speaking contest.
(3) She baked bread every day _____ _____.

04 다음 주어진 문장의 밑줄 친 부분과 같은 의미로 쓰인 것을 고르시오.

> Emily went on working until late at night.

① Let's go on to the next page.
② What's going on here?
③ We should go on a picnic on such a beautiful day.
④ The hot weather will go on for this week.
⑤ You don't have to go on a diet.

05 다음 우리말을 주어진 단어를 활용하여 영작하시오.

(1) 너는 홈런을 쳐 본 적이 있니? (hit)
➡ _____

(2) 나는 종종 여가 시간에 탁구를 쳐. (free)
➡ _____

(3) 그는 어떤 일을 하나요? (living)
➡ _____

[06~08] 다음 대화를 읽고, 물음에 답하시오.

Jean: I'm so happy. It's Friday!
Tom: What are you going to do on the weekend, Jean?
Jean: I'm going to play badminton.
Tom: Do you play badminton often?
Jean: Yes, it's my favorite free time activity.
Tom: _____(A)_____
Jean: My dad. What do you do in your free time?
Tom: I often go to the Han River and ride my bike.

06 위 대화의 빈칸 (A)에 들어갈 말을 <보기>에 주어진 단어를 모두 배열하여 완성하시오.

> ┌─ 보기 ─┐
> usually / who / with / you / play /
> do

➡ _____

07 What does Jean do in her free time?

➡ _____

08 위 대화의 주제로 적절한 것은?

① volunteer activity
② school activity
③ leisure activity
④ club activity
⑤ festival activity

[09~11] 다음 대화를 읽고, 물음에 답하시오.

> Suji: Mike, have you ever heard ⓐof flying yoga?
> Mike: Yeah! ⓑI've seen it on TV. People were hanging in the air!
> Suji: Guess what? I'm learning it these days.
> Mike: Really? It looked so scary. Do you like it, Suji?
> Suji: At first, I was a little ⓒscaring, but now I'm enjoying it.
> Mike: _____(A)_____ I think I should ⓓexercise more, too.
> Suji: Do you want to join my yoga class?
> Mike: No, that's too scary ⓔfor me. I'll just play basketball.

09 위 대화의 ⓐ~ⓔ 중 어법상 어색한 것을 찾아 바르게 고치시오.

➡ _____

10 위 대화의 빈칸 (A)에 들어갈 말로 어색한 것은?

① Sounds great!
② Good for you.
③ That's really cool.
④ I'm happy to hear that.
⑤ That's all right.

11 위 대화를 읽고 대답할 수 없는 것은?

① Has Mike ever seen flying yoga?
② What is Suji learning these days?
③ What does Mike think he should do?
④ Does Mike want to join Suji's yoga class?
⑤ Why does Suji like doing yoga these days?

[12~14] 다음 대화를 읽고, 물음에 답하시오.

> Hojin: Judy, what do you do in your free time?
> Judy: I often go rock climbing with my dad.
> Hojin: _____(A)_____
> Judy: No, Hojin. I usually do it at a gym near my house.
> Hojin: I see. Have you ever done it on a real mountain?
> Judy: Not yet. But I hope to do it someday.
> Hojin: That's really cool. Can I come and join you next time?
> Judy: Sure. I'm going this Saturday.
> Hojin: That sounds great.
> Judy: You're going to love it.

12 위 대화에서 다음 영영풀이가 가리키는 말을 찾아 쓰시오.

> the sport or activity of climbing steep rock surfaces

➡ _____

13 위 대화의 빈칸 (A)에 <보기>에 주어진 단어를 모두 배열하여 문장을 완성하시오.

┌─── 보기 ───
│ to / what / you / do / mountain / go
└─────────────

➡ _____

14 위 대화의 내용과 일치하지 <u>않는</u> 것은?

① Judy는 여가 시간에 종종 아빠와 함께 암벽 등반을 간다.

② Judy는 주로 집 근처의 체육관에서 암벽 등반을 한다.

③ Judy는 실제 산에서 암벽 등반을 해 본 적이 없다.

④ Judy는 이번 주 토요일에 암벽 등반을 하러 산에 갈 것이다.

⑤ Judy는 Hojin이 암벽 등반을 좋아하게 될 것이라고 생각한다.

15 다음 대화가 자연스럽게 이어지도록 순서대로 배열하시오.

┌──────────────────────────────
│ (A) That's great! I'm sure you'll like it a lot.
│ (B) Have you ever been to Jeju-do?
│ (C) I've never been there, but I'm going there this summer.
│ (D) Yes, I have. I went there last winter vacation. What about you?
└──────────────────────────────

➡ _____

16 다음 중 밑줄 친 부분의 쓰임이 적절하지 <u>않은</u> 것은?

① He is the man <u>who</u> I really look up to.

② I apologized to the girl <u>whose</u> milk I spilled.

③ Kyle made friends with a boy <u>which</u> is in my class.

④ Harvard is the best university <u>that</u> I have ever visited.

⑤ Did the woman <u>who</u> stepped on your toes apologize to you?

17 주어진 단어를 활용하여 다음 우리말을 영어로 쓰시오.

┌──────────────────────────────
│ 네가 오늘 수영한 호수는 우리나라에서 가장 깊은 호수이다.
│ (which / swim in / deep)
└──────────────────────────────

➡ _____
  _____

18 다음 중 의미가 같지 <u>않은</u> 것은?

① This is the longest bridge in our country.
→ This bridge is longer than any other bridge in our country.

② I worked at a company whose employees were really happy.
→ I worked at a company. Its employees were really happy.

③ Jake is the fastest boy in our school.
→ No other boy in our school is faster than Jake.

④ The woman who had found my wallet called me.
→ I called the woman whose wallet I had found.

⑤ The teacher is excellent. I am taking her lessons.
→ The teacher whose lessons I am taking is excellent.

19 다음 중 어법상 바르지 <u>않은</u> 것은?

> The woman ①<u>whose</u> hair ②<u>is</u> blond ③<u>is</u> Taylor Swift. She is ④<u>one</u> of the most famous ⑤<u>singer</u> in America.

①   ②   ③   ④   ⑤

20 다음 중 밑줄 친 부분을 생략할 수 <u>없는</u> 것은?

① The book <u>that</u> you bought yesterday is very interesting.
② The woman <u>who</u> I wanted to meet was on vacation.
③ I wish to get the job <u>which</u> I applied for.
④ The doctor <u>who</u> lives next door is my father's best friend.
⑤ Is this the key <u>that</u> you lost the other day?

[21~22] 다음 글을 읽고 빈칸에 알맞은 답을 쓰시오.

> There are three boxes on the table. They are named box A, box B, and box C. Box A is smaller than any other box on the table. And no other box is as big as box C. However, box C is the lightest of the three boxes and box A is heavier than all the other boxes.

21 Which is the biggest box?

> Box C is _____ _____ _____ _____ box on the table.

22 Which is the heaviest box?

> No other box on the table is _____ _____ _____ box A.

23 다음 문장의 빈칸에 들어갈 말과 같은 것은?

> There were many children _____ made a lot of noise in the library. (that 사용 불가)

① That is the boy _____ mother is a farmer.
② Picasso painted many pictures _____ are now very expensive.
③ I have two sisters _____ I should take care of.
④ Look at the house _____ roof is red.
⑤ I saw a man and a dog _____ were running together.

24 다음 글을 읽고 빈칸에 알맞은 말을 쓰시오.

> Your friend meets a lot of people, and some of them are very famous. So you ask your friend like this, "Who is _____ person _____ you've ever met?

➡ _____

25 다음 빈칸에 들어갈 말이 바르게 짝지어진 것은?

> • I know a girl _____ dream is to be a singer.
> • They liked the house _____ was very large.

① who – which   ② whom – that
③ whose – that   ④ whose – who
⑤ who – whose

Reading

[26~28] 다음 글을 읽고 물음에 답하시오.

Imagine you are ____ⓐ____ a great desert. The sands go on and on in every direction. The sun ____ⓑ____ a giant ball of fire. The hot wind burns your face and throat. You open your backpack to drink some water. Oh, no! You're almost ____ⓒ____ water. You wet your throat with ____ⓓ____ water and keep going.

26 위 글의 빈칸 ⓐ~ⓓ에 적합한 말이 <u>아닌</u> 것은?

① feels like
② in the middle of
③ out of
④ full of
⑤ a drop of

27 위 글의 내용과 일치하지 <u>않는</u> 것은? (2개)

① The sands are everywhere.
② The wind is so hot that you are too thirsty.
③ Your water was in your pocket.
④ You have a lot of water.
⑤ You keep walking after drinking a little water.

28 위 글의 내용에 맞게 빈칸에 알맞은 말을 쓰시오.

> A: Due to the hot wind, how does your face feel?
> B: My face feels _____ due to the hot wind.

➡ _____

[29~31] 다음 글을 읽고, 물음에 답하시오.

Only the greatest runners on the planet can take part in 4 Deserts Race, right? Not exactly. Many of the (A)participants are ordinary people like you and me. So why do they do ⓐ [it / them]? Adrianna, a librarian from France, says, "It's a chance to test your limits and ⓑ [makes / make] your own history. Anyone who ⓒ[crosses / cross] the finish line can do anything."

29 다음은 밑줄 친 (A)를 설명하는 문장이다. 빈칸에 알맞은 말을 위 글에서 찾아 쓰시오.

> A participant means a person _____ _____ _____ _____ an event.

➡ _____

30 위 글의 ⓐ~ⓒ에 들어갈 말이 바르게 짝지어진 것은?

① it – makes – crosses
② it – make – crosses
③ it – make – cross
④ them – make – crosses
⑤ them – makes – cross

31 위 글의 내용과 일치하는 것은?

① Only expert runners can be found in the 4 Deserts Race.
② Ordinary people can't participate in the 4 Deserts Race.
③ A German woman took part in the 4 Deserts Race.
④ Adrianna works in the library.
⑤ Adrianna doesn't want to know her limits.

출제율 90%

01 다음 짝지어진 단어의 관계가 같도록 빈칸에 알맞은 말을 쓰시오.

> early : late = melt : _____

출제율 95%

02 다음 주어진 문장의 밑줄 친 부분과 같은 의미로 쓰인 것은?

> They succeeded in completing the <u>tough</u> project by cooperating with each other.

① He was in charge of the <u>tough</u> work as a leader.
② My mother's <u>tough</u> hands made me so sad.
③ Tom applied the lotion to relieve his <u>tough</u> skin.
④ He had his teeth broken because of the <u>tough</u> meat.
⑤ She became as <u>tough</u> as nails after moving to China.

[03~04] 다음 대화를 읽고, 물음에 답하시오.

Jean: I'm so happy. It's Friday!
Tom: ⓐ<u>What</u> are you going to do on the weekend, Jean?
Jean: I'm going to play badminton.
Tom: Do you play badminton ⓑ<u>often</u>?
Jean: Yes, it's my favorite free time activity.
Tom: ⓒ<u>Where</u> do you usually play with?
Jean: My dad. ⓓ<u>What</u> do you do in your free time?
Tom: I often go to the Han River and ⓔ<u>ride</u> my bike.

출제율 100%

03 위 대화의 밑줄 친 ⓐ~ⓔ 중 어색한 것을 찾아 바르게 고치시오.

➡ _____

출제율 85%

04 위 대화의 내용과 일치하지 않는 것은?

① Jean feels so good because it's Friday.
② Jean is planning to play badminton.
③ Jean loves playing badminton in her free time.
④ Jean usually plays badminton with her father.
⑤ Jean is going to ride a bike with Tom this Saturday.

출제율 90%

05 다음 주어진 단어를 써서 우리말과 일치하도록 영작하시오.

(1) 나는 종종 여가 시간에 그림을 그려요. (draw, free)
➡ _____

(2) 당신은 일본에 가 본 적이 있나요? (ever, to)
➡ _____

(3) 저는 중국에 가 본 적이 없어요. (never)
➡ _____

출제율 90%

06 다음 주어진 단어를 모두 배열하여 빈칸에 들어갈 말을 영작하시오.

> Tony: Bomi, _____
> (free / do / what / you / do / in / time / your / ?)
> Bomi: I often bake cookies.

➡ _____

Mina: Tom, have you ever been to Jeju-do?

Tom: Yes, I have. I went there last winter vacation. What about you?

Mina: (A)나는 거기에 가 본 적이 없어, but I'm going there this summer.

Tom: That's great! I'm (B)sure you'll like it a lot.

출제율 95%

07 위 대화의 밑줄 친 우리말 (A)를 4단어를 사용하여 영작하시오.

➡ _____

출제율 100%

08 위 대화의 밑줄 친 (B)와 바꾸어 쓸 수 있는 것은?

① certain   ② doubtful

③ clear   ④ likely

⑤ believable

출제율 90%

09 Who has been to Jeju-do?

➡ _____

[10~11] 다음 대화를 읽고 물음에 답하시오.

Suji: Mike, ⓐ너는 플라잉 요가에 대해 들어 본 적이 있니? (of, flying yoga)

Mike: Yeah! I've seen it on TV. People were hanging in the air!

Suji: Guess what? I'm learning it these days.

Mike: (A) Really? It looked so scary. Do you like it, Suji?

Suji: (B) At first, I was a little scared, but now I'm enjoying it.

Mike: (C) Sounds great! I think I should exercise more, too.

Suji: (D) Do you want to join my yoga class?

Mike: (E) I'll just play basketball.

출제율 90%

10 위 대화의 밑줄 친 ⓐ의 우리말을 주어진 단어를 사용하여 영작하시오.

➡ _____

출제율 95%

11 위 대화의 (A)~(E) 중 주어진 문장이 들어가기 적절한 곳은?

No, that's too scary for me.

① (A)   ② (B)   ③ (C)   ④ (D)   ⑤ (E)

출제율 100%

12 다음 빈칸에 공통으로 들어갈 말은?

- The problem is not _____ difficult.
- Everything _____ you made for me is beautiful.
- I think _____ Tom wants you to help him.

① what   ② who   ③ that

④ which   ⑤ whom

출제율 90%

13 다음 우리말을 바르게 영작한 것을 모두 고르시오.

나는 머리가 긴 그 소녀를 안다.

① I know the girl which has long hair.

② I know the girl who is long hair.

③ I know the girl whose hair is long.

④ I know the girl that hair is long.

⑤ I know the girl who has long hair.

14 다음 중 어법상 바르지 <u>않은</u> 것은?

① Is this the oldest building in the country?
② Tom is the funniest boy in the class.
③ You are the latest person I want to talk with.
④ Julia is the most creative and beautiful person I know.
⑤ It is the dirtiest room I've ever seen.

15 다음 중 나머지 넷과 의미가 <u>다른</u> 하나는?

① Honesty is more important than any other thing.
② Nothing is more important than honesty.
③ Honesty is the most important thing of all.
④ Nothing is so important as honesty.
⑤ Nothing is less important than honesty.

16 주어진 단어를 활용하여 다음 우리말을 영어로 쓰시오.

> 그것은 내 생애에서 가장 고통스러운 순간이었다.
> (it, painful)

➡ _____

17 다음 두 문장을 관계대명사 whose를 써서 한 문장으로 만드시오.

> • Kelly bought a book.
> • Its cover looked familiar to him.

➡ _____
_____

18 주어진 단어를 어법에 맞게 각각 쓰시오.

> (diligent)

> A: What do you think is _____ _____ _____ insect on earth?
> B: I think no other insect on earth is _____ _____ _____ bees.

➡ _____
_____

[19~20] 다음 글을 읽고, 물음에 답하시오.

The first race takes place in the Atacama Desert in Chile. It is the driest desert in the world. In fact, it ⓐhasn't rained in some parts of the Atacama Desert for 400 years! ① The next race goes to the Gobi Desert in China. It is the windiest desert on earth. ② The third race heads to the Sahara Desert in Egypt. It is the hottest of the four deserts. ③ Finally, the race travels to the coldest desert on earth, Antartica. ④ If you throw boiling water into the air here, it freezes! ⑤

19 다음 주어진 문장이 들어가기에 가장 적절한 곳은?

> Temperatures can reach up to 50℃.

①   ②   ③   ④   ⑤

20 위 글의 밑줄 친 ⓐ와 쓰임이 같은 것은?

① She <u>has</u> just <u>had</u> dinner with me.
② <u>Have</u> you ever <u>heard</u> about the news?
③ How long <u>have</u> you <u>seen</u> each other?
④ Jimmy <u>has lost</u> his cell phone.
⑤ My mom <u>has gone</u> out.

21 다음 우리말을 관계대명사를 이용하여 영어로 쓰시오.

> 중국에 있는 고비 사막은 지구상에서 가장 바람이 많이 부는 사막이다.

➡ _____

_____

[22~26] 다음 글을 읽고, 물음에 답하시오.

The 4 Deserts Race is a series of four races across the world's ①toughest deserts. Each race is 250 kilometers long and ⓐ seven days.

The first race ⓑ place in the Atacama Desert in Chile. It is the driest desert in the world. In fact, it ②hasn't rained in some parts of the Atacama Desert for 400 years! The next race goes to the Gobi Desert in China. It is ③windier than any other desert on earth. The third race heads to the Sahara Desert in Egypt. It is the hottest of the four deserts. Temperatures can reach ④down to 50℃. Finally, the race travels to the coldest desert on earth, Antarctica. If you throw boiling water into the air here, it ⑤freezes!

Only the greatest runners on the planet can take part in 4 Deserts Race, right? Not exactly. Many of the participants are ordinary people like you and me. So why do they do it? Adrianna, a librarian from France, says, "It's a chance to test your limits and make your own history. ⓒ "

22 위 글의 빈칸 ⓐ, ⓑ에 공통으로 들어갈 말은?

① makes   ② has   ③ takes
④ holds   ⑤ gets

23 다음 ①~⑤ 중 글의 흐름상 어색한 것은?

①   ②   ③   ④   ⑤

24 (A)~(E) 중 글의 내용과 일치하는 것의 개수는?

> (A) The Antarctica Desert race is 250km long.
> (B) The Sahara Desert is in Egypt.
> (C) It takes 14 days to run through two deserts.
> (D) The participants are made up of only ordinary people.
> (E) The last race is held in Antarctica.

① 1개   ② 2개   ③ 3개   ④ 4개   ⑤ 5개

25 위 글의 내용에 맞도록 빈칸에 알맞은 말을 쓰시오.

> Not only _____ _____ _____ but also _____ _____ take part in the 4 Deserts Race.

➡ _____

26 주어진 단어를 바르게 배열하여 빈칸 ⓒ를 알맞게 채우시오.

> (anything / who / do / can / anyone / the finish line / crosses)

➡ _____

[01~03] 다음 대화를 읽고 물음에 답하시오.

> Mina: Tom, (A)너는 제주도에 가 본 적이 있니?
> Tom: Yes, I have. I went there last winter vacation. What about you?
> Mina: I've never been there, but I'm going there this summer.
> Tom: That's great! I'm sure you'll like (B)it a lot.

01 위 대화의 밑줄 친 우리말 (A)를 영작하시오.

➡ _____

02 위 대화의 밑줄 친 (B)가 가리키는 것을 영어로 쓰시오.

➡ _____

03 What is Mina planning to do this summer?

➡ _____

04 다음 우리말을 여러 가지 표현을 이용하여 영어로 쓰시오.

> Kevin은 그의 가족 구성원 중에서 가장 어리다.

➡ _____
➡ _____
➡ _____
➡ _____
➡ _____

05 다음 문장을 하나의 문장으로 만드시오.

> • You are sitting on the chair.
> • Is it comfortable?

➡ _____

06 다음 빈칸에 알맞은 말을 쓰시오.

> The town _____ I grew up in is very small. People in the town is nicer _____ any other people in the world. If you visit there, you will see many people _____ smile is very bright.

➡ _____

07 주어진 조건에 맞도록 다음 우리말을 영어로 쓰시오.

> • 최상급을 한 번 사용할 것
> • laugh를 두 번 사용할 것
> • 관계대명사를 사용할 것

> 마지막에 웃는 사람이 가장 잘 웃는 사람이다.
> (= 마지막에 웃는 사람이 최후의 승자이다.)

➡ He _____ .

08 주어진 단어를 바르게 배열하여 문장을 완성하시오.

> A myth _____ .
> (traditional / is / expresses / a story / beliefs / which)

➡ _____

[09~11] 다음 글을 읽고, 물음에 답하시오.

> Imagine you are in the middle of a great desert. The sands ___ⓐ___ on and on in every direction. The sun feels like a giant ball of fire. The hot wind burns your face and throat. You open your backpack to drink some water. Oh, no! You're almost out of water. You wet your throat with a drop of water and keep ___ⓑ___ .

Sounds like a bad dream? Well, this is not a dream for the people who take part in the 4 Deserts Race. The 4 Deserts Race is a series of four races across the world's toughest deserts. Each race is 250 kilometers long and takes seven days.

(A)The first race takes place in the Atacama Desert in Chile. It is the driest desert in the world.   (B)   fact, it hasn't rained in some parts of the Atacama Desert for 400 years! The next race   ⓒ   to the Gobi Desert in China. It is the windiest desert on earth.

중요
9 주어진 동사를 어법에 맞게 빈칸 ⓐ~ⓒ에 쓰시오.

(go)

ⓐ _____   ⓑ _____   ⓒ _____

10 적절한 관계대명사를 이용하여 밑줄 친 (A)를 하나의 문장으로 쓰시오.

➡ _____

_____

11 위 글의 빈칸 (B)에 알맞은 전치사를 쓰시오.

➡ _____

[12~13] 다음 글을 읽고, 물음에 답하시오.

The third race heads to the Sahara Desert in Egypt. It is the hottest of the four deserts. Temperatures can reach up to 50℃. Finally, the race travels to the coldest desert on earth, Antarctica. If you throw boiling water into the air here, it freezes!

Only the greatest runners on the planet can take part in 4 Deserts Race, right? Not exactly. Many of the participants are ordinary people like you and me. So why do they do it? Adrianna, a librarian from France, says, "It's a chance to test your limits and make your own history. Anyone who crosses the finish line can do anything."

중요
12 원급을 이용하여 다음 질문에 답하시오.

Q: Which desert is colder than any other desert on earth?
A: No other desert _____.

➡ _____

13 '4 Deserts Race' 광고에 알맞은 말을 쓰시오.

_____ _____ _____ 4 Deserts Race _____ offers you a chance _____ _____ _____ _____ and _____ _____ _____ _____. 당신의 한계를 시험하고 당신의 역사를 만들 기회를 제공하는 '4 Deserts Race'에 참가하세요.

➡ _____

_____

01 다음 대화의 내용과 일치하도록 Mike의 일기를 완성하시오.

> **Suji:** Mike, have you ever heard of flying yoga?
>
> **Mike:** Yeah! I've seen it on TV. People were hanging in the air!
>
> **Suji:** Guess what? I'm learning it these days.
>
> **Mike:** Really? It looked so scary. Do you like it, Suji?
>
> **Suji:** At first, I was a little scared, but now I'm enjoying it.
>
> **Mike:** Sounds great! I think I should exercise more, too.
>
> **Suji:** Do you want to join my yoga class?
>
> **Mike:** No, that's too scary for me. I'll just play basketball.

> Today, I talked about (1)_____ with Suji. I have seen it on TV. Surprisingly, she was learning and enjoying it recently. She suggested (2)_____, but it looked so (3)_____ for me. Although I didn't accept her suggestion, I decided to (4)_____.

02 관계대명사를 이용하여 〈보기〉와 같이 직업과 사물을 설명하는 문장을 쓰시오.

> ── 보기 ──
> A coward is a person who is not brave.

(1) English teachers are people _____.

(2) Hair designers are people _____.

(3) A computer is a machine _____.

(4) A car is a vehicle _____.

(5) The Wright Brothers were people _____.

03 다음 〈보기〉에 나오는 형용사를 이용하여 최상급을 나타내는 문장을 쓰시오.

> ── 보기 ──
> beautiful   delicious   spicy   hard   soft

(1) _____

(2) _____

(3) _____

(4) _____

(5) _____

단원별 모의고사

01 다음 영영풀이가 나타내는 말을 쓰시오.

> the measurement in degrees of how hot or cold a thing or place is

➡ _____

02 다음 문장의 빈칸에 들어갈 말을 〈보기〉에서 골라 쓰시오.

> ┌─── 보기 ───┐
> temperature / direction / scary / boiling

(1) I'm afraid you're going in the wrong _____.

(2) I had a nightmare because I saw the _____ movie yesterday.

(3) Be careful! There is lots of _____ water in the pot.

(4) My doctor was measuring my _____.

03 다음 주어진 문장의 밑줄 친 부분과 같은 의미로 쓰인 것은?

> Many tourists head to Jeju-do in Korea.

① You look so tired. Why don't you head to the house?

② Mike shook his head during the meeting.

③ I hit my head on the window.

④ Tony is not the head of our company.

⑤ The head of the department has been changed.

04 다음 우리말을 주어진 어구를 사용하여 영작하시오.

(1) 이 소설은 일련의 역사적 사실에 관해 쓰여졌다. (a series of)

➡ _____

(2) 경주는 매년 봄에 개최된다. (take place)

➡ _____

(3) 고양이가 길 한 가운데에서 발견되었다. (in the middle of, road)

➡ _____

[05~06] 다음 대화를 읽고 물음에 답하시오.

> Jean: I'm so happy. It's Friday!
> Tom: What are you going to do on the weekend, Jean?
> Jean: I'm going to play badminton.
> Tom: (A)[Do / Have] you play badminton often?
> Jean: Yes, it's my favorite free time activity.
> Tom: Who do you usually play (B)[by / with]?
> Jean: My dad. What do you do in your free time?
> Tom: I often go to the Han River and (C)[ride / riding] my bike.

05 위 대화의 괄호 (A)~(C)에 들어갈 말이 바르게 짝지어진 것은?

	(A)	(B)	(C)
①	Do	by	ride
②	Do	with	riding
③	Do	with	ride
④	Have	with	riding
⑤	Have	by	ride

06 What sport does Jean like best as her free time activity?

➡ _____

[07~09] 다음 대화를 읽고, 물음에 답하시오.

Suji: Mike, have you ever heard of flying yoga?

Mike: Yeah! I've seen ⓐit on TV. People were hanging in the air!

Suji: Guess what? I'm learning ⓑit these days.

Mike: Really? ⓒIt looked so scary. Do you like it, Suji?

Suji: At first, I was a little scared, but now I'm enjoying ⓓit.

Mike: Sounds great! I think ⓔit is necessary for me to exercise more, too.

Suji: Do you want to join my yoga class?

Mike: No, that's too (A)scary for me. I'll just play basketball.

07 위 대화의 ⓐ~ⓔ 중 가리키는 대상이 나머지와 넷과 다른 것은?

① ⓐ　　② ⓑ　　③ ⓒ　　④ ⓓ　　⑤ ⓔ

08 위 대화의 밑줄 친 (A)와 의미가 다른 것은?

① terrifying　　② scaring

③ frightening　　④ fearful

⑤ terrific

09 위 대화의 내용과 일치하지 않는 것은?

① Suji is learning flying yoga these days.

② Mike feels scary about flying yoga.

③ Mike has seen flying yoga on TV.

④ Mike is going to join the yoga class with Suji.

⑤ Mike thinks he needs to exercise more.

[10~11] 다음 대화를 읽고, 물음에 답하시오.

Hojin: Judy, what do you do in your free time?

Judy: I often go rock climbing with my dad.

Hojin: What mountain do you go to?

Judy: No, Hojin. I usually do it at a gym near my house.

Hojin: I see. (A)너는 실제 산에서 그것을 해 본 적이 있니?

Judy: Not yet. But I hope to do it someday.

Hojin: That's really cool. (B)＿＿＿＿＿＿

Judy: Sure. I'm going this Saturday.

Hojin: That sounds great.

Judy: You're going to love it.

10 위 대화의 밑줄 친 (A)의 우리말과 일치하도록 〈보기〉에 주어진 단어를 모두 배열하시오.

┤ 보기 ├
ever / mountain / have / done / you / a / real / it / on

➡ ＿＿＿＿＿＿＿＿＿＿＿＿＿＿＿＿

11 위 대화의 빈칸 (B)에 들어갈 말로 어색한 것은?

① Can I come and join you next time?

② Do you wonder if I come and join you next time?

③ Is it okay for me to come and join you next time?

④ May I come and join you next time?

⑤ Would it be possible for me to come and join you next time?

12 주어진 문장에 대화가 자연스럽게 이어지도록 순서대로 배열하시오.

What are you going to do on the weekend?

(A) Who do you usually play with?
(B) My dad.
(C) Do you play badminton often?
(D) Yes, it's my favorite free time activity.
(E) I'm going to play badminton.

➡ ＿＿＿＿＿＿＿＿＿＿＿＿＿＿＿＿

13 다음 중 빈칸에 들어갈 말이 바르게 짝지어진 것은?

> • What is the name of the boy _____ pen you borrowed?
> • What is the name of the boy _____ you lent your pen?

① whom – who
② who – whose
③ whose – whom
④ whom – that
⑤ whose – whose

14 다음 우리말을 영어로 바르게 옮기지 않은 것은?

① 그건 내가 할 수 있는 최소한이야.
  → It's the least I can do.
② 그는 그 소년들 중에서 가장 행복해 보여.
  → He looks happiest of the boys.
③ 그것은 내 인생에서 가장 무서웠던 순간이었어.
  → It was the scariest moment of my life.
④ 이 사탕이 그 슈퍼마켓에서 가장 싼 사탕이야.
  → This candy is cheaper than all the other candies in the supermarket.
⑤ 그것은 그 주에서 가장 좋은 대학이야.
  → It is the best college in the state.

15 다음 빈칸에 적절한 것을 모두 고르시오.

> These are the blue jeans _____ Tom Cruise wore in the movie.

① who
② whose
③ which
④ that
⑤ whom

16 주어진 단어를 바르게 배열하여 다음 문장을 완성하시오.

> August _____
> September.
> (before / that / the / comes / month / is)

➡ _____

17 주어진 단어를 활용하여 다음 우리말을 영어로 쓰시오.

> 그것은 내 생애 최악의 경험들 중 하나야. (bad)

➡ _____

[18~20] 다음 글을 읽고, 물음에 답하시오.

> Imagine you are in the middle of a great desert. The sands go on and on in every direction. The sun feels like a giant ball of ⓐfire. The hot wind ⓑburns your face and throat. You open your backpack to drink some water. Oh, no! You're almost out of water. You wet your throat with ⓒplenty of water and keep going.
>
> Sounds like a ⓓbad dream? Well, this is not a dream for the people who take part in the 4 Deserts Race. The 4 Deserts Race is a series of four races across the world's ⓔtoughest deserts. Each race is 250 kilometers long and takes seven days.

18 위 글의 밑줄 친 ⓐ~ⓔ 중 문맥상 어색한 것은?

① ⓐ
② ⓑ
③ ⓒ
④ ⓓ
⑤ ⓔ

19 위 글의 내용과 일치하는 것은?

① You can see the sands only in one direction.
② The hot sun makes the wind cold.
③ You are thirsty because of a long walk.
④ There are people who participate in the 4 Deserts Race.
⑤ The 4 Deserts Race is 250km long.

20 위 글의 내용에 맞게 빈칸에 알맞은 답을 하시오.

> A: How long does it take to finish a race?
> B: _____

➡ _____

[21~23] 다음 글을 읽고, 물음에 답하시오.

The first race takes place ①in the Atacama Desert in Chile. It is the driest desert in the world. In fact, it hasn't rained in some parts of the Atacama Desert ②since 400 years! The next race goes to the Gobi Desert in China. It is ③the windiest desert on earth. The third race heads to the Sahara Desert in Egypt. It is the hottest of the four deserts. Temperatures can reach up ④ to 50℃. Finally, the race travels to the coldest desert on earth, Antarctica. If you throw ⑤ boiling water into the air here, it freezes!

21 위 글의 ①~⑤ 중 어법상 바르지 <u>않은</u> 것은?

①   ②   ③   ④   ⑤

22 위 글의 내용에 맞도록 빈칸에 알맞은 말을 쓰시오.

No other desert on earth is _____ _____ Antarctica.
= No other desert on earth is _____ _____ _____ Antarctica.

➡ _____ , _____

23 다음 중 위 글을 읽고 답할 수 <u>없는</u> 것은?

① Where is the Atacama Desert?
② How long hasn't it rained in some parts of the Atacama Desert?
③ Where do the participants go after the first race?
④ Which desert is hotter than any other desert?
⑤ Why do people take part in the desert race?

[24~25] 다음 글을 읽고, 물음에 답하시오.

Only the greatest runners on the planet can take part in 4 Deserts Race, right? Not exactly. Many of the participants are ordinary people like you and me. So why do they do it? Adrianna, a librarian from France, says, "It's a chance to test your limits and make your own history. Anyone who crosses the finish line can do anything."

24 위 글을 읽고 답할 수 있는 것은?

① How many people participate in the 4 Deserts Race?
② Where is the first race held?
③ What is the reason people take part in the race?
④ How many deserts has Adrianna run through?
⑤ Why does Adrianna want to test her limits?

25 다음 우리말에 맞게 빈칸을 채우시오.

Anyone _____ wants to _____ his or her _____ can _____ in 4 Deserts Race.
자신의 한계를 시험하기를 원하는 사람은 누구든 사막 레이스에 참가할 수 있다.

➡ _____

26 주어진 문장에 자연스럽게 연결되도록 (A)~(C)를 바르게 나열하시오.

Imagine you are in the middle of a great desert. The sands go on and on in every direction.

(A) Oh, no! You're almost out of water. You wet your throat with a drop of water and keep going.
(B) Sounds like a bad dream? Well, this is not a dream for the people who take part in the 4 Deserts Race.
(C) The sun feels like a giant ball of fire. The hot wind burns your face and throat. You open your backpack to drink some water.

➡ _____ → _____ → _____

Summer on a Stick

Words & Expressions

Key Words

- **about** [əbáut] 부 대략, 약
- **add** [æd] 동 더하다, 추가하다
- **apple juice** 사과 주스
- **blend** [blend] 동 섞다, 혼합하다
- **blender** [bléndər] 명 믹서
- **close** [klouz] 동 (문, 가게를) 닫다, (눈을) 감다
- **cold** [kould] 형 추운, 찬 명 감기
- **cool** [ku:l] 형 시원한, 냉정한, 멋진
- **cut** [kʌt] 동 자르다
- **enjoy** [indʒɔ́i] 동 즐기다, (즐겁게) 맛보다
- **excellent** [éksələnt] 형 우수한, 훌륭한
- **finish** [fíniʃ] 동 끝내다, 마치다
- **freezer** [frí:zər] 명 냉동고
- **health** [helθ] 명 건강
- **ice pop** 막대 아이스크림
- **kiwi** [kí:wi] 명 키위
- **maker** [méikər] 명 ~을 만드는 기계(사람, 회사)
- **mix** [miks] 명 혼합(물) 동 섞다, 혼합하다
- **need** [ni:d] 동 필요하다

- **orange** [ɔ́:rindʒ] 명 오렌지
- **own** [oun] 형 자기 자신의, 고유한
- **peel** [pi:l] 동 껍질을 벗기다 명 껍질
- **piece** [pi:s] 명 조각, 일부, 부분
- **pineapple** [painæpəl] 명 파인애플
- **pour** [pɔ:r] 동 붓다, 따르다
- **pretty** [príti] 형 예쁜, 귀여운 부 꽤, 상당히
- **share** [ʃɛər] 동 나누다, 공유하다
- **slice** [slais] 동 얇게 썰다[베다] 명 얇은 조각
- **smooth** [smu:ð] 형 매끄러운, 부드러운
- **source** [sɔ:rs] 명 원천, 근원
- **stay** [stei] 동 ~인 채로 있다, 남다, 머무르다
- **step** [step] 명 단계
- **stick** [stik] 명 막대기, 지팡이
- **strawberry** [strɔ́:bèri] 명 딸기
- **tip** [tip] 명 조언, 비결
- **try** [trai] 동 시도하다, 해 보다
- **until** [əntíl] 전 ~까지
- **vitamin** [váitəmin] 명 비타민

Key Expressions

- **a cup of** ~ 한 잔[컵]의
- **a half** (= **one half**) 2분의 1
- **cut A into B** A를 B(상태)로 자르다
- **have a cold** 감기에 걸리다

- **mix up** ~을 섞다
- **pour A into B** A를 B에 붓다
- **put A into B** A를 B에 넣다
- **stay cool** 시원함을 유지하다

Word Power

※ 서로 반대되는 뜻을 가진 어휘

- □ **smooth** 매끄러운, 부드러운 ↔ **rough** 거친
- □ **part** 부분 ↔ **whole** 전체, 전부
- □ **cool** 시원한 ↔ **warm** 따뜻한
- □ **close** 닫다 ↔ **open** 열다
- □ **ask** 묻다 ↔ **answer** 대답하다
- □ **add** 더하다 ↔ **subtract** 빼다

- □ **finish** 끝내다 ↔ **begin** 시작하다
- □ **high** 높은 ↔ **low** 낮은

English Dictionary

- □ **add** 더하다
  → to put something together with something else so as to increase the size, number, amount, etc.
  크기, 수, 양 등을 증가시키기 위해 무언가에 다른 무언가를 더하다

- □ **blender** 믹서
  → an electric machine for mixing soft food or liquid
  부드러운 음식이나 음료를 섞기 위한 전기 기기

- □ **cut** 자르다
  → to divide something into two or more pieces with a knife, etc.
  칼 등으로 무언가를 두 개 또는 그 이상의 조각으로 나누다

- □ **excellent** 훌륭한, 우수한
  → extremely good
  극히 좋은

- □ **mix** 혼합
  → a combination of things that you need to make something
  무언가를 만들기 위해 필요한 것들의 결합

- □ **peel** 껍질을 벗기다
  → to take the outer layer off fruit, vegetables, etc.
  과일이나 야채 등의 외면을 벗겨 내다

- □ **pineapple** 파인애플
  → a large tropical fruit with thick rough skin, sweet yellow flesh with a lot of juice and stiff leaves on top
  두껍고 거친 표면을 가졌으며 많은 즙이 있는 달콤한 노란색의 과육과 맨 윗부분의 뻣뻣한 나뭇잎을 가진 큰 열대 과일

- □ **pour** 붓다, 따르다
  → to make a liquid or other substance flow from a container in a continuous stream
  액체나 다른 물질을 용기로부터 계속 흐르게 만들다

- □ **slice** 얇은 조각
  → a thin flat piece of food that has been cut off a larger piece
  큰 조각을 잘라낸 음식의 얇고 평평한 조각

- □ **smooth** 매끄러운
  → completely flat and even, without any lumps, holes or rough areas
  어떤 혹, 구멍, 또는 거친 부분이 없이 완전히 평평하고 균일한

- □ **step** 단계
  → one of a series of things that you do in order to achieve something
  무언가를 성취하기 위해 당신이 하는 일련의 것들 중 하나

- □ **stick** 막대기
  → a thin piece of wood that has fallen or been broken from a tree
  나무로부터 떨어지거나 부서진 나무의 얇은 조각

- □ **tip** 조언, 비결
  → a small piece of advice about something practical
  어떤 실제적인 것에 관한 사소한 조언

- □ **vitamin** 비타민
  → a natural substance found in food that is an essential part of what humans and animals eat to help them grow and stay healthy
  성장하고 건강을 유지하는 데 도움을 주기 위해 동물이나 사람들이 먹는 것의 필수적인 부분으로 음식에서 발견되는 자연적 물질

Reading

Pineapple Ice Pops

The hot days of summer are here. How can we <u>stay cool</u>? Let's make
<small>stay(2형식 동사)+형용사: ~한 상태로 있다</small>

ice pops together!

You need:

1/2 pineapple
<small>분자는 기수로, 분모는 서수로 읽음 = a half 또는 one half</small>

2 kiwis

1 cup of apple juice

ice pop makers

Steps

1. Cut the pineapple <u>into</u> small pieces. 2. Peel the kiwis and slice <u>them</u>.
<small>cut A into B: A를 B(상태)로 자르다</small>   <small>= the kiwis</small>

3. Put the pineapple pieces <u>into</u> the blender. 4. Add the apple juice. 5.
<small>put A into B: A를 B에 넣다</small>

Blend <u>until</u> the mix is smooth. 6. Pour <u>the mix</u> into the ice pop makers.
<small>~할 때까지(접속사)</small>   <small>혼합물(명사)</small>

7. Add the kiwi slices. 8. Close the ice pop makers. 9. Put <u>them</u> in the
<small>= the ice pop makers</small>

freezer for about three hours.
<small>~동안 (전치사)</small>

Finished!

Enjoy your summer on a stick!

---

stay cool 시원함을 유지하다

let's ~ ~하자

ice pop 막대 아이스크림

maker 만드는 기계

peel 껍질을 벗기다

slice 얇게 썰다

blender 믹서기, 분쇄기

add ~을 첨가하다

blend ~을 섞다

smooth (덩어리 없이) 고루 잘 섞인

pour ~을 붓다

freezer 냉동고

about 대략

확인문제

● 다음 문장이 본문의 내용과 일치하면 T, 일치하지 <u>않으면</u> F를 쓰시오.

1 It is a recipe for pineapple ice pops. ☐

2 You don't need apple juice to make pineapple ice pops. ☐

3 The first step is cutting pineapples. ☐

4 You don't have to peel the kiwis. ☐

5 What you need to put into the blender first is kiwis. ☐

Health Tips

Pineapples are an excellent source of vitamin C. They have more
vitamin C than oranges. So when you have a cold, try pineapples.

Share Your Ideas!

How will you make your own ice pops? Share your ideas!

Jinsu

I will use kiwis and strawberries. I will cut them into big pieces. I will
put them into the ice pop makers with apple juice. I think my ice pops
will be pretty.

---

tip 조언

excellent 탁월한, 훌륭한

source 원천

vitamin 비타민

have a cold 감기에 걸리다

share 공유하다

own 자신의

cut A into B A를 B로 자르다

pretty 예쁜

확인문제

• 다음 문장이 본문의 내용과 일치하면 T, 일치하지 않으면 F를 쓰시오.

1   Pineapples are good for us when we have a cold. ☐

2   Oranges have more vitamin C than pineapples. ☐

3   There is only one way to make ice pops. ☐

4   You don't need to cut strawberries to make ice pops. ☐

5   Ice pops are made from kiwis, strawberries and apple juice. ☐

● 우리말을 참고하여 빈칸에 알맞은 말을 쓰시오.

1   The _____ _____ of summer _____ here.

2   How can we _____ _____?

3   Let's _____ ice pops together!

4   You need:

    1/2 _____

    2 _____

    1 _____ of apple juice

    ice pop _____

5   _____

6   _____ the pineapple _____ _____ _____.

7   _____ the kiwis and _____ _____.

8   _____ the pineapple _____ _____ the blender.

9   _____ the apple juice.

10   _____ _____ the mix is _____.

11   _____ the mix _____ the ice pop makers.

12   _____ the kiwi _____.

13   _____ the ice pop makers.

14   _____ _____ in the freezer _____ _____ three hours.

1	더운 여름날이 왔어요.
2	우리는 어떻게 시원하게 지낼 수 있을까요?
3	막대 아이스크림을 함께 만들어 봐요!
4	여러분은 필요해요:
	파인애플 1/2개
	키위 2개
	사과 주스 1컵
	막대 아이스크림 틀
5	단계
6	파인애플을 작은 조각으로 자르세요.
7	키위의 껍질을 벗기고 얇게 자르세요.
8	파인애플 조각들을 믹서에 넣으세요.
9	사과 주스를 첨가하세요.
10	혼합물이 덩어리 없이 골고루 잘 섞일 때까지 섞으세요.
11	혼합물을 막대 아이스크림 틀에 부으세요.
12	키위 조각을 추가하세요.
13	막대 아이스크림 틀을 닫으세요.
14	약 세 시간 동안 그것들을 냉동고에 넣으세요.

15 _____!

16 _____ your summer _____ _____ _____!

17 Health _____

18 Pineapples _____ _____ _____ _____ _____ vitamin C.

19 They have _____ _____ _____ _____ oranges.

20 So _____ you have _____ _____, _____ pineapples.

21 _____ Your Ideas!

22 How will you _____ _____ _____ ice pops?

23 _____ your ideas!

24 I will _____ kiwis and strawberries.

25 I will _____ _____ _____ big pieces.

26 I will _____ _____ _____ the ice pop makers _____ apple juice.

27 I think my ice pops _____ _____ _____.

15 끝났어요!

16 막대 위의 여름을 맛보세요!

17 건강 조언들

18 파인애플은 비타민 C의 훌륭한 원천이에요.

19 파인애플에는 비타민 C가 오렌지보다 더 많이 들어 있어요.

20 그러니 감기에 걸리면 파인애플을 먹어 보세요.

21 여러분의 생각을 나누세요!

22 여러분은 어떻게 막대 아이스크림을 만들 건가요?

23 여러분의 생각을 나누세요!

24 저는 키위와 딸기를 사용할 거예요.

25 저는 그것들을 크게 자를 거예요.

26 그것들을 사과 주스와 함께 막대 아이스크림 틀에 넣을 거예요.

27 제 막대 아이스크림은 예쁠 것 같아요.

● 우리말을 참고하여 본문을 영작하시오.

1 ▶ 더운 여름날이 왔어요.

➡ _____

2 ▶ 우리는 어떻게 시원하게 지낼 수 있을까요?

➡ _____

3 ▶ 막대 아이스크림을 함께 만들어 봐요!

➡ _____

4 ▶ 여러분은 필요해요: 파인애플 1/2개, 키위 2개, 사과 주스 1컵, 막대 아이스크림 틀

➡ _____

5 ▶ 단계

➡ _____

6 ▶ 파인애플을 작은 조각으로 자르세요.

➡ _____

7 ▶ 키위의 껍질을 벗기고 얇게 자르세요.

➡ _____

8 ▶ 파인애플 조각들을 믹서에 넣으세요.

➡ _____

9 ▶ 사과 주스를 첨가하세요.

➡ _____

10 ▶ 혼합물이 덩어리 없이 골고루 잘 섞일 때까지 섞으세요.

➡ _____

11 ▶ 혼합물을 막대 아이스크림 틀에 부으세요.

➡ _____

12 ▶ 키위 조각을 추가하세요.

➡ _____

13 ▶ 막대 아이스크림 틀을 닫으세요.

➡ _____

14 ▶ 약 세 시간 동안 그것들을 냉동고에 넣으세요.

➡ _____

15 끝났어요!

➡ _____

16 막대 위의 여름을 맛보세요!

➡ _____

17 건강 조언들

➡ _____

18 파인애플은 비타민 C의 훌륭한 원천이에요.

➡ _____

19 파인애플에는 비타민 C가 오렌지보다 더 많이 들어 있어요.

➡ _____

20 그러니 감기에 걸리면 파인애플을 먹어 보세요.

➡ _____

21 여러분의 생각을 나누세요!

➡ _____

22 여러분은 어떻게 막대 아이스크림을 만들 건가요?

➡ _____

23 여러분의 생각을 나누세요!

➡ _____

24 저는 키위와 딸기를 사용할 거예요.

➡ _____

25 저는 그것들을 크게 자를 거예요.

➡ _____

26 그것들을 사과 주스와 함께 막대 아이스크림 틀에 넣을 거예요.

➡ _____

27 제 막대 아이스크림은 예쁠 것 같아요.

➡ _____

서술형 실전문제

01 다음 빈칸에 알맞은 말을 〈보기〉에서 골라 쓰시오.

┌── 보기 ──┐
slice / freezer / source / pour

(1) My sister hid the chocolates in the _____, but I found them.

(2) I put some peanut butter on a _____ of bread.

(3) _____ the milk, banana and honey into a blender.

(4) Pineapples are a good _____ of vitamin C.

[02~03] 다음 영영풀이에 해당하는 단어를 쓰시오.

02
┌─────────────────────────────┐
│ an electric machine for mixing soft food │
│ or liquid │
└─────────────────────────────┘

➡ _____

03
┌─────────────────────────────┐
│ a large tropical fruit with thick rough │
│ skin, sweet yellow flesh with a lot of │
│ juice and stiff leaves on top │
└─────────────────────────────┘

➡ _____

04 주어진 단어를 바르게 배열하여 우리말 의미에 맞는 문장을 완성하시오.

(1) 그 쓰레기를 휴지통에 넣어라.
(the garbage / can / put / the trash / into)
➡ _____

(2) 물속으로 다이빙해서 그녀와 함께 수영하여라.
(her / dive / with / into / swim / the water / and)
➡ _____

05 대·소문자에 유의하여 빈칸에 알맞은 말을 〈보기〉에서 골라 쓰시오.

┌── 보기 ──┐
until / when / and

(1) What do you usually do _____ you are at home on the weekend?

(2) Let's wait _____ the rain stops.

(3) Stay focused, _____ you will understand it better.

06 다음 주어진 단어를 이용하여 우리말을 영어로 옮기시오.

(1) 당근을 작은 조각으로 잘라라. (cut, a carrot)
➡ _____

(2) 나는 그 책이 매우 유용할 것이라고 생각해. (think, useful)
➡ _____

[07~11] 다음 글을 읽고, 물음에 답하시오.

The hot days of summer are here. How can we stay cool? Let's make ice pops together!

Steps

1. Cut the pineapple into small ⓐ_____.
2. Peel the kiwis and slice them.
3. Put the pineapple ⓑ_____ into the blender.
4. Add the apple juice.
5. Blend until the mix is smooth.
6. Pour the mix into the ice pop makers.
7. Add the kiwi slices.
8. Close the ice pop makers.
9. Put ⓒthem in the freezer for about three hours.

Finished!

Enjoy your summer on a stick!

07 위 글의 빈칸 ⓐ와 ⓑ에 공통으로 들어갈 말을 쓰시오.

➡ _____

08 다음 설명에 해당하는 단어를 위 글에서 찾아 쓰시오.

> You use this word when you remove skins of something.

➡ _____

09 Where do we have to pour the apple juice? Answer in English.

➡ _____

10 위 글의 밑줄 친 ⓒ가 가리키는 것을 영어로 쓰시오.

➡ _____

11 위 글의 내용에 맞게 빈칸에 알맞은 말을 쓰시오.

> Jina: How long do I have to blend?
> Kelly: If it looks _____, then you can
>   stop _____ it.

➡ _____

[12~15] 다음 글을 읽고, 물음에 답하시오.

Health Tips

 Pineapples are an excellent source of vitamin C. They have more vitamin C than oranges. So when you have a cold, try pineapples.
Share Your Ideas!
Kyle: How will you make your own ice pops? Share your ideas!
Jinsu: I will use kiwis and strawberries. I will cut them into big pieces. I will put them into the ice pop makers with apple juice. I think ___ⓐ___ my ice pops will be pretty.

12 위 글의 내용에 맞게 빈칸에 알맞은 말을 쓰시오.

> Pineapples are rich in _____.

➡ _____

13 What kind of fruit will Jinsu use to make his own ice pops? Answer in English.

➡ _____

14 위 글의 빈칸 ⓐ에 들어갈 알맞은 접속사를 쓰시오.

➡ _____

15 진수의 막대 아이스크림을 본 친구의 반응을 영어로 쓰시오.

> 진수야, 그것은 예뻐 보인다!

➡ _____

단원별 예상문제

[01~02] 다음 영영풀이에 해당하는 단어를 쓰시오.

01 출제율 90%

> to take the outer layer off fruit, vegetables, etc.

➡ _____

02 출제율 90%

> a thin flat piece of food that has been cut off a larger piece

➡ _____

03 출제율 85%

다음 짝지어진 두 단어의 관계가 같도록 빈칸에 알맞은 말을 쓰시오.

> close : open = _____ : rough

04 출제율 95%

다음 중 밑줄 친 부분의 뜻풀이가 바르지 <u>않은</u> 것은?

① I ate a <u>piece</u> of cake. 조각
② Would you <u>add</u> some salt to the boiling water? 더하다
③ <u>Pour</u> some water into the pot. 휘젓다
④ It took an hour for me to <u>peel</u> these onions. 껍질을 벗기다
⑤ You need to <u>blend</u> eggs with the flour. 섞다

05 출제율 90%

다음 주어진 문장의 밑줄 친 부분과 같은 의미로 쓰인 것은?

> <u>Close</u> ice pop makers.

① Would you mind <u>closing</u> the window?
② Brian, the police officer, is my <u>close</u> friend.
③ I want to live <u>close</u> to the river.
④ Can you sit <u>close</u> to Mike?
⑤ Jake is one of my <u>close</u> friends.

06 출제율 100%

다음 문장의 빈칸에 들어갈 말을 〈보기〉에서 골라 쓰시오.

> ┌─ 보기 ─┐
> stay / mix / cut / put

(1) First, _____ sweet potatoes into small pieces.
(2) My mother _____ the ice cream in the freezer.
(3) Let's _____ the brown sugar, honey and butter.
(4) What is the best way to _____ cool in summer?

07 출제율 95%

다음 문장의 빈칸에 공통으로 들어갈 말로 적절한 것은?

> • This color does not _____ with the white wall.
> • My daughters _____ in well with the new classmates.
> • Will you _____ milk and flour together?

① add　　　　　② stay
③ blend　　　　④ finish
⑤ try

08 다음 중 쓰임이 다른 하나는?

① I have enough money to buy a car.
② Julia went to the hospital to see a doctor.
③ He came here to meet me.
④ To keep the promise, Dan studied hard.
⑤ You had better bring a book not to be bored.

09 다음 우리말을 조건에 맞도록 주어진 단어를 이용하여 영어로 쓰시오.

그 방을 깨끗하게 치우지 않으면, 너희 엄마가 화내실 거야. (upset)

(1) 명령문으로
➡ _____

(2) Unless를 사용하여
➡ _____

10 다음 중 〈보기〉의 밑줄 친 부분과 쓰임이 같은 것은?

┌─── 보기 ───┐
I haven't seen her for a while.
└───────────┘

① She has lost her wallet.
② Jimmy has lived in Seoul since he was seven.
③ Have you ever used the machine?
④ I have been to the place three times.
⑤ Danny has already finished his homework.

11 같은 의미의 문장이 되도록 빈칸에 알맞은 말을 쓰시오.

(1) The doctor advised that I should eat regularly.
➡ The doctor advised _____ _____
_____ _____ .

(2) Jenny told me that I had better make more friends.
➡ Jenny told _____ _____ _____
_____ .

12 다음 문장의 빈칸에 알맞은 것은?

사람들은 Brady에 대해 좋게 말해.
➡ Brady is _____ people.

① spoken
② spoken by
③ spoken well
④ spoken well of
⑤ spoken well of by

13 다음 문장을 수동태로 전환하시오.

People around the world look up to Mother Theresa.

➡ _____
_____

14 다음 빈칸에 공통으로 들어갈 말은?

• Tom is the last man _____ tells a lie.
• Mike, _____ do you think is the most intelligent?
• Frank is the boy _____ Linda fell in love with.

① that
② whom
③ who
④ which
⑤ whose

15 괄호 안에 주어진 어휘를 어법에 맞게 쓰시오.

• If I (be) not busy tomorrow, I (call) on you.
• I don't know if they (take part in) the contest tomorrow.

➡ _____

[16~20] 다음 대화를 읽고, 물음에 답하시오.

Pineapple Ice Pops

The hot days of summer ①are here. How can we stay ②cool? Let's make ice pops together!

You need:
1/2 pineapple
2 kiwis
1 cup of apple juice
ice pop makers

Steps

1. Cut the pineapple into small ③pieces.
2. Peel the kiwis and slice them.
3. Put the pineapple pieces into the blender.
4. Add the apple juice.
5. Blend until the mix is ④smoothly.
6. Pour the mix into the ice pop makers.
7. Add the kiwi slices.
8. Close the ice pop makers.
9. Put ⑤them in the freezer for about three hours.
Finished!
Enjoy your summer on a stick!

출제율 100%

16 다음과 같이 풀이되는 단어를 위 글에서 찾아 쓰시오.

> You find pleasure and satisfaction in doing something or experiencing something.

➡ _____

출제율 100%

17 위 글의 내용과 일치하지 <u>않는</u> 것은?

① Ice pops help us stay cool.
② We need half of a pineapple to make the ice pops.
③ Ice pop makers are needed.
④ We need pineapple juice.
⑤ Two kiwis are used to make the ice pops.

출제율 90%

18 위 글의 ①~⑤ 중 어법상 바르지 <u>않은</u> 것은?

①　　②　　③　　④　　⑤

출제율 95%

19 What do you have to do with kiwis before you slice them? Answer in English.

➡ _____

출제율 95%

20 Where do we put the closed ice pop makers? Answer in English.

➡ _____

[21~24] 다음 글을 읽고 물음에 답하시오.

Health Tips

Pineapples are an excellent source of vitamin C. They have more vitamin C than oranges. So when you have a cold, try pineapples.
Share Your Ideas!

Kyle: ____ⓐ____ will you make your own ice pops? Share your ideas!

Jinsu: I will use kiwis and strawberries. I will cut ⓑthem into big pieces. I will put them into the ice pop makers with apple juice. I think my ice pops will be pretty.

출제율 90%

21 위 글의 빈칸 ⓐ에 들어갈 말로 가장 적절한 것은?

① When　② What　③ Who
④ How　⑤ Where

출제율 95%

22 위 글을 읽고 답할 수 <u>없는</u> 것은?

① What can you try when you have a cold?
② What do pineapples have more than oranges?
③ What will Jinsu use to make his own ice pops?
④ Why will Jinsu use apple juice?
⑤ What kind of ideas does Kyle want to share?

✎ 출제율 85%

23 밑줄 친 ⓑ가 가리키는 것을 영어로 쓰시오.

➡ _____

✎ 출제율 90%

24 Write the reason why the writer advises us to try pineapples when we have a cold. Answer in Korean.

➡ _____

[25~29] 다음 설명을 읽고 빈칸에 알맞은 답을 쓰시오.

Pineapple Ice Pops

　The hot days of summer are here. How can we stay cool? Let's make ice pops together!

You need:

1/2 pineapple

2 kiwis

1 cup of apple juice

ice pop makers

Steps

1. Cut the pineapple into small pieces.

2. Peel the kiwis and slice them.

(A) Blend until the mix is smooth.

(B) Add the apple juice.

(C) Pour the mix into the ice pop makers.

(D) Put the pineapple pieces into the blender.

7. Add the kiwi slices.

8. Close the ice pop makers.

9. Put them in the freezer ⓐfor about three hours.

ⓑFinished!

Enjoy your summer on a stick!

✎ 출제율 95%

25 위 글을 읽고 답할 수 없는 것은?

① How many pineapples do we need?

② How much apple juice do we need?

③ How many ice pop makers do we need?

④ What do we first do with the pineapple?

⑤ What do we do after peeling the kiwis?

✎ 출제율 100%

26 위 글의 (A)~(D)의 순서를 바르게 배열한 것은?

① (B) – (A) – (C) – (D)

② (B) – (D) – (A) – (C)

③ (C) – (B) – (A) – (D)

④ (D) – (A) – (B) – (C)

⑤ (D) – (B) – (A) – (C)

✎ 출제율 95%

27 위 글의 밑줄 친 ⓐ와 쓰임이 같은 것은?

① They are anxious for his safety.

② What can I do for you?

③ She is working for Google.

④ I'm for you.

⑤ I'm going away for a few days.

✎ 출제율 90%

28 After adding the kiwi slices, what do we do next? Answer in English.

➡ _____

✎ 출제율 85%

29 주어진 단어를 활용하여 밑줄 친 ⓑ의 의미를 완성하시오.

(you, make)

➡ _____

[30~33] 다음 글을 읽고 물음에 답하시오.

Health Tips

　Pineapples are an excellent source of vitamin C. ⓐThey have more vitamin C than oranges. So ⓑ감기에 걸리면, 파인애플을 먹어 보세요.

Share Your Ideas!

Kyle: How will you make your own ice pops? Share your ideas!

Jinsu: I will use kiwis and strawberries. I will cut them into big pieces. I will put ⓒthem into the ice pop makers with apple juice. I think my ice pops will be pretty.

30 출제율 90%

다음 중 밑줄 친 ⓐ와 같은 의미의 문장은?

① Pineapples have as much vitamin C as oranges.
② Pineapples don't have as much vitamin C as oranges.
③ Oranges have less vitamin C than pineapples.
④ Oranges don't have much vitamin C.
⑤ No other fruit on earth has more vitamin C than pineapples.

31 출제율 95%

주어진 단어를 활용하여 밑줄 친 우리말 ⓑ를 영어로 쓰시오.

have / try

➡ _____

32 출제율 90%

다음은 밑줄 친 ⓒ가 가리키는 말이다. 빈칸에 알맞은 말을 쓰시오.

_____ _____ of _____ _____ _____

➡ _____

33 출제율 95%

위 글의 내용과 일치하지 않는 것은?

① Pineapples are rich in vitamin C.
② Kyle wants to share ideas about making ice pops.
③ There will be strawberries in Jinsu's ice pops.
④ Jinsu thinks his ice pops will be delicious.
⑤ Jinsu's strawberries and kiwis will be cut into big pieces.

[34~36] 다음 글을 읽고, 물음에 답하시오.

Pineapple Ice Pops

The hot days of summer are here. ①How can we stay cool? Let's make ice pops together!

You need: 1/2 pineapple, 2 ②kiwis, 1 cup of apple juice, ice pop makers

Steps

1. Cut the pineapple into small pieces.
2. Peel the kiwis and slice ③it.
3. Put the pineapple pieces into the blender.
4. Add the apple juice.
5. Blend ④until the mix is smooth.
6. Pour the mix into the ice pop makers.
7. Add the kiwi slices.
8. Close the ice pop makers.
9. Put ⑤them in the freezer for about three hours.

Finished!

Enjoy your summer on a stick!

34 출제율 90%

위 글의 내용과 일치하는 것은?

① We need three kinds of fruits to make ice pops.
② A bottle of apple juice will be used.
③ A blender is needed to mix the fruit.
④ We don't need to peel the kiwis.
⑤ We need to cut the pineapple as big as possible.

35 출제율 100%

위 글의 ①~⑤ 중 어법상 바르지 않은 것은?

①   ②   ③   ④   ⑤

36 출제율 100%

How long do we put the ice pop makers in the freezer? Answer in English.

➡ _____

Lesson 5

Come One, Come All

🎙 의사소통 기능

- 길 묻고 답하기

  A: How can I get to the post office?

  B: Go straight to 1st Street and make a right.

- 소요 시간 말하기

  A: How long will it take to make the sandwiches?

  B: Maybe it will take about an hour.

🎙 언어 형식

- 가주어 It

  It is a lot of fun **to throw** colorful powder at everyone.

- 지각동사

  You can **hear** musicians **playing** beautiful live music.

Words & Expressions

교과서

Key Words

- **adult**[ədʌ́lt] 명 성인, 어른
- **advertise**[ǽdvərtàiz] 동 광고하다
- **almost**[ɔ́:lmoust] 부 거의
- **amazing**[əméiziŋ] 형 놀라운
- **appear**[əpíər] 동 나타나다
- **arrow**[ǽrou] 명 화살
- **artwork**[á:rtwərk] 명 예술 작품
- **bakery**[béikəri] 명 빵집, 제과점
- **block**[blɑk] 명 블록, 구획
- **boat**[bout] 명 배, 선박
- **celebrate**[séləbrèit] 동 축하하다, 기념하다
- **chase**[tʃeis] 동 뒤쫓다
- **colorful**[kʌ́lərfəl] 형 형형색색의
- **competition**[kàmpətíʃən] 명 대회, 시합, 경쟁
- **completely**[kəmplí:tli] 부 완전히
- **cross**[krɔ:s] 동 가로지르다, 가로질러 건너다
- **dark**[dɑ:rk] 형 어두운
- **decorate**[dékərèit] 동 장식하다
- **during**[djúəriŋ] 전 ~ 동안
- **far**[fɑ:r] 형 먼 부 멀리
- **festival**[féstəvəl] 명 축제

- **firework**[fáiərwə:rk] 명 폭죽, 불꽃놀이
- **follow**[fálou] 동 따르다
- **gather**[gǽðər] 동 모이다, 모으다
- **hold**[hould] 동 개최하다
- **hometown**[hóumtaun] 명 고향
- **huge**[hju:dʒ] 형 거대한
- **last**[læst] 동 지속하다
- **live**[laiv] 형 라이브의, 실황인
- **musician**[mju:zíʃən] 명 음악가
- **near**[niər] 형 가까운, 가까이에 있는
- **neighborhood**[néibərhùd] 명 근처, 이웃, 인근
- **outdoor**[áutdɔːr] 형 야외의
- **parade**[pəréid] 명 퍼레이드, 행진
- **pile**[pail] 명 더미
- **post**[poust] 동 게시하다
- **powder**[páudər] 명 가루
- **sail**[seil] 명 돛
- **shape**[ʃeip] 명 형태 동 ~ 모양으로 만들다
- **sled**[sled] 명 썰매
- **solve**[sɑlv] 동 해결하다
- **take**[teik] 동 (시간이) 걸리다, (탈 것을) 타다
- **throw**[θrou] 동 던지다

Key Expressions

- **because of** ~ 때문에
- **between A and B** A와 B 사이에
- **come out** 나오다
- **each other** 서로
- **from beginning to end** 처음부터 끝까지
- **get off** 내리다
- **go on** 지속되다, 계속되다

- **go straight** 앞으로 곧장 가다
- **in front of** ~ 앞에
- **make a left[right]** 왼쪽[오른쪽]으로 돌다
- **more and more** 더욱 더
- **next to** ~ ~ 옆에
- **on one's right** ~의 오른편에
- **out of hand** 손을 쓸 수 없는

Word Power

※ 서로 반대되는 뜻을 가진 단어

- far 먼 ↔ near 가까운
- dark 어두운 ↔ bright 밝은
- outdoor 야외의 ↔ indoor 실내의
- complete 완전한 ↔ incomplete 불완전한
- huge 거대한 ↔ tiny 작은
- get on (탈 것을) 타다 ↔ get off 내리다

- appear 나타나다 ↔ disappear 사라지다
- adult 어른, 성인 ↔ child 아이, 어린이
- live 살아 있는 ↔ dead 죽은
- follow 뒤따르다 ↔ precede 선행하다, 앞서다
- compete 경쟁하다 ↔ cooperate 협력하다, 협동하다
- throw 던지다 ↔ receive 받다

English Dictionary

- **adult** 어른
  → a fully grown person
  완전히 자란 사람

- **advertise** 광고하다
  → to tell the public about goods to make people buy them
  사람들이 물건을 사게 만들도록 물건에 대해 대중에게 이야기하다

- **artwork** 예술 작품
  → objects produced by artists
  예술가들에 의해 만들어진 물체

- **celebrate** 축하하다
  → to do something special for an important event, holiday, etc.
  중요한 행사나 휴일 등을 위해 특별한 무언가를 하다

- **chase** 뒤쫓다
  → to follow and try to catch
  따라가서 잡으려고 노력하다

- **competition** 대회, 경쟁
  → an event or contest in which people compete
  사람들이 경쟁하는 행사 또는 대회

- **completely** 완전히
  → totally, fully
  완전히

- **decorate** 장식하다
  → to make something look more beautiful by putting things on it
  위에 물건들을 올려놓음으로써 더 아름답게 보이도록 만들다

- **festival** 축제
  → a day or period of celebration
  축하하는 날이나 기간

- **gather** 모이다
  → to come together to form a group
  모임을 형성하기 위해 함께 모이다

- **hold** 개최하다
  → to have a meeting, competition, conversation, etc.
  만남, 경쟁, 대화 등을 갖다

- **hometown** 고향
  → the city or town where you were born or grew up
  당신이 태어나거나 자란 도시나 마을

- **last** 지속하다
  → to continue in time
  시간에 있어서 계속되다

- **lift** 들어올리다
  → to move something or someone to a higher position
  어떤 것이나 어떤 사람을 높은 위치로 옮기다

- **live** 라이브의, 실황인
  → given or made when people are watching, not pre-recorded
  미리 녹화되지 않고 사람들이 보고 시청하고 있을 때 주어지거나 만들어진

- **pile** 더미
  → a mass of something that has been placed somewhere
  어딘가에 놓여진 무언가의 덩어리

- **shape** ~ 모양으로 만들다
  → to make something into a particular shape
  무언가를 특정한 모양으로 만들다

- **sled** 썰매
  → a small vehicle used for sliding over snow
  눈 위에서 미끄러지기 위해 사용된 작은 탈 것

서답형

01 다음 짝지어진 단어의 관계가 같도록 빈칸에 알맞은 말을 쓰시오.

> heavy: light = _____ : near

서답형

02 다음 영영풀이가 가리키는 말을 쓰시오.

> the city or town where you were born or grew up

➡ _____

03 다음 중 밑줄 친 부분의 뜻풀이가 바르지 않은 것은?

① That yacht with white sails is my dad's. 항해하다
② He raked the leaves into piles. 더미
③ I heard the band playing live music. 라이브의, 실황의
④ This movie lasts two hours. 지속하다
⑤ The technique is completely new. 완전히

서답형

04 다음 문장의 빈칸에 들어갈 말을 〈보기〉에서 골라 쓰시오.

> ┌─ 보기 ─┐
> parade / neighborhood / pile / advertise / regularly

(1) Is there a bakery in this _____?
(2) The band is marching in a _____.
(3) We made a plan to _____ our new product.
(4) He is looking at a _____ of newspapers.
(5) She attended church _____.

중요

05 다음 주어진 문장의 밑줄 친 live와 같은 의미로 쓰인 것은?

> Musicians played beautiful live music.

① This program is live from Time Square.
② We used to live in Jeju-do.
③ Mike needs to find somewhere to live.
④ This moment will live in our memory for a long time.
⑤ Bears can live for several days without food.

06 다음 문장에 공통으로 들어갈 말을 고르시오.

> • You should _____ the sea to get to the island.
> • My brother is waiting to _____ the street.
> • I put a _____ on the map to show where the hotel is.

① follow
② chase
③ parade
④ shape
⑤ cross

서답형

07 다음 우리말에 맞게 빈칸에 알맞은 말을 쓰시오.

(1) 그들은 개 썰매로 이동하곤 했다.
➡ They used to travel by dog _____.
(2) 사진 속의 형형색색의 꽃들을 보세요.
➡ Look at the _____ flowers in the picture.
(3) 시간이 화살처럼 지나갔다.
➡ Time flew like an _____.

01 다음 짝지어진 단어의 관계가 같도록 빈칸에 알맞은 말을 쓰시오.

complete : incomplete = appear : _____

02 다음 문장의 빈칸에 들어갈 말을 〈보기〉에서 골라 쓰시오.

┌─ 보기 ├─
almost / live / artwork / fireworks

(1) I'm looking forward to the _____ music performance.

(2) They celebrate the festival with _____.

(3) It's been _____ 5 years since I moved to Korea.

(4) His _____ is going to be displayed in a gallery.

03 다음 우리말에 맞게 주어진 빈칸을 완성하시오.

(1) 나는 이 책을 처음부터 끝까지 읽을 거야.
  ➡ I'll read this book from beginning _____ _____.

(2) 경쟁이 더욱 더 심해졌다.
  ➡ The competition became _____ _____ severe.

(3) 언제 그 책이 나왔습니까?
  ➡ When did the book _____ _____?

(4) 일이 아주 엉망이 되었다.
  ➡ Things really got _____ _____.

04 다음 우리말을 주어진 단어를 이용하여 영작하시오.

(1) 음악 축제가 언제 열리나요? (will, held)
  ➡ _____

(2) 나는 크리스마스 트리 장식하는 것을 즐겼다. (enjoyed)
  ➡ _____

(3) 사람들이 그 가수를 보기 위해 함께 모였다. (gathered)
  ➡ _____

05 다음 우리말과 일치하도록 주어진 어구를 배열하여 완성하시오.

(1) 사람들이 이틀 동안 여기저기서 축제를 기념한다.
  (two / everywhere / days / people / the festival / celebrate / for)
  ➡ _____
     _____

(2) 내가 가장 좋아하는 가수를 직접 본 것은 정말 놀라웠다.
  (singer / in / amazing / it / to / see / favorite / person / my / was)
  ➡ _____
     _____

(3) 사람들은 미술가들이 그들의 작품을 만드는 것을 처음부터 끝까지 지켜본다.
  (watch / the / shaping / artists / from / end / works / beginning / to / their / people)
  ➡ _____
     _____

Conversation

1 길 묻고 답하기

> **A** How can I get to the post office? 우체국에 어떻게 가나요?
>
> **B** Go straight to 1st Street and make a right. 1가로 곧장 간 후 오른쪽으로 도세요.

■ 'How can I get to + 장소 명사?'는 '~에 어떻게 갈 수 있나요?'라는 뜻으로 길을 묻는 표현이다. 'How can I go to ~?'로 물을 수도 있다. 대답으로 길을 안내할 때는 보통 'Go straight.'처럼 명령문의 형태로 대답한다.

길 묻고 답하기

- Where can I find the police station? 경찰서가 어디에 있나요?
- Do you know where the library is? 도서관이 어디에 있는지 아세요?
- Is there a bakery around here? 이곳 주위에 빵집이 있나요?
- Walk straight ahead. 앞쪽으로 곧장 걸어가세요.
- You can't miss it. 쉽게 찾을 수 있을 거야.
- It's just around the corner. 그것은 바로 모퉁이를 돌면 있어.
- It's across from the museum. 그것은 박물관 건너편에 있어.

핵심 Check

1. 다음 우리말과 일치하도록 빈칸에 알맞은 말을 쓰시오.

(1) **A**: _____ _____ _____ _____ _____ the museum?

(박물관에 어떻게 가나요?)

B: Come out from the school and go straight one block.

(학교에서 나와서 한 구역 곧장 가세요.)

(2) **A**: Where can I find the theater? (극장이 어디에 있나요?)

B: _____ _____ _____ and _____ _____ two blocks.

(길을 건너서 두 구역을 곧장 가세요.)

(3) **A**: _____ _____ _____ _____ around here? (이곳 주위에 병원이 있나요?)

B: Yes, it's _____ _____ the corner. (네, 그것은 바로 모퉁이를 돌면 있어요.)

2 소요 시간 말하기

> **A** How long will it take to make the sandwiches? 샌드위치를 만드는 데 시간이 얼마나 걸릴까?
> **B** Maybe it will take about an hour. 아마도 약 한 시간 정도 걸릴 거야.

■ 'How long will it take to ~?'는 '~하는 데 시간이 얼마가 걸릴까?'라는 뜻으로, 소요 시간을 묻는 표현이다. 대답으로 '(시간이) ~ 걸리다'의 뜻을 나타내는 동사 take를 사용하여 소요 시간을 말한다. 대답할 때는 소요 시간을 구체적으로 말하는 것이 보통이다.

- How long will it take to finish your work? 일을 마치는 데 얼마나 걸리겠어요?
- How long will it take to go to London? 런던까지 가는 데는 얼마나 걸립니까?
- It will take more than an hour. 한 시간 이상 걸릴 것이다.
- It will take about ten minutes on foot. 걸어서 10분 정도 걸립니다.

✏️ 핵심 Check

2. 다음 우리말과 일치하도록 빈칸에 알맞은 말을 쓰시오.

(1) **A**: How long will it take to clean the classroom? (교실을 청소하는 데 얼마나 걸릴까?)
   B: It'll _____ _____ _____ _____ _____. (약 30분 정도 걸릴 거야.)

(2) **A**: _____ _____ _____ _____ _____ get to the theater?
   (영화관까지 가는 데 시간이 얼마가 걸릴까?)
   B: It'll take about 15 minutes _____ _____. (버스로 약 15분 정도 걸릴 거야.)

(3) **A**: _____ _____ _____ _____ _____ _____ _____
   _____? (교실을 장식하는 데 얼마나 걸릴까?)
   B: It'll _____ _____ _____ _____. (약 두 시간 정도 걸릴 거야.)

Listen and Speak 1-B

(*A phone rings.*)

Minsu: Hi, Emma. What's up?

Emma: Hey, Minsu. Are you free this Saturday?

Minsu: Yes. Why do you ask?

Emma: Well, ❶how about having lunch together?

Minsu: Sure.

Emma: Let's try the new Chinese restaurant, Ming's. ❷It's near the school.

Minsu: Okay. ❸How can I get there from the school?

Emma: ❹Come out from the school and go straight to Green Street. ❺Make a left, and the restaurant will be on your left.

Minsu: All right. Let's meet at 12 o'clock.

Emma: Wonderful. See you then.

(전화벨이 울린다.)

Minsu: 안녕, Emma. 잘 지내니?

Emma: 안녕, 민수야. 이번 토요일에 한가하니?

Minsu: 응. 왜 묻는 거니?

Emma: 그럼, 함께 점심 먹는 게 어떠니?

Minsu: 좋아.

Emma: Ming's라는 새로 생긴 중국 음식점에 가 보자. 학교 근처에 있어.

Minsu: 좋아. 학교에서 거기까지 어떻게 가니?

Emma: 학교에서 나와서 Green Street까지 곧장 가. 왼쪽으로 돌면 음식점이 네 왼쪽에 있을 거야.

Minsu: 알겠어. 12시에 만나자.

Emma: 좋아. 그때 보자.

❶ 'How about ~?'은 '~하는 게 어때?'라고 제안하는 표현으로 'Why don't we ~?' 또는 'What about ~?'으로 바꾸어 쓸 수 있다.

❷ be near ~: ~와 가깝다

❸ How can I get ~?은 '~에 어떻게 가니?'라고 길을 묻는 표현이다.

❹ 동사원형으로 시작하는 명령문이다.

❺ make a left: 왼쪽으로 돌다(= turn left)

Check(√) True or False

(1) Minsu and Emma will have lunch together.　　T ☐ F ☐

(2) The Chinese restaurant is far from the school.　　T ☐ F ☐

Real Life Talk

Man: Excuse me. How can I get to Suwon Hwaseong from here?

Mina: It's easy. Do you see the bus stop over there?

Man: Yes, I do.

Mina: Take the No. 11 bus and ❶get off at the sixth stop.

Man: ❷How long will it take to get there?

Mina: It will take ❸about 20 minutes.

Man: Thank you very much.

Mina: No problem. ❹Are you going there for the festival?

Man: Yes. I heard it's a lot of fun.

Mina: I hope you have a great time.

Man: 실례합니다. 여기에서 수원 화성까지 어떻게 가나요?

Mina: 쉬워요. 저쪽에 버스 정류장 보이세요?

Man: 네, 보여요.

Mina: 11번 버스를 타서 여섯 번째 정류장에서 내리세요.

Man: 그곳까지 가는 데 시간이 얼마나 걸릴까요?

Mina: 대략 20분 정도 걸릴 거에요.

Man: 정말 고마워요.

Mina: 별말씀을요. 그곳에 축제 때문에 가시는 건가요?

Man: 네. 그 축제가 무척 재미있다고 들었어요.

Mina: 즐거운 시간 보내길 바라요.

❶ get off: 내리다 ↔ get on: 타다

❷ How long will it take to get there?: '그곳에 가는 데 얼마나 걸리나요?'라는 의미로 소요 시간을 묻는 표현이다.

❸ about: 대략

❹ 수원 화성에 가는 목적을 묻고 있다.

Check(√) True or False

(3) It'll take about 20 minutes for the man to go to Suwon Hwaseong by bus.　　T ☐ F ☐

(4) Mina wants to visit the festival in Suwon Hwaseong.　　T ☐ F ☐

Listen and Speak 1-A

Sora: Excuse me. ❶How can I get to the library?

Tom: Oh, the library? ❷Cross the street and go straight two blocks. Then ❸make a left.

Sora: Thank you very much.

❶ 도서관에 가는 법을 묻는 표현이다.
❷ cross: 건너다
❸ make a left: 왼쪽으로 돌다(= turn left)

Listen and Speak 1-C

A: Excuse me. How can I get to the post office?

B: Go straight to 1st Street and make a right. It will be ❶on your right.

A: Is it ❷far from here?

B: No, it's not.

A: Thank you very much.

❶ on one's right: ~의 오른편에
❷ far: 먼; 멀리

Listen and Speak 2-A

Amy: Jinho, hurry up. We're going to be late for the movie.

Jinho: Okay. ❶How long will it take to get to the theater?

Amy: It will take about 15 minutes ❷by bus.

Jinho: All right. I'm ❸almost ready.

❶ 극장에 가는 소요 시간을 묻고 있다.
❷ by bus: 버스로
❸ almost: 거의

Listen and Speak 2-B

Andy: I'm so excited about the school festival this Friday.

Mike: ❶Me, too. What can we do to advertise ❷it, Andy?

Andy: How about making posters?

Mike: Great idea. We can post ❸them in our neighborhood.

Andy: Right. ❹How long will it take to make them?

Mike: Well, it will take about three hours.

Andy: Okay, I hope many people come to the festival.

❶ '나도 그래.'라는 의미로 'So am I.'와 바꾸어 쓸 수 있다.
❷ it은 the school festival을 가리킨다.
❸ them은 posters를 가리킨다.
❹ 포스터를 제작하는 데 걸리는 소요 시간을 묻고 있다.

Listen and Speak 2-C

Rachel: Chris, what will you do for the class party?

Chris: I'll make sandwiches.

Rachel: Great idea. How long will it take to make ❶them?

Chris: Maybe it'll take ❷about an hour.

❶ them은 sandwiches를 가리킨다.
❷ about: 약, 대략

다음 우리말과 일치하도록 빈칸에 알맞은 말을 쓰시오.

Listen and Speak 1-A

Sora: Excuse me. _____ _____ _____ _____ _____
_____ _____?

Tom: Oh, the library? _____ the street and _____ _____ two
blocks. Then _____ a left.

Sora: Thank you very much.

Listen and Speak 1-B

(*A phone rings.*)

Minsu: Hi, Emma. _____ _____?

Emma: Hey, Minsu. Are you _____ this Saturday?

Minsu: Yes. _____ do you _____?

Emma: Well, how about _____ lunch together?

Minsu: Sure.

Emma: _____ try the new Chinese restaurant, Ming's. It's _____
the school.

Minsu: Okay. _____ _____ _____ _____ _____
_____ _____?

Emma: _____ _____ from the school and _____ _____ to
Green Street. _____ _____ _____, and the restaurant
will be _____ _____ _____.

Minsu: All right. _____ _____ at 12 o'clock.

Emma: Wonderful. _____ you _____.

Listen and Speak 1-C

A: Excuse me. _____ _____ I _____ _____ the post office?

B: _____ _____ to 1st Street and _____ a right. It will _____
_____ _____ _____.

A: Is it _____ _____ here?

B: No, it's _____.

A: Thank you very much.

Sora: 실례합니다. 도서관까지 어떻게
가나요?

Tom: 아, 도서관이요? 길을 건너서 두
구역을 곧장 가세요. 그런 다음 왼
쪽으로 도세요.

Sora: 정말 고마워요.

(전화벨이 울린다.)

Minsu: 안녕, Emma. 잘 지내니?

Emma: 안녕, 민수야. 이번 토요일에 한
가하니?

Minsu: 응. 왜 묻는 거니?

Emma: 음, 함께 점심 먹는 게 어떠니?

Minsu: 좋아.

Emma: Ming's라는 새로 생긴 중국 음
식점에 가 보자. 학교 근처에 있
어.

Minsu: 좋아. 학교에서 거기까지 어떻게
가니?

Emma: 학교에서 나와서 Green Street
까지 곧장 가. 왼쪽으로 돌면 음
식점이 네 왼쪽에 있을 거야.

Minsu: 알겠어. 12시에 만나자.

Emma: 좋아. 그때 보자.

A: 실례합니다. 우체국에 어떻게 갈 수
있나요?

B: 1st Street까지 곧장 가서 오른쪽으로
도세요. 그것은 오른쪽에 있을 거예
요.

A: 여기서 먼가요?

B: 아니요, 멀지 않아요.

A: 정말 고마워요.

Listen and Speak 2-A

Amy: Jinho, hurry up. We're going to _____ _____ _____ the movie.

Jinho: Okay. _____ _____ _____ _____ _____ _____ _____ _____ _____ ?

Amy: It will _____ _____ 15 minutes _____ _____ .

Jinho: All right. I'm _____ ready.

Amy: 진호야, 서둘러. 우리 영화 시간에 늦겠어.
Jinho: 응. 영화관까지 가는 데 시간이 얼마나 걸릴까?
Amy: 버스로 대략 15분 정도 걸릴 거야.
Jinho: 알겠어. 나 거의 준비됐어.

Listen and Speak 2-B

Andy: I'm so _____ about the school festival this Friday.

Mike: _____ , _____ . What can we do to _____ it, Andy?

Andy: How _____ _____ posters?

Mike: Great idea. We can _____ _____ in our _____ .

Andy: Right. _____ _____ _____ _____ _____ _____ _____ make them?

Mike: Well, it will _____ _____ three hours.

Andy: Okay, I hope many people _____ _____ the festival.

Andy: 나는 이번 금요일 학교 축제가 정말 기대돼.
Mike: 나도. 축제를 광고하기 위해 무엇을 할 수 있을까, Andy?
Andy: 포스터를 만들면 어떨까?
Mike: 좋은 생각이야. 이 근방에 포스터를 붙일 수 있겠다.
Andy: 맞아. 포스터를 만드는 데 시간이 얼마나 걸릴까?
Mike: 음, 대략 세 시간 정도 걸릴 거야.
Andy: 좋아, 많은 사람들이 축제에 왔으면 좋겠다.

Real Life Talk

Man: Excuse me. How can I _____ _____ Suwon Hwaseong from here?

Mina: It's easy. Do you see the bus stop _____ _____ ?

Man: Yes, I do.

Mina: _____ the No. 11 bus and _____ _____ at the sixth stop.

Man: _____ _____ _____ _____ _____ _____ _____ _____ _____ ?

Mina: It will _____ _____ 20 minutes.

Man: Thank you very much.

Mina: No problem. Are you going there for _____ _____ ?

Man: Yes. I heard _____ _____ _____ _____ .

Mina: I hope you _____ _____ _____ _____ .

Man: 실례합니다. 여기에서 수원 화성까지 어떻게 가나요?
Mina: 쉬워요. 저쪽에 버스 정류장 보이세요?
Man: 네, 보여요.
Mina: 11번 버스를 타서 여섯 번째 정류장에서 내리세요.
Man: 그곳까지 가는 데 시간이 얼마나 걸릴까요?
Mina: 대략 20분 정도 걸릴 거에요.
Man: 정말 고마워요.
Mina: 별말씀을요. 그곳에 축제 때문에 가시는 건가요?
Man: 네. 그 축제가 무척 재미있다고 들었어요.
Mina: 즐거운 시간 보내길 바라요.

Conversation 시험대비 기본평가

01 다음 대화의 빈칸에 들어갈 말을 〈보기〉에 주어진 단어를 배열하여 완성하시오.

A: How long will it take to get to the pharmacy?

B: _____

┤ 보기 ├

by / car / about / take / it / 5 minutes / will

➡ _____

02 다음 대화가 자연스럽게 이어지도록 순서대로 배열하시오.

(A) Thank you very much.
(B) Excuse me. How can I get to the post office?
(C) Is it far from here?
(D) No, it's not.
(E) Go straight to 1st Street and make a right. It will be on your right.

➡ _____

[03~04] 다음 대화를 읽고 물음에 답하시오.

A: Excuse me. How can I get ⓐto the police station?
B: Go straight to Green Street. ⓑCross the street. Then make a right. The police station is between the flower shop ⓒor the bakery.
A: How ⓓlong will it take to get there?
B: It will take ⓔabout 5 minutes.
A: Thank you very much.

03 위 대화의 밑줄 친 ⓐ~ⓔ 중 어법상 바르지 않은 것을 찾아 바르게 고치시오.

➡ _____

04 위 대화의 내용과 일치하지 않는 것은?

① A는 경찰서를 찾고 있다.
② 경찰서는 꽃가게와 빵집 사이에 위치해 있다.
③ 경찰서까지 5분 정도 걸릴 것이다.
④ 경찰서에 가기 위해 Green Street까지 직진해서 길을 건넌 후 오른쪽으로 돌아야 한다.
⑤ B는 A에게 버스를 타고 경찰서 가는 법을 설명하고 있다.

[01~02] 다음 대화를 읽고 물음에 답하시오.

Amy: Jinho, hurry up. We're going to be late for the movie.

Jinho: Okay. _____(A)_____?

Amy: It will take about 15 minutes ___(B)___ bus.

Jinho: All right. I'm almost ready.

서답형

01 위 대화의 빈칸 (A)에 들어갈 말을 〈보기〉의 단어를 배열하여 완성하시오.

┌─── 보기 ───┐
take / get / it / the / to / to / theater / how / will / long
└─────────────┘

➡ _____

중요

02 위 대화의 빈칸 (B)에 들어갈 말로 적절한 것은?

① by　　② at　　③ from
④ on　　⑤ for

[03~04] 다음 대화를 읽고 물음에 답하시오.

Minsu: Hi, Emma. What's up?

Emma: Hey, Minsu. Are you free this Saturday?

Minsu: Yes. Why do you ask?

Emma: Well, (A)how about having lunch together?

Minsu: Sure.

Emma: Let's try the new Chinese restaurant, Ming's. It's near the school.

Minsu: Okay. How can I get there from the school?

Emma: Come out from the school and go straight to Green Street. Make a left, and the restaurant will be on your left.

Minsu: All right. Let's meet at 12 o'clock.

Emma: Wonderful. See you then.

서답형

03 위 대화의 밑줄 친 (A)와 의미가 같도록 why를 사용하여 다시 쓰시오.

➡ _____

04 위 대화를 읽고 대답할 수 <u>없는</u> 것은?

① What are Emma and Minsu going to do this Saturday?

② What restaurant are Emma and Minsu going to try?

③ How can Minsu get to Ming's?

④ What time are Emma and Minsu going to meet?

⑤ How long does it take for Emma to go to Ming's?

[05~07] 다음 대화를 읽고 물음에 답하시오.

Andy: I'm so excited about the school festival this Friday.

Mike: Me, too. What can we do to advertise ⓐit, Andy?

Andy: How about making posters?

Mike: Great idea. We can post them in our neighborhood.

Andy: Right. How long will it take to make ⓑ them?

Mike: Well, it will take about three hours.

Andy: Okay, I hope many people come to the festival.

05 위 대화에서 다음 영영풀이가 나타내는 말을 찾아 쓰시오.

> to tell the public about goods to make people buy them

➡ _____

06 위 대화의 밑줄 친 ⓐ와 ⓑ가 각각 가리키는 것을 쓰시오.

➡ ⓐ _____ ⓑ _____

07 위 대화의 내용과 일치하지 <u>않는</u> 것은?

① Andy and Mike are excited about the school festival.
② The school festival is going to be held this Friday.
③ Andy and Mike are going to make posters to advertise the school festival.
④ It will take about three hours to make the posters.
⑤ Andy and Mike are going to post the posters with their neighbors.

[08~10] 다음 대화를 읽고 물음에 답하시오.

> Man: Excuse me. How can I get to Suwon Hwaseong from here?
> Mina: It's easy. Do you see the bus stop over there?
> Man: Yes, I do.
> Mina: Take the No. 11 bus and get off at the sixth stop.
> Man: How long will it take to get there?
> Mina: It will take about 20 minutes.
> Man: Thank you very much.

> Mina: No problem. Are you going there for the festival?
> Man: Yes. I heard it's a lot of fun.
> Mina: I hope you have a great time.

08 How will the man go to Suwon Hwaseong?

➡ _____

09 Why does the man want to join the festival?

➡ _____

10 Which bus should the man take to go to Suwon Hwaseong?

➡ _____

11 다음 대화에 알맞은 말을 <보기>에서 골라 쓰시오.

> ┤ 보기 ├
> a right / front / get / one block /
> go straight

> A: Excuse me. How can I ____(A)____ to the market?
> B: ____(B)____ to Green Street. Make ____(C)____. Go straight ____(D)____ and cross the street. The market will be in ____(E)____ of you.
> A: Thank you very much.

➡ (A) _____
  (B) _____
  (C) _____
  (D) _____
  (E) _____

[01~02] 다음 대화를 읽고 물음에 답하시오.

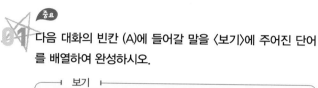

Sora: Excuse me. _____(A)_____ ?

Tom: Oh, the library? Cross the street and go straight two blocks. Then ___(B)___ .

Sora: Thank you very much.

01 다음 대화의 빈칸 (A)에 들어갈 말을 〈보기〉에 주어진 단어를 배열하여 완성하시오.

> ┤ 보기 ├
>
> get / how / I / to / library / can / the

➡ _____

02 다음 표지판의 내용과 일치하도록 빈칸 (B)를 완성하시오.

➡ _____

[03~05] 다음 대화를 읽고 물음에 답하시오.

Andy: I'm so ⓐexciting about the school festival this Friday.

Mike: Me, too. What can we do ⓑto advertise it, Andy?

Andy: How about ⓒmaking posters?

Mike: Great idea. We can post them in our neighborhood.

Andy: Right. How long will it take to make them?

Mike: Well, it will take ⓓabout three hours.

Andy: Okay, I hope many people ⓔcome to the festival.

03 위 대화의 ⓐ~ⓔ 중 어법상 바르지 않은 것을 찾아 바르게 고치시오.

➡ _____

04 What are Andy and Mike going to advertise?

➡ _____

05 What are Andy and Mike going to make?

➡ _____

06 다음 그림의 내용과 일치하도록 빈칸 (A)와 (B)를 완성하시오.

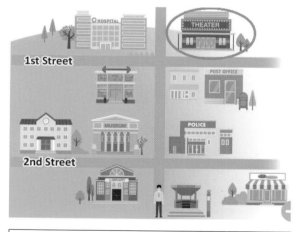

Aram: Excuse me. How can I get to the theater?

Brian: _____(A)_____ . It will be on your ___(B)___ .

Aram: Thank you so much.

➡ (A) _____

   (B) _____

교과서
Grammar

① 가주어 It

- **It** is a pleasure **to talk** with you. 너와 대화하는 것은 즐거워.
- **It** was difficult **to stop** my bad habit. 나의 나쁜 습관을 멈추는 것은 어려웠다.

■ to부정사구가 문장의 주어로 쓰여 주어가 길어진 경우, 주어부를 문장의 맨 뒤로 보내고 이 자리에 It을 쓰는 것이 가주어 It이다.

- **To exercise** regularly is very important.
  = **It** is very important **to exercise** regularly. 규칙적으로 운동하는 것은 매우 중요하다.

■ 가주어 It은 따로 해석하지 않으며 to부정사구를 주어로 해석해야 한다. to부정사구의 부정은 'not+to V'로 나타낸다.

- **It** is fun **to learn** a foreign language. 외국어를 배우는 것은 재미있다.
- **It** was hard **to say** sorry to you. 너에게 미안하다고 말하는 것은 힘들었어.
- **It** is good **to know** how to say hello. 인사하는 방법을 아는 것은 좋다.
- **It** is important **not to use** your phone while walking. 걷는 동안 휴대 전화기를 사용하지 않는 것이 중요하다.

핵심 Check

1. 다음 우리말과 일치하도록 빈칸에 알맞은 말을 쓰시오.

(1) 아침 일찍 운동하는 것은 좋다.
➡ _____ is good _____ _____ early in the morning.

(2) 부주의하게 운전하는 것은 위험하다.
➡ _____ is dangerous _____ _____ carelessly.

(3) 너의 친구에게 거짓말하는 것은 옳지 않아.
➡ It is wrong _____ _____ to your friend.

② 지각동사

- I **heard** her **crying**. 나는 그녀가 우는 소리를 들었어.
- They **saw** the boy **playing** the piano. 그들은 그 소년이 피아노를 연주하는 것을 보았다.

■ 지각동사란 신체 감각과 관련된 동사로 보고, 듣고, 느끼는 동사인 see, watch, hear, feel 등이 이에 해당한다. 5형식 동사에 해당하여 목적어와 목적격보어를 취한다.

- June **heard** the dog **barking** at someone. June은 그 개가 누군가를 향해 짖는 소리를 들었다.

■ '지각동사+목적어+V(ing)'로 쓰이는 경우, 목적어와 목적격보어는 능동 관계가 된다. 동작이 진행 중인 것을 강조하고 싶을 때에는 보통 현재분사를 쓴다. '지각동사+목적어+p.p.'로 쓰이는 경우 목적어와 목적격보어의 관계는 수동이다.

- We **watched** our children **singing** songs. 우리는 우리 아이들이 노래 부르는 것을 지켜보았다.
- Did you **see** the glass **broken**? 너는 그 유리잔이 깨어진 것을 봤니?

■ 사역동사의 쓰임과 혼동하지 않도록 한다. 사역동사 make, have, let 역시 5형식 동사로 목적어와 목적격보어를 취하지만, 사역동사의 목적격보어는 원형부정사이며 '목적어가 ~하게 시키다'라는 의미이다.

- Mom **makes** me **eat** carrots. 엄마는 내가 당근을 먹게 하신다.
- The teacher **had** us **do** some homework. 그 선생님은 우리가 약간의 숙제를 하도록 시키셨다.

핵심 Check

2. 다음 우리말과 일치하도록 빈칸에 알맞은 말을 쓰시오.

(1) 그 사냥꾼은 누군가가 그를 따라오는 것을 느꼈다.

➡ The hunter _____ someone _____ him.

(2) 우리는 그가 집으로 들어가는 것을 보았다.

➡ We _____ him _____ the house.

(3) 아빠는 내가 내 방 청소를 하도록 시키셨다.

➡ Dad _____ me _____ my room.

Grammar 시험대비 기본평가

01 다음 문장에서 어법상 어색한 부분을 바르게 고쳐 쓰시오.

(1) It is natural for you get angry.

_____ ➡ _____

(2) It was impossible to changing the plan.

_____ ➡ _____

(3) Didn't you hear him said he was busy?

_____ ➡ _____

(4) We watched Jane to dance on the stage.

_____ ➡ _____

02 주어진 단어를 어법에 맞게 빈칸에 쓰시오.

(1) Perry saw her friend _____ off the stairs. (fall)
(2) It is really exciting _____ on a picnic. (go)
(3) I saw the boy _____ the window. (break)
(4) It was fun _____ with your sisters. (play)

03 주어진 단어를 바르게 배열하여 다음 우리말을 영어로 쓰시오. 필요하다면 단어를 추가하거나 변형하시오.

(2) wake up: 일어나다
(3) island: 섬

(1) 나는 그 아기가 우는 소리를 들었어. (cry / the baby / heard / I)

➡ _____

(2) 너가 일찍 일어나는 것은 좋은 생각이야. (early / it / a good idea / for / you / wake up / is)

➡ _____

(3) Emma는 그들이 섬 주변에서 수영하는 것을 보았다. (the island / Emma / them / swim / saw / around)

➡ _____

(4) 사람들은 미술가들이 그들의 작품을 만드는 것을 처음부터 끝까지 지켜본다. (from beginning to end / the artists / people / their / create / watch / works)

➡ _____

01 다음 중 밑줄 친 부분의 쓰임이 <u>다른</u> 하나는?

① <u>It</u> is nice to clean your room by yourself.

② <u>It</u> is not that difficult to speak Korean well.

③ <u>It</u> is under the sofa in the living room.

④ <u>It</u> was hard to tell the truth to her.

⑤ <u>It</u> was easy to find the way to get there.

02 다음 빈칸에 들어갈 말로 가장 적절한 것은?

> James saw his friends _____ football on the playground.

① to play ② play ③ played
④ plays ⑤ to playing

03 다음 우리말을 영어로 바르게 옮긴 것은?

> 이 책을 읽는 것은 어려웠다.

① It is difficult to read this book.

② I was difficult to read this book.

③ It was difficult read this book.

④ It was difficult to read this book.

⑤ It is difficult to reading this book.

04 주어진 단어를 이용하여 다음 우리말을 영어로 쓰시오.

> 거짓말을 하는 것은 잘못된 일이다.
> (it / wrong)

➡ _____

05 다음 중 어법상 바르지 <u>않은</u> 것은?

① It is good to do your job on your own.

② David saw his brother wearing his cap.

③ It is important to help others.

④ Wendy saw the bus leaving right in front of her eyes.

⑤ Mom made me to wash my clothes every day.

06 다음 빈칸에 들어갈 말이 바르게 짝지어진 것은?

> • I heard the couple _____ last night.
> • Did you feel the house _____?

① to fight – to shake

② fight – shaken

③ fighting – shake

④ fight – to shake

⑤ fighting – shaken

07 다음 중 어법상 바르지 <u>않은</u> 것은?

> I like ①<u>to listen</u> ②<u>to</u> ③<u>the birds</u> ④ <u>to sing</u> when I ⑤<u>get up</u> early in the morning.

①　　②　　③　　④　　⑤

08 주어진 단어를 바르게 배열하여 다음 우리말을 영어로 쓰시오. 필요하다면 단어를 추가하시오.

> 헬멧을 쓰지 않고 오토바이를 타는 것은 위험해. (dangerous / a helmet / without / a motorcycle / is / it / ride)

➡ _____

09 다음 우리말을 영어로 바르게 옮긴 것을 고르시오.

> 최선을 다하는 것은 중요해.

① It was important to do best.
② It is important to doing your best.
③ It is important do your best.
④ It is important to do your best.
⑤ It is important for doing your best.

10 다음 중 어법상 바르지 않은 것은?

① I saw the man got into the car alone.
② Julia heard Bill talking with someone.
③ It is fun to live in a dormitory.
④ It was careless of you to fall asleep while you were driving.
⑤ It is not easy to learn how to swim.

11 다음 중 쓰임이 다른 하나는?

① It is wrong to say like that to your friend.
② I am so happy to hear the news from you.
③ To see is to believe.
④ It is easy to solve the problem.
⑤ Is it difficult to write a poem?

서답형
12 다음 대화의 빈칸에 알맞은 말을 세 단어로 쓰시오.

> A: Did anybody go out?
> B: I don't think so. I didn't see _____ .

➡ _____

13 다음 빈칸에 들어갈 말로 가장 적절한 것은?

> I didn't hear you _____ in. You must have been very quiet.

① will come
② come
③ came
④ to come
⑤ to coming

14 다음 중 (A)~(C)에서 어법상 옳은 것끼리 바르게 짝지은 것은?

> • I saw my friend (A)[running / to run] down the street.
> • It was thoughtful of you (B)[to give / give] her a present.
> • Jason heard somebody (C)[say / to say] something to her.

① to run – give – to say
② to run – to give – to say
③ running – to give – say
④ running – give – say
⑤ running – to give – to say

15 다음 중 주어진 문장의 It과 쓰임이 같은 것은?

> It is kind of you to help your mom.

① It is time to go to bed now.
② It was too dark outside.
③ It was made of 100 blocks of stone.
④ It makes me nervous.
⑤ It is not easy to plant a tree.

서답형
16 주어진 단어를 활용하여 다음 우리말을 영어로 쓰시오.

> 말을 타는 것은 매우 재미있어. (it / lot / of / fun)

➡ _____

17 다음 상황을 읽고 빈칸에 들어갈 말로 가장 적절한 것을 고르시오.

> Brad was walking along the street. I saw that when I drove past in my car.
> → I _____ .

① saw Brad driving past
② heard Brad drive my car
③ saw Brad in my car
④ saw Brad walking along the street
⑤ heard Brad walking with someone

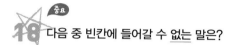

18 다음 중 빈칸에 들어갈 수 <u>없는</u> 말은?

> We _____ the boys playing the guitars.

① watched   ② listened to   ③ saw
④ heard   ⑤ made

19 다음 빈칸에 알맞은 말은?

> **A:** Did I close the window when I went out?
> **B:** Yes, you did. I _____ .

① saw you go out
② heard you go out
③ saw you closing the window
④ heard you closed the window
⑤ heard you going out through the window

서답형

20 다음 대화의 밑줄 친 우리말을 영어로 옮기시오.

> **A:** What was Jane doing then?
> **B:** <u>나는 그녀가 누군가에게 전화하고 있는 것을 보았어.</u>

➡ _____

21 빈칸에 알맞은 말이 바르게 짝지어진 것을 <u>모두</u> 고르시오.

> It is fun _____ someone _____ comedy.

① seeing – doing   ② see – doing
③ seeing – to do   ④ to see – do
⑤ see – do

중요

22 다음 중 밑줄 친 부분이 어법상 <u>틀린</u> 것은?

① It is really fun <u>to play</u> tennis with you.
② I want <u>to play</u> computer games.
③ It is exciting <u>to play</u> basketball.
④ Tom was tired of <u>playing</u> alone.
⑤ It is dangerous <u>to playing</u> with a knife.

서답형

23 다음 두 문장을 하나의 문장으로 쓰시오.

> • The boy fell off the tree yesterday.
> • I saw that.

➡ _____

서답형

24 다음 대화를 읽고 빈칸에 알맞은 말을 쓰시오.

> **Kelly:** What is Jimmy doing over there?
> **Amelia:** He is using his phone.

➡ Amelia sees Jimmy _____ .

서답형

25 주어진 단어를 활용하여 다음 우리말을 7 단어로 이루어진 한 문장으로 쓰시오.

> 여기에 머무는 것은 안전하지 않아.
> (safe / stay)

➡ _____

01 다음 대화의 빈칸에 알맞은 말을 쓰시오.

> A: How do you know I rode a bike yesterday?
> B: I know because I saw _____.

➡ _____

02 가주어 It을 이용하여 다음 우리말을 영어로 쓰시오.

> 계단에서 뛰는 것은 나쁘다.

➡ _____

03 다음 두 문장을 하나의 문장으로 쓰시오.

> • The accident happened.
> • Did you see that?

➡ _____

04 다음 빈칸에 알맞은 말을 쓰시오.

> To hear you say that was true.
> = _____ to hear you say that.

➡ _____

05 주어진 단어를 바르게 배열하여 다음 우리말을 영어로 쓰시오. 한 단어는 두 번 쓰시오.

> 학생들이 학교에서 휴대전화를 이용하도록 허락하는 것은 좋은 생각이 아니다.
> (in school / a good idea / students / allow / cell phones / to / it / not / is / use)

➡ _____

06 주어진 단어를 이용하여 다음 대화의 빈칸에 알맞은 말을 쓰시오.

> A: Did Susan cross the street?
> B: Yes, she did. I _____.(see)

➡ _____

07 주어진 단어를 이용하여 다음 우리말을 9 단어로 이루어진 한 문장으로 쓰시오.

> 네가 예의 바르게 인사하지 않는 것은 무례하다.
> (it / bow / politely / of)

➡ _____

08 주어진 문장을 지시에 맞게 영어로 쓰시오.

> 물을 절약하는 것은 중요합니다.

(1) to부정사 주어를 써서 작문할 것

➡ _____

(2) 가주어를 써서 작문할 것

➡ _____

09 다음 빈칸에 알맞은 말을 쓰시오.

> A: Who opened the window?
> B: I saw a man _____ but I don't know who he was.

➡ _____

10 다음 우리말을 영어로 쓰시오.

> 화살을 쏘는 것은 어렵다.

➡ _____

11 다음 대화의 빈칸에 알맞은 말을 7 단어로 쓰시오.

> A: I heard that you carried out a campaign to reduce food waste in school cafeteria. Did it work?
> B: It was a little hard _____, but the campaign turned out to be successful.

➡ _____

12 다음 상황을 읽고 빈칸에 알맞은 말을 쓰시오.

> There are many people in the park. Musicians play beautiful live music. Children play catch. Couples sing a song.

➡ In the park, you can hear _____

_____. Also, you can see children _____ and couples _____.

13 밑줄 친 말의 반의어를 이용하여 빈칸에 알맞은 말을 쓰시오.

> A: Brian, isn't it difficult to look up a word in a dictionary?
> B: No. _____

➡ _____

14 다음 우리말을 영어로 쓰시오.

> 나는 누군가가 피아노를 연주하는 소리를 들었다.

➡ _____

15 주어진 문장과 같은 의미의 문장을 쓰시오.

> To be honest and fair is important.

➡ _____

16 다음 중 어법상 어색한 것을 골라 바르게 고치고, 그렇게 고친 이유를 서술하시오.

> Brady saw Clara to do something and wondered what she was doing.

➡ 잘못된 곳: _____ ➡ _____
고친 이유: _____

17 주어진 단어를 활용하여 다음 우리말을 영어로 쓰시오.

> 의사가 되는 것은 쉽지 않아. (It)

➡ _____

18 다음 우리말에 맞게 빈칸에 알맞은 말을 쓰시오.

> 그들이 그 탁자를 옮기는 것을 지켜보는 것은 아주 재미있었다.
> It was a lot of fun _____.

➡ _____

19 다음 우리말을 영어로 쓰시오.

> 나는 어제 누군가가 나를 따라오는 것을 느꼈다.

➡ _____

교과서

Let's Party!

Holi, the Festival of Colors

Amala from Delhi, India
출신을 나타내는 전치사 from

Holi is the most popular festival in my country. It is usually in March.
가장 인기 있는(최상급)　　　　　　= Holi　　　　연도 앞에

During the festival, we say goodbye to cold winter and hello to warm
전치사(~ 동안)　　　　~에게 작별 인사를 하다

spring. We celebrate the festival everywhere for two days. On the first
전치사(~ 동안)+구체적인 기간　　特정 날짜 앞에

day, people gather around a big fire at night and sing and dance. The
등위접속사: sing과 dance를 대등하게 연결

main event begins the next day. Children and adults chase each other
그 다음 날　　　　　　　　　　서로(chase의 목적어)

with *gulal*. What is *gulal*? It is blue, yellow, green and pink powder.

It's a lot of fun to run around and throw colorful powder at everyone.
가주어 It　　　진주어 to부정사　　　throw A at B: B를 향해 A를 던지다

We also join street parades!

White Nights Festival

Victor from St. Petersburg, Russia

Have you heard of the *White Nights*? Every summer, this amazing
~에 대해 들어봤니?(경험을 묻는 현재완료)　　every+단수명사: 모든 ~, 매 ~　　the White

thing happens in my hometown. The night sky does not get completely
Nights를 지칭　　　　　　　　　　get+형용사: (어떤 상태가) 되다

dark.

📎 확인문제

● 다음 문장이 본문의 내용과 일치하면 T, 일치하지 <u>않으면</u> F를 쓰시오.

1 Holi is held in India. ☐

2 People in India celebrate Holi for two weeks. ☐

3 There is a big fire at night on the second day of Holi. ☐

4 We can see white nights in Victor's hometown every summer. ☐

---

usually 주로
celebrate 축하하다, 기념하다
gather 모이다, 모으다
adult 어른
chase 뒤쫓다
throw 던지다
parade 퍼레이드, 행진
happen 발생하다
completely 완전히

During that time, we hold the White Nights Festival. It usually starts
= the White Nights   = the White Nights Festival
in May and lasts for about a month. During the festival, there is a
                        약
ballet or an opera almost every night. The most popular event is the
                    거의   가장 인기 있는
Scarlet Sails celebration. A boat with red sails slowly appears on the
                              전치사(~가 부착된, ~가 달린)   자동사(수동태 안 됨)
river. Soon, fireworks begin and a water show follows. You can also
                                              (시간, 순서상으로) 뒤를 잇다
hear musicians playing beautiful live music.
지각동사+목적어+현재분사

Kiruna Snow Festival

Ebba from Kiruna, Sweden

Winter is my favorite season because of the Kiruna Snow Festival.
                                ~ 때문에
The festival starts in the last week of January and goes on for five or
                        마지막 주   진행되다
six days. The largest event is the snow design competition. The artists
        가장 큰(최상급)
shape huge piles of snow into animals, buildings, and other beautiful
shape A into B: A를 B의 형태로 만들다
artworks. People watch the artists shaping their works from beginning
            지각동사+목적어+현재분사   처음부터 끝까지(= from start to finish)
to end. My favorite activity is the dog sled ride. It is amazing to fly
                                    타기, 타는 것(명사) 가주어 It   진주어 to부정사
through a world of snow on a dog sled.

last 지속하다
celebration 축하, 기념, 축하 행사
appear 나타나다
follow 따라가다, 따라오다
fireworks 불꽃놀이
live 라이브의, 실황인
musician 음악가
favorite 가장 좋아하는
competition 대회, 시합, 경쟁
other 다른
from A to B A부터 B까지
sled 썰매

확인문제

● 다음 문장이 본문의 내용과 일치하면 T, 일치하지 않으면 F를 쓰시오.

1 The White Nights Festival continues for about a month. ☐

2 A boat with no sails appears on the river during the Scarlet Sails celebration. ☐

3 The Kiruna Snow Festival is held in Kiruna. ☐

4 The Kiruna Snow Festival starts in the first week of January. ☐

5 At the Kiruna Snow Festival, artists shape huge piles of snow into animals,

buildings, and other artworks. ☐

● 우리말을 참고하여 빈칸에 알맞은 말을 쓰시오.

1 Holi, the _____ of Colors

2 Amala _____ Delhi, India

3 Holi is _____ _____ _____ festival in my country.

4 It _____ _____ in March.

5 During the festival, we _____ _____ to cold winter and _____ to warm spring.

6 We _____ the festival everywhere _____ two days.

7 _____ the first day, people _____ _____ a big fire _____ _____ and sing and dance.

8 The main event _____ _____ _____ _____ .

9 Children and adults _____ _____ _____ with *gulal*.

10 _____ is *gulal*? It is blue, yellow, green and pink _____ .

11 It's a lot of fun _____ _____ _____ and _____ colorful powder _____ everyone.

12 We also _____ _____ _____ !

13 _____ _____ Festival

14 Victor _____ St. Petersburg, Russia

15 _____ you _____ _____ the *White Nights*?

16 Every summer, this _____ thing _____ in my hometown.

1 홀리, 색의 축제

2 인도, 델리의 Amala

3 '홀리'는 우리나라에서 가장 인기 있는 축제예요.

4 그것은 보통 3월에 있어요.

5 축제 기간 동안에, 우리는 추운 겨울에게 작별 인사를 하고 따뜻한 봄을 맞는 인사를 해요.

6 우리는 이틀 동안 어디서든 축제를 기념해요.

7 첫째 날, 사람들은 밤에 큰 모닥불 주변에 모여 노래하고 춤을 춰요.

8 주요 행사는 다음 날에 시작돼요.

9 어린이들과 어른들이 'gulal'을 지니고 서로를 쫓아다녀요.

10 'gulal'이 무엇이냐고요? 그것은 파랑, 노랑, 초록, 분홍의 가루예요.

11 주변을 뛰어다니며 형형색색의 가루를 모든 사람들에게 던지는 것은 정말 재미있어요.

12 우리는 거리 행진에도 참가해요!

13 백야 축제

14 러시아, 상트페테르부르크의 Victor

15 '백야'에 대해 들어 봤나요?

16 매년 여름, 이 놀라운 일이 나의 고향에서 벌어져요.

17 The night sky _____ dark.

18 _____ that time, we _____ the White Nights Festival.

19 It usually _____ _____ May and _____ for _____ a month.

20 During the festival, _____ _____ a ballet or an opera _____ _____ _____ .

21 The most _____ event is the Scarlet Sails _____ .

22 A boat with red sails slowly _____ _____ _____ _____ .

23 Soon, fireworks _____ and a water show _____ .

24 You can also _____ musicians _____ beautiful live music.

25 Kiruna _____ _____

26 Ebba _____ Kiruna, Sweden

27 Winter is _____ _____ _____ _____ _____ the Kiruna Snow Festival.

28 The festival _____ _____ _____ _____ _____ of January and _____ _____ for five or six days.

29 _____ _____ _____ is the snow design competition.

30 The artists _____ huge piles of snow _____ animals, buildings, and _____ beautiful artworks.

31 People _____ the artists _____ their works _____ beginning _____ end.

32 My _____ _____ is the dog sled ride.

33 It is amazing _____ _____ _____ a world of snow _____ a dog sled.

17 밤하늘이 완전히 어두워지지 않아요.

18 그 시기 동안, 우리는 백야 축제를 열어요.

19 축제는 보통 5월에 시작되고 약 한 달 동안 지속돼요.

20 축제 기간 동안 거의 매일 밤 발레나 오페라 공연이 있어요.

21 가장 인기 있는 행사는 '붉은 돛 축하 행사'예요.

22 빨간 돛을 단 배가 강 위에 서서히 나타나요.

23 곧 불꽃놀이가 시작되고 물 쇼가 이어져요.

24 또한 여러분은 음악가들이 아름다운 라이브 음악을 연주하는 것을 들을 수 있어요.

25 키루나 눈 축제

26 스웨덴, 키루나의 Ebba

27 겨울은 키루나 눈 축제 때문에 내가 가장 좋아하는 계절이에요.

28 축제는 1월 마지막 주에 시작해서 5일이나 6일 동안 계속돼요.

29 가장 큰 행사는 '눈 디자인 대회'예요.

30 미술가들이 거대한 눈 덩어리를 동물, 건물, 다른 아름다운 작품의 모양으로 만들어요.

31 사람들은 미술가들이 그들의 작품을 만드는 것을 처음부터 끝까지 지켜봐요.

32 내가 가장 좋아하는 활동은 개썰매 타기예요.

33 개썰매를 타고 눈 세상을 날아가는 것은 정말 놀라워요.

● 우리말을 참고하여 본문을 영작하시오.

1 홀리, 색의 축제

➡ _____

2 인도, 델리의 Amala

➡ _____

3 '홀리'는 우리나라에서 가장 인기 있는 축제예요.

➡ _____

4 그것은 보통 3월에 있어요.

➡ _____

5 축제 기간 동안에, 우리는 추운 겨울에게 작별 인사를 하고 따뜻한 봄을 맞는 인사를 해요.

➡ _____

6 우리는 이틀 동안 어디서든 축제를 기념해요.

➡ _____

7 첫째 날, 사람들은 밤에 큰 모닥불 주변에 모여 노래하고 춤을 춰요.

➡ _____

8 주요 행사는 다음 날에 시작돼요.

➡ _____

9 어린이들과 어른들이 'gulal'을 지니고 서로를 쫓아다녀요.

➡ _____

10 'gulal'이 무엇이냐고요? 그것은 파랑, 노랑, 초록, 분홍의 가루예요.

➡ _____

11 주변을 뛰어다니며 형형색색의 가루를 모든 사람들에게 던지는 것은 정말 재미있어요.

➡ _____

12 우리는 거리 행진에도 참가해요!

➡ _____

13 백야 축제

➡ _____

14 러시아, 상트페테르부르크의 Victor

➡ _____

15 '백야'에 대해 들어 봤나요?

➡ _____

16 매년 여름, 이 놀라운 일이 나의 고향에서 벌어져요.

➡ _____

17 밤하늘이 완전히 어두워지지 않아요.

➡ _____

18 그 시기 동안, 우리는 백야 축제를 열어요.

➡ _____

19 축제는 보통 5월에 시작되고 약 한 달 동안 지속돼요.

➡ _____

20 축제 기간 동안 거의 매일 밤 발레나 오페라 공연이 있어요.

➡ _____

21 가장 인기 있는 행사는 '붉은 돛 축하 행사'예요.

➡ _____

22 빨간 돛을 단 배가 강 위에 서서히 나타나요.

➡ _____

23 곧 불꽃놀이가 시작되고 물 쇼가 이어져요.

➡ _____

24 또한 여러분은 음악가들이 아름다운 라이브 음악을 연주하는 것을 들을 수 있어요.

➡ _____

25 키루나 눈 축제

➡ _____

26 스웨덴, 키루나의 Ebba

➡ _____

27 겨울은 키루나 눈 축제 때문에 내가 가장 좋아하는 계절이에요.

➡ _____

28 축제는 1월 마지막 주에 시작해서 5일이나 6일 동안 계속돼요.

➡ _____

29 가장 큰 행사는 '눈 디자인 대회'예요.

➡ _____

30 미술가들이 거대한 눈 덩어리를 동물, 건물, 다른 아름다운 작품의 모양으로 만들어요.

➡ _____

31 사람들은 미술가들이 그들의 작품을 만드는 것을 처음부터 끝까지 지켜봐요.

➡ _____

32 내가 가장 좋아하는 활동은 개썰매 타기예요.

➡ _____

33 개썰매를 타고 눈 세상을 날아가는 것은 정말 놀라워요.

➡ _____

[01~06] 다음 글을 읽고 물음에 답하시오.

Holi, the Festival of Colors
Amala from Delhi, India
Holi is the most popular festival in my country. It is usually in March. During the festival, we say goodbye to cold winter and hello to warm spring. We celebrate the festival everywhere for two days. On the first day, people gather around a big fire ____ⓐ____ night and sing and dance. The main event begins the next day. Children and adults chase each other with *gulal*. What is *gulal*? It is blue, yellow, green and pink powder. It's a lot of fun ____ⓑ____ around and throw colorful powder ____ⓒ____ everyone. We also join street parades!

01 빈칸 ⓐ와 ⓒ에 공통으로 들어갈 말로 가장 적절한 것은?

① by   ② on   ③ to
④ at   ⑤ in

서답형
02 빈칸 ⓑ에 동사 run을 어법에 맞게 쓰시오.

➡ _____

중요
03 다음 중 위 글의 내용과 일치하지 않는 것은?

① Holi is usually in March.
② The festival lasts for two days.
③ There is the main event on the first day.
④ *Gulal* is colorful powder.
⑤ There are street parades at the festival.

서답형
04 According to the passage, what is the most popular festival in India?

➡ _____

서답형
05 다음 빈칸에 들어갈 말을 위 글에서 찾아 쓰시오.

If people _____ somewhere, they come together in a group.

➡ _____

06 다음 중 홀리 축제 기간에 볼 수 없는 것은?

① people gathering around a big fire
② people singing and dancing at night
③ street parades
④ adults and children chasing each other with *gulal*
⑤ children throwing colorful balls

[07~10] 다음 글을 읽고 물음에 답하시오.

White Nights Festival
Victor from St. Petersburg, Russia
(A)Have you heard of the *White Nights*? Every summer, (B)this amazing thing happens in my hometown. The night sky does not get completely dark. During that time, we (C)hold the White Nights Festival. It usually starts in May and lasts for about a month. During the festival, there is a ballet or an opera almost every night. The most popular event is the Scarlet Sails celebration. A boat with red sails slowly appears on the river. Soon, fireworks begin and a water show follows. You can also hear musicians playing beautiful live music.

07 밑줄 친 (A)와 현재완료의 용법이 같은 것은?

① We have known each other for ten years.
② Nora has been to Vietnam three times.
③ The employer has just arrived at the airport.
④ David has lost his car key.
⑤ Karen has played the guitar since she was twelve years old.

서답형

08 밑줄 친 (B)가 의미하는 것을 위 글에서 찾아 쓰시오.

➡ _____

09 다음 중 밑줄 친 (C)와 같은 의미로 쓰인 것은?

① Janet held her head because of headache.
② The chair is strong enough to hold your weight.
③ Tom held his girl friend's hand tightly.
④ Can you hold a minute, please?
⑤ We hold our class meeting every Monday.

서답형

10 During the festival, what can you see almost every night? Answer the question with a full sentence.

➡ _____

[11~14] 다음 글을 읽고 물음에 답하시오.

Kiruna Snow Festival
Ebba from Kiruna, Sweden
Winter is my favorite season (A)[because / because of] the Kiruna Snow Festival. The festival starts in the last week of January and goes on for five or six days. The largest event

is the snow design competition. The artists shape huge piles of snow into animals, buildings, and (B)[other / another] beautiful artworks. People watch the artists ____ⓐ____ their works from beginning to end. My favorite activity is the dog sled ride. It is (C)[amazing / amazed] to fly through a world of snow on a dog sled.

서답형

11 동사 shape를 어법에 맞게 활용하여 빈칸 ⓐ에 쓰시오.

➡ _____

12 (A)~(C)에서 어법상 옳은 것끼리 바르게 묶은 것은?

① because of – another – amazed
② because of – other – amazing
③ because – other – amazed
④ because – other – amazing
⑤ because – another – amazed

13 다음 중 위 글을 읽고 답할 수 없는 것은?

① When does the festival start?
② What is the largest event of the festival?
③ What do the artists do at the festival?
④ What is Ebba's favorite activity?
⑤ How many artists take part in the snow design competition?

서답형

14 How long does the festival last? Answer in English with a full sentence.

➡ _____

[15~19] 다음 글을 읽고 물음에 답하시오.

Holi, the Festival of Colors

Amala ___(A)___ Delhi, India

Holi is ①the most popular festival in my country. It is usually ___(B)___ March. ___(C)___ the festival, we say goodbye to cold winter and hello to warm spring. We celebrate the festival everywhere ②for two days. ③On the first day, people gather around a big fire at night and sing and dance. The main event begins the next day. Children and adults chase each other with *gulal*. What is *gulal*? It is blue, yellow, green and pink powder. It's ④a lot of fun to run around and throw colorful powder at everyone. We also ⑤join with street parades!

15 빈칸 (A)~(C)에 들어갈 말이 바르게 짝지어진 것은?

① from – at – While
② from – in – During
③ at – on – For
④ in – about – At
⑤ in – by – About

16 다음 중 위 글의 내용과 일치하는 것은?

① Holi is not a famous festival in India.
② Holi is held in summer.
③ People celebrate the festival at a special place.
④ People dance and sing on the first night of the festival.
⑤ Amala doesn't like throwing *gulal* at the festival.

17 밑줄 친 ①~⑤ 중 어법상 옳지 <u>않은</u> 것은?

① ② ③ ④ ⑤

서답형

18 위 글의 내용에 맞게 빈칸에 알맞은 말을 쓰시오.

> On the last day of the festival, we can see children and adults _____.

➡ _____

서답형

19 If you want to see only the main event of the festival, when should you go to the festival?

➡ _____

[20~23] 다음 글을 읽고 물음에 답하시오.

White Nights Festival

Victor from St. Petersburg, Russia

Have you heard of the *White Nights*? Every summer, this amazing thing happens in my hometown. The night sky does not get completely dark. During that time, we hold the White Nights Festival. It usually starts in May and lasts for about a month. During the festival, there is a ballet or an opera almost every night. The most popular event is the Scarlet Sails celebration. A boat with red sails slowly appears on the river. Soon, fireworks begin and a water show follows. You can also hear musicians ___(A)___ beautiful live music.

서답형

20 play를 어법에 맞게 빈칸 (A)에 쓰시오.

➡ _____

서답형

21 위 글의 내용에 맞게 빈칸에 알맞은 말을 쓰시오.

> The White Nights Festival is held in Victor's hometown _____ _____.

22 다음 중 위 글을 읽고 답할 수 없는 것은?

① Where is Victor from?

② What is Victor mainly talking about?

③ When is the White Nights Festival held?

④ How long does the festival last?

⑤ Where does the boat come from?

23 다음 중 백야 축제에 관한 내용으로 바르지 않은 것은?

① It is held in St. Petersburg in Russia.

② Scarlet Sails celebration is more popular than any other event.

③ There is a boat with red sails.

④ The boat moves really fast on the river.

⑤ After the boat appears, fireworks begin.

[24~28] 다음 글을 읽고 물음에 답하시오.

Kiruna Snow Festival

Ebba from Kiruna, Sweden

Winter is my favorite season because of the Kiruna Snow Festival. The festival starts in ①the last week of January and ②goes on for five or six days. ③The largest event is the snow design competition. The artists shape huge piles of snow into animals, buildings, and other beautiful artworks. People watch the artists shaping their works ④from beginning to end. My favorite activity is the dog sled ride. (A)It is amazing to fly through ⑤a world of snow on a dog sled.

24 다음 중 ①~⑤의 뜻풀이로 바르지 않은 것은?

① 1월 마지막 주   ② 나아가다

③ 가장 큰 행사   ④ 처음부터 끝까지

⑤ 눈 세상

25 Which is NOT true about Ebba?

① She is from Sweden.

② Her favorite season is winter.

③ She likes the dog sled ride.

④ She thinks flying through a world of snow on a dog sled is amazing.

⑤ She can shape huge piles of snow into animals.

26 위 글의 내용에 맞게 빈칸에 알맞은 말을 세 단어로 쓰시오.

At the Kiruna Snow Festival, you can see the artists _____ from beginning to end.

➡ _____

27 다음 중 위 글의 내용을 잘못 이해한 사람은?

① Kelly: The Kiruna Snow Festival lasts five or six days.

② Susan: I will be able to see many artists in the snow design competition.

③ Jason: Many artists make their works in front of people.

④ Brian: The artists have to make only animals and buildings with snow.

⑤ David: I will ride the dog sled at the festival.

28 다음 중 밑줄 친 (A)와 쓰임이 같은 것을 모두 고르시오.

① It made Jenny upset.

② It is hot and humid outside.

③ It is surprising to meet you here.

④ It was found under the sofa.

⑤ It was difficult for me to study hard.

[01~05] 다음 글을 읽고 물음에 답하시오.

Holi, the Festival of Colors

Amala from Delhi, India

Holi is the most popular festival in my country. It is usually in March. During the festival, we say goodbye to cold winter and hello to warm spring. We celebrate the festival everywhere for two days. On the first day, people gather around a big fire at night and sing and dance. The main event begins the next day. Children and adults chase each other with *gulal*. What is *gulal*? It is blue, yellow, green and pink powder. (A) To run around and throw colorful powder at everyone is a lot of fun. We also join street parades!

01 How long do Indians celebrate the festival? Answer the question with seven words.

➡ _____

02 글의 내용에 맞게 대화의 빈칸에 알맞은 말을 쓰시오.

A: I heard about a festival, Holi.
B: What is it?
A: It is the festival of colors. On the first day of the festival, we can see people _____ a big fire at night and _____.

➡ _____, _____

03 주어진 단어를 주어로 하여 밑줄 친 문장 (A)를 다시 쓰시오.

➡ It _____
_____

04 글의 내용에 맞게 빈칸에 알맞은 말을 세 단어로 쓰시오.

A: I want to see the festival, Holi.
B: Oh, then you have to go to _____.
It is usually held then.

➡ _____

05 What is *gulal*? Answer in English with a full sentence.

➡ _____

[06~11] 다음 글을 읽고 물음에 답하시오.

White Nights Festival

Victor from St. Petersburg, Russia

Have you heard of the *White Nights*? Every summer, this amazing thing happens in (A) my hometown. The night sky does not get completely dark. During that time, we hold the White Nights Festival. (B)It starts in May and lasts for about a month. During the festival, there is a ballet or an opera almost every night. The most popular event is the Scarlet Sails celebration. A boat with red sails slowly appears on the river. Soon, fireworks begin and a water show follows. You can also hear musicians playing beautiful live music.

06 밑줄 친 (A)를 구체적으로 쓰시오.

➡ _____

07 단어 usually를 넣어 밑줄 친 문장 (B)를 다시 쓰시오.

➡ _____

08 위 글에서 백야를 설명하는 문장을 찾아 쓰시오.

➡ _____

09 According to the passage, what kinds of events are at the White Nights Festival?

➡ _____

_____

10 다음은 백야 축제를 다녀온 학생이 쓴 일기의 일부이다. 빈칸에 알맞은 말을 다섯 단어로 쓰시오.

> ... I saw a boat _____. It had red sails. Shortly, fireworks began. ...

➡ _____

[11~15] 다음 글을 읽고 물음에 답하시오.

Kiruna Snow Festival

Ebba from Kiruna, Sweden

Winter is my favorite season because of the Kiruna Snow Festival. The festival starts in the last week of January and goes on for five or six days. The largest event is the snow design competition. The artists shape huge piles of snow into animals, buildings, and other beautiful artworks. People watch the artists shaping their works from beginning to end. My favorite activity is the dog sled ride. It is amazing ___(A)___ through a world of snow on a dog sled.

11 동사 fly를 어법에 맞게 빈칸 (A)에 쓰시오.

➡ _____

12 Write the reason why winter is Ebba's favorite season.

➡ _____

_____

13 다음 대화의 빈칸에 알맞은 말을 쓰시오.

> A: I heard that you will visit _____ to see the Kiruna Snow Festival.
> B: Yes. I'm so excited.
> A: Then you should see _____.
>   It is the largest event at the festival.

➡ _____ , _____

14 According to the passage, how long does the Kiruna Snow Festival last? Answer in English with a full sentence.

➡ _____

15 다음은 축제를 방문한 두 사람의 대화이다. 우리말에 맞게 주어진 어구를 바르게 배열하시오.

> A: What are you watching?
> B: 나는 저 미술가가 하나의 거대한 눈 덩어리를 코끼리 모양으로 바꾸는 것을 보고 있어.
> (a huge pile of / an elephant / I / shaping / watching / snow / am / into / the artist)

➡ _____

_____

해석

Listen and Speak 2-C

A: Chris, what will you do for the class party?

B: I'll make sandwiches.

A: Great idea. How long will it take to make them?
= sandwiches

B: Maybe it'll take about an hour.
= Perhaps   대략, ~ 정도

구문해설 • **take:** (시간이) 걸리다

A: Chris, 학급 파티를 위해 무엇을 할 거니?

B: 나는 샌드위치를 만들 거야.

A: 좋은 생각이야. 그것들을 만드는 데 얼마가 걸릴까?

B: 아마도 약 한 시간 정도 걸릴 거야.

Think and Write

I Love Gangneung

I live in Gangneung. There are beautiful beaches in my neighborhood. It's a
~이 있다 (뒤에 있는 명사에 수의 일치)   나의 이웃에   가주어 It

lot of fun to swim at the beach. There is a famous hanok in Gangneung. It is
진주어(to부정사)

called Ojukheon. Yulgok was born there. The most famous food in Gangneung
수동태   in Ojukheon

is potato tteok. It is soft and sweet. Come and enjoy Gangneung!
= Potato tteok

구문해설 • **beach:** 해변   • **neighborhood:** 이웃   • **be born:** 태어나다

강릉이 정말 좋아요

저는 강릉에 살아요. 나의 이웃에는 아름다운 해변들이 있어요. 해변에서 수영하는 것은 정말 재미있어요. 강릉에는 유명한 한옥이 있어요. 그것은 오죽헌이라고 불려요. 율곡이 거기에서 태어났어요. 강릉에서 가장 유명한 음식은 감자떡이에요. 그것은 부드럽고 달콤해요. 와서 강릉을 즐기세요!

Project Culture

I want to introduce Boryeong Mud Festival. It is held in Daecheon Beach
to부정사를 목적어로 취하는 동사   수동태

in July. There are many interesting events in the festival. First, you can
월, 연도 앞에 쓰는 전치사   흥미를 유발할 때 쓰는 현재분사형 형용사

see people do Ssireum in mud. Also it is fun to do colorful mud body painting
지각동사+목적어+동사원형   가주어   진주어

on your body. Lastly, there is an outdoor concert. You can hear musicians play
지각동사+목적어+동사원형

beautiful musics.

구문해설 • **introduce:** 소개하다   • **mud:** 진흙   • **festival:** 축제   • **interesting:** 흥미로운
• **event:** 행사

나는 보령 진흙 축제를 소개하고 싶어요. 그것은 7월에 대천 해수욕장에서 열립니다. 그 축제에는 많은 흥미로운 행사가 있습니다. 우선, 당신은 사람들이 진흙 속에서 씨름하는 것을 볼 수 있어요. 또한 당신의 몸에 형형색색의 진흙을 바르는 것은 재미있어요. 마지막으로, 실외 콘서트가 있습니다. 당신은 음악가들이 아름다운 음악을 연주하는 것을 들을 수 있습니다.

Words & Expressions

01 다음 짝지어진 단어의 관계가 같도록 빈칸에 알맞은 말을 쓰시오.

> _____ : bright = give : receive

02 다음 영영풀이가 가리키는 것을 고르시오.

> to follow and try to catch

① chase   ② advertise
③ decorate   ④ hold
⑤ gather

03 다음 중 밑줄 친 부분의 뜻풀이가 바르지 않은 것은?

① Time goes by and you will become an adult soon. 어른
② The painting is my son's latest artwork. 예술 작품
③ We made a poster to advertise our school festival. 광고하다
④ The police officers chased the thief. 체포했다
⑤ There is a competition between players. 경쟁

04 다음 우리말에 맞게 빈칸에 알맞은 말을 쓰시오.

(1) 한 블록 곧장 간 후 왼쪽으로 도세요.
 ➡ _____ _____ one block and _____ a left.

(2) 우리는 서로 너무 다르다.
 ➡ We are too different from _____ _____.

(3) 어느 버스 정류장에서 내려야 하나요?
 ➡ Which bus stop should I _____ at?

05 다음 주어진 문장의 밑줄 친 sail과 같은 의미로 쓰인 것은?

> A boat with a red sail appeared on the river.

① After retirement, I want to sail around the world.
② The navigator extended the sail on the boat.
③ The sailors couldn't sail against the wind.
④ The ferry will sail to the Atlantic.
⑤ We are ready to sail to New York.

06 다음 주어진 우리말을 영작하시오.

(1) 당신의 고향은 어디입니까?
 ➡ _____

(2) 그것은 박물관 건너편에 있어요.
 ➡ _____

(3) 내 친구들이 내 생일을 축하해 주기 위해 모였다.
 ➡ _____

Conversation

[07~08] 다음 대화를 읽고 물음에 답하시오.

Minsu: Hi, Emma. What's up?
Emma: Hey, Minsu. Are you free this Saturday?
Minsu: Yes. Why do you ask?
Emma: Well, how about having lunch together?
Minsu: Sure.
Emma: Let's try the new Chinese restaurant, Ming's. It's near the school.
Minsu: Okay.   (A)

Emma: Come out from the school and go straight to Green Street. Make a left, and the restaurant will be on your left.

Minsu: All right. Let's meet at 12 o'clock.

Emma: Wonderful. See you then.

07 위 대화의 빈칸 (A)에 들어갈 말을 〈보기〉에 주어진 단어를 배열하여 완성하시오.

┌─ 보기 ─┐
the / how / school / from / I / get / there / can

➡ _____

08 위 대화의 내용과 일치하지 <u>않는</u> 것은?

① Emma and Minsu are going to have lunch together this Saturday.

② Emma and Minsu are going to visit Ming's, the new Chinese restaurant.

③ Ming's is located near the school.

④ Minsu should make a left in the front of the school and go straight to Green Street to get to Ming's.

⑤ Emma and Minsu are going to meet at 12 o'clock this Saturday.

[09~10] 다음 대화를 읽고 물음에 답하시오.

Andy: I'm so excited about the school festival this Friday.

Mike: Me, too. What can we do to advertise it, Andy?

Andy: How about making posters?

Mike: Great idea. We can post them in our neighborhood.

Andy: Right. How long will it take to make them?

Mike: Well, it will take about three hours.

Andy: Okay, _____ (A)

09 위 대화의 빈칸 (A)에 들어갈 말을 주어진 단어를 배열하여 완성하시오.

┌─ 보기 ─┐
hope / many / the / to / festival / come / I / people

➡ _____

10 위 대화를 읽고 대답할 수 <u>없는</u> 것은?

① What are Andy and Mike looking forward to?

② What do Andy and Mike want to advertise?

③ What do Andy and Mike decide to make?

④ How long will it take to make the poster?

⑤ Where will Andy and Mike make the posters?

[11~13] 다음 대화를 읽고 물음에 답하시오.

Man: Excuse me. How can I (A)[take / get] to Suwon Hwaseong from here?

Mina: It's easy. Do you see the bus stop over there?

Man: Yes, I do.

Mina: Take the No. 11 bus and get (B)[on / off] at the sixth stop.

Man: How (C)[long / far] will it take to get there?

Mina: It will take about 20 minutes.

Man: Thank you very much.

Mina: _____ⓐ_____ Are you going there for the festival?

Man: Yes. I heard it's a lot of fun.

Mina: I hope you have a great time.

11 위 대화의 빈칸 ⓐ에 들어갈 말로 적절하지 <u>않은</u> 것은?

① No problem.　　② You're welcome.

③ Don't mention it.　　④ It's my pleasure.

⑤ Of course not.

12 위 대화의 (A)~(C)에 알맞은 것으로 짝지어진 것은?

	(A)	(B)	(C)
①	take	on	long
②	take	off	far
③	get	off	far
④	get	off	long
⑤	get	on	long

13 위 대화를 읽고 대답할 수 <u>없는</u> 것은?

① What does the man want?
② How can the man get to Suwon Hwaseong?
③ How long will it take to get to Suwon Hwaseong?
④ Why does the man want to visit Suwon Hwaseong?
⑤ Has Mina ever visited the festival of Suwon Hwaseong?

Grammar

14 다음 빈칸에 들어갈 수 <u>없는</u> 것은?

> It is good to _____ you laugh.

① see   ② hear   ③ watch
④ make   ⑤ encourage

15 다음 중 밑줄 친 부분의 쓰임이 <u>다른</u> 하나는?

① It is five miles from here to the beach.
② Is it possible to get there in time?
③ Was it cloudy this afternoon?
④ It is five past three.
⑤ It is not dark in this cave.

---

16 다음 우리말을 영어로 바르게 옮긴 것은?

> 나는 누군가가 문을 열고 나가는 소리를 들었어.

① I heard someone opened the door and went out.
② I heard someone opened the door and go out.
③ I heard someone open the door and went out.
④ I heard someone open the door and go out.
⑤ I heard someone opening the door and went out.

17 다음 대화의 빈칸에 알맞은 말을 쓰시오.

> A: Did you see Tom shouting at someone?
> B: Yes, I did. It was surprising _____ _____ _____ _____ _____ because he is known to us as a kind and quiet man.

18 다음 중 어법상 바르지 <u>않은</u> 것은?

① I felt someone pulling my hair.
② It was my fault to believe such a thing.
③ Did you see the boys kicked the ball?
④ To make you laugh is my job.
⑤ The situation made me tell a lot of lies.

19 다음 중 주어진 문장의 밑줄 친 부분과 쓰임이 같은 것은?

> It is necessary for you <u>to buy</u> a concert ticket now.

① My brother wanted you <u>to call</u> him.
② Karen went out <u>to eat</u> lunch alone.
③ Do you have a chair <u>to sit</u> on?
④ I didn't plan <u>to do</u> it.
⑤ It is good <u>to hear</u> from you.

20 다음 문장에서 어법상 바르지 <u>않은</u> 것을 찾아 바르게 고치시오.

> It is very boring to hearing someone talking constantly.

➡ _____ ➡ _____

21 주어진 단어를 활용하여 다음 우리말을 영어로 쓰시오.

> 영어를 배우는 것은 흥미롭다. (it / excite)

➡ _____

22 다음 중 어법상 <u>틀린</u> 문장의 개수는?

> ⓐ It is impossible to understand her.
> ⓑ Is it possible for me to visit your office?
> ⓒ We listened to the old man told his story from beginning to end.
> ⓓ Yesterday, I saw Kate to wait for a bus alone.
> ⓔ It was not easy to find your house.

① 1개 ② 2개 ③ 3개 ④ 4개 ⑤ 5개

23 빈칸에 들어갈 말이 바르게 짝지어진 것은?

> • It is dangerous _____ the mountain alone.
> • Did you see the man _____ the mountain alone?

① climb – climb
② to climb – climbed
③ to climb – climbing
④ to climb – to climb
⑤ to climbing – climbing

24 다음 우리말을 영어로 쓰시오.

> 나는 누군가가 내 어깨를 만지는 것을 느꼈다.

➡ _____

Reading

[25~28] 다음 글을 읽고 물음에 답하시오.

Holi, the Festival of Colors
Amala from Delhi, India
Holi is the most popular festival in my country. ① It is usually in March. During the festival, we say goodbye to cold winter and hello to warm spring. ② We ___ⓐ___ the festival everywhere for two days. On the first day, people gather around a big fire at night and sing and dance. ③ The main event begins the next day. ④ What is *gulal*? It is blue, yellow, green and pink powder. It's a lot of fun ⓑto run around and throw colorful powder at everyone. ⑤ We also join street parades!

25 다음과 같이 풀이되는 단어를 빈칸 ⓐ에 쓰시오.

> to do something special for an important event, holiday, etc.

➡ _____

26 ①~⑤ 중 주어진 문장이 들어가기에 가장 적절한 곳은?

> Children and adults chase each other with *gulal*.

①   ②   ③   ④   ⑤

27 위 글의 밑줄 친 ⓑ와 쓰임이 같은 것은?

① Tim went to Rome to see his girlfriend.
② Sarah was sad to hear the news.
③ To see her crying was painful for me.
④ I need something warm to wear.
⑤ The problem was very difficult to solve.

28 다음 중 위 글을 읽고 답할 수 없는 것은?

① What is Holi?
② What do people in India do during the festival?
③ How long does the festival last?
④ When does the main event begin?
⑤ How much *gulal* do people have at the festival?

[29~33] 다음 글을 읽고 물음에 답하시오.

Kiruna Snow Festival
Ebba from Kiruna, Sweden
Winter is my favorite season because of the Kiruna Snow Festival. The festival starts in the last week of January and (A)goes on for five or six days. The largest event is the snow design competition. The artists shape huge piles of snow into animals, buildings, and other beautiful artworks. People watch the artists shaping their works from beginning to end. My favorite activity is the dog sled ride. It is amazing to fly through a world of snow on a dog sled.

29 다음 중 밑줄 친 (A) 대신에 쓰일 수 있는 것은?

① quits   ② goes by
③ continues   ④ increases
⑤ expects

30 위 글의 내용에 맞게 다음 물음에 완전한 문장의 영어로 답하시오.

Q: What can we see at the snow design competition?

➡ _____
_____

31 다음 대화에서 위 글의 내용과 일치하지 않는 것은?

A: ①As we are here in Sweden, I want to visit Kiruna.
B: ②Oh, there is the snow festival in Kiruna, right?
A: ③Yes. I heard it starts in the last week of January, so we can see the festival.
B: That's nice. ④I'm so excited to see the largest event, the dog sled ride.
A: Me, too. ⑤I will also see how huge piles of snow are turned into various artworks.

①   ②   ③   ④   ⑤

32 위 글의 표현을 이용하여 다음 우리말을 영어로 쓰시오. 주어진 단어를 사용하시오.

미술가들이 그들의 작품을 만드는 것을 처음부터 끝까지 지켜보는 것은 흥미롭다.
(it / interesting)

➡ _____
_____

33 다음과 같이 풀이되는 단어를 위 글에서 찾아 쓰시오.

a small vehicle used for sliding over snow

➡ _____

[01~02] 다음 그림을 보고 물음에 답하시오.

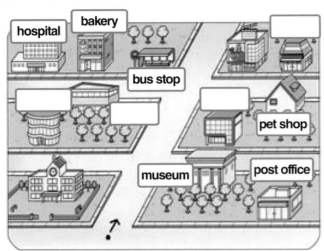

✏ 출제율 90%

01 다음 대화를 읽고 bank의 위치를 그림에 표시하시오.

> A: Excuse me. Is there a bank around here?
>
> B: Yes, there is. It's not far from here.
>
> A: How can I get there?
>
> B: Go straight two blocks and make a right. It's across from the pet shop. You can't miss it.
>
> A: Thank you so much.

✏ 출제율 95%

02 위 그림의 내용과 일치하도록 대화의 빈칸을 완성하시오.

> A: Excuse me. How can I get to the bakery?
>
> B: _____
>
> A: Is it far from here?
>
> B: No, it's not.
>
> A: Thank you.

➡ _____

_____

✏ 출제율 100%

03 다음 짝지어진 대화가 <u>어색한</u> 것을 고르시오.

① A: How can I get to the post office?
  B: Go straight to 1st Street and make a right.

② A: How long will it take to make the sandwiches?
  B: Maybe it will take about an hour.

③ A: Do you know where the subway station is?
  B: Sure. Walk straight ahead.

④ A: Is there a pet shop around here?
  B: It's just around the corner.

⑤ A: Where can I find a museum?
  B: It will take about 15 minutes by taxi.

[04~05] 다음 대화를 읽고 물음에 답하시오.

> Man: Excuse me. How can I get to Suwon Hwaseong from here?
>
> Mina: It's easy. Do you see the bus stop over there?
>
> Man: Yes, I do.
>
> Mina: Take the No. 11 bus and get off at the sixth stop.
>
> Man: (A)그곳까지 가는 데 시간이 얼마나 걸릴까요?
>
> Mina: It will take about 20 minutes.
>
> Man: Thank you very much.
>
> Mina: No problem. Are you going there for the festival?
>
> Man: Yes. I heard it's a lot of fun.
>
> Mina: I hope you have a great time.

✏ 출제율 85%

04 위 대화의 밑줄 친 (A)의 우리말을 주어진 단어를 써서 영어로 옮기시오.

(long, it, get)

➡ _____

05 위 대화의 내용과 일치하지 <u>않는</u> 것은?

① The man wants to go to Suwon Hwaseong on foot.

② Mina tells the man how to get to Suwon Hwaseong.

③ The man should take the No. 11 bus and get off at the sixth stop to get to Suwon Hwaseong.

④ It will take about 20 minutes for the man to get to Suwon Hwaseong by bus.

⑤ The festival is being held in Suwon Hwaseong.

06 다음 대화의 내용과 일치하도록 빈칸을 완성하시오.

> Andy: I'm so excited about the school festival this Friday.
>
> Mike: Me, too. What can we do to advertise it, Andy?
>
> Andy: How about making posters?
>
> Mike: Great idea. We can post them in our neighborhood.
>
> Andy: Right. How long will it take to make them?
>
> Mike: Well, it will take about three hours.
>
> Andy: Okay, I hope many people come to the festival.

> Andy and Mike are excited about the school festival this Friday. To advertise it, they decide to _____(A)_____ and post them in _____(B)_____. It will take _____(C)_____ to make them. They want many people to come and enjoy _____(D)_____.

➡ (A) _____

(B) _____

(C) _____

(D) _____

[07~08] 다음 대화를 읽고 물음에 답하시오.

> Minsu: Hi, Emma. What's up?
>
> Emma: Hey, Minsu. Are you free this Saturday?
>
> Minsu: Yes. Why do you ask?
>
> Emma: Well, how about having lunch together?
>
> Minsu: (A) Sure.
>
> Emma: (B) Let's try the new Chinese restaurant, Ming's. It's near the school.
>
> Minsu: (C) Okay. How can I @get there from the school?
>
> Emma: (D) Make a left, and the restaurant will be on your left.
>
> Minsu: (E) All right. Let's meet at 12 o'clock.
>
> Emma: Wonderful. See you then.

07 위 대화의 (A)~(E) 중에서 다음 문장이 들어가기에 적절한 곳은?

> Come out from the school and go straight to Green Street.

① (A) ② (B) ③ (C) ④ (D) ⑤ (E)

08 위 대화의 밑줄 친 @get과 같은 의미로 쓰인 것은?

① Get me something to drink, please.

② We're going to be late. Let's <u>get</u> a taxi.

③ I didn't <u>get</u> your letter yesterday.

④ Jane will <u>get</u> the prize at the dancing contest.

⑤ You can <u>get</u> to the city hall by bus.

[09~10] 다음 대화를 읽고 물음에 답하시오.

A: Excuse me. How can I get to the post office?
B: Go straight to 1st Street and make a right. It will be on your right.
A: (A)여기서 먼가요?
B: No, it's not.
A: Thank you very much.

출제율 90%

09 위 대화에 나타난 우체국의 위치를 우리말로 설명하시오.

➡ _____

출제율 95%

10 위 대화의 우리말 (A)를 영작하시오.

➡ _____

출제율 100%

11 다음 빈칸에 들어갈 말이 바르게 짝지어진 것은?

> • It is interesting _____ a book.
> • David saw me _____ a book in the library.

① reading – to read ② read – reading
③ to read – reading ④ read – to read
⑤ read – read

출제율 95%

12 다음 중 밑줄 친 부분의 쓰임이 다른 하나는?

① It was a bad idea to call you late at night.
② It was my mistake to give you my phone number.
③ It was the hat that I bought for him.
④ It is useful to discuss the issue.
⑤ It is strange for him to say so.

출제율 95%

13 주어진 단어를 활용하여 다음 우리말을 영어로 쓰시오.

> 나는 Kevin이 프랑스어를 말하는 것을 들었다. (hear / French)

➡ _____

출제율 90%

14 다음 우리말을 영어로 바르게 옮긴 것은?

> 목표를 정하고 최선을 다하는 것은 중요하다.

① It is important to set a goal and does your best.
② It is important to set a goal and do your best.
③ It is important setting a goal and to do your best.
④ It is important setting a goal and do your best.
⑤ It is important to set a goal and your best.

출제율 95%

15 다음 중 어법상 바르지 않은 것은?

① Jason heard two girls talking to each other loudly.
② It is not easy to take care of a pet.
③ Did you feel the house shaking?
④ I think it is important to listen to other people's opinion carefully.
⑤ Ms. Kim watched her students to solve the problems.

출제율 85%

16 주어진 단어를 활용하여 다음 우리말을 영어로 쓰시오.

> 그녀가 바이올린을 연주하는 것을 듣는 것은 좋은 기회야. (it / a good chance)

➡ _____

출제율 95%

17 다음 우리말을 영어로 쓰시오.

> 한 소년이 호수에서 수영하고 있는 것이 보이니?

➡ _____

[18~20] 다음 글을 읽고 물음에 답하시오.

White Nights Festival
Victor from St. Petersburg, Russia
Have you heard ___ⓐ___ the *White Nights*?
[A] During that time, we hold the White Nights Festival. It usually starts in May and lasts for about a month.
[B] A boat with red sails slowly appears on the river. Soon, fireworks begin and a water show follows. You can also hear musicians playing beautiful live music.
[C] Every summer, this amazing thing happens in my hometown. The night sky does not get completely dark.
[D] During the festival, there is a ballet or an opera almost every night. The most popular event is the Scarlet Sails celebration.

출제율 95%

18 다음 중 빈칸 ⓐ에 들어갈 말과 같은 말이 들어가는 것은?

① Emily gets tired _____ eating the same food.
② Jason came up _____ a brilliant idea.
③ My hobby is looking _____ plants in the garden.
④ I really look up _____ King Sejong.
⑤ They had to put _____ their event because of the bad weather.

출제율 90%

19 자연스러운 글이 되도록 [A]~[D]를 바르게 나열한 것은?

① [B] – [D] – [C] – [A]
② [B] – [C] – [A] – [D]
③ [C] – [B] – [D] – [A]
④ [C] – [A] – [D] – [B]
⑤ [D] – [B] – [A] – [C]

출제율 100%

20 다음 중 위 글을 읽고 답할 수 <u>없는</u> 것은?

① Where is St. Petersburg?
② What do people in Russia do during the White Nights?
③ What color of sails does the boat have?
④ What can people see after the firework?
⑤ How many musicians are there at the festival?

[21~22] 다음 글을 읽고 물음에 답하시오.

Holi, the Festival of Colors
Amala from Delhi, India
Holi is the most popular festival in my country. ① It is usually in March. During the festival, we say goodbye to cold winter and hello to warm spring. ② On the first day, people gather around a big fire at night and sing and dance. ③ The main event begins the next day. ④ Children and adults chase each other with *gulal*. ⑤ What is *gulal*? It is blue, yellow, green and pink powder. It's a lot of fun to run around and throw (A)<u>colorful powder</u> at everyone. We also join street parades!

출제율 90%

21 ①~⑤ 중 주어진 문장이 들어가기에 가장 적절한 곳은?

> We celebrate the festival everywhere for two days.

①   ②   ③   ④   ⑤

출제율 95%

22 밑줄 친 (A)가 가리키는 것을 위 글에서 찾아 쓰시오.

➡ _____

[01~03] 다음 대화를 읽고 물음에 답하시오.

Minsu: Hi, Emma. What's up?

Emma: Hey, Minsu. Are you free this Saturday?

Minsu: Yes. Why do you ask?

Emma: Well, how about having lunch together?

Minsu: Sure.

Emma: Let's try the new Chinese restaurant, Ming's. It's near the school.

Minsu: Okay. How can I get there from the school?

Emma: Come out from the school and go straight to Green Street. Make a left, and the restaurant will be on your left.

Minsu: All right. Let's meet at 12 o'clock.

Emma: Wonderful. See you then.

01 What are Emma and Minsu going to do this Saturday?

➡ _____

_____

02 What time are Emma and Minsu going to meet?

➡ _____

03 중요 Minsu가 Ming's를 어떻게 찾아가야 하는지 우리말로 간략히 설명하시오.

➡ _____

_____

04 다음 빈칸에 call을 어법에 맞게 쓰시오.

- I heard someone _____ my name.
- I heard my name _____.

05 중요 주어진 단어를 활용하여 다음 우리말을 영어로 쓰시오.

나의 영어 실력을 향상시키는 것은 필수적이다.
(it / essential / skill / improve)

➡ _____

06 다음 대화의 빈칸에 알맞은 말을 다섯 단어로 쓰시오.

A: Do you think that having a balanced diet is important?

B: Sure. It is really important _____.

➡ _____

07 다음 두 문장을 하나의 문장으로 쓰시오.

- The cat jumped up onto the chair.
- Did you see that?

➡ _____

08 중요 주어진 단어를 바르게 배열하여 다음 우리말을 영어로 쓰시오.

나는 그 소년이 수영장에서 수영하고 있는 것을 보았다.
(in / the boy / I / the pool / saw / swimming)

➡ _____

Holi, the Festival of Colors

Amala from Delhi, India

Holi is the most popular festival in my country. It is usually in March. During the festival, we say goodbye to cold winter and hello to warm spring. We celebrate the festival everywhere for two days. On the first day, people gather around a big fire at night and sing and dance. The main event begins the next day. Children and adults chase each other with *gulal*. What is *gulal*? It is blue, yellow, green and pink powder. (A)주변을 뛰어다니며 형형색색의 가루를 모든 사람들에게 던지는 것은 정말 재미있어요. We also join street parades!

09 주어진 단어를 활용하여 밑줄 친 우리말 (A)를 영어로 쓰시오.

(a lot of / run around / colorful)

➡ _____

_____

10 위 글의 내용에 맞게 빈칸에 알맞은 말을 세 단어로 쓰시오.

A: Did you _____ _____ _____ at the Holi festival?

B: Yeah. People march in public to celebrate the festival. It was amazing.

11 When do people in India celebrate Holi? Answer in English with a full sentence.

➡ _____

I live in Gangneung. There are beautiful beaches in my neighborhood. It's a lot of fun to swim at the beach. Many people swim there. There is a famous hanok in Gangneung. It is called Ojukheon. Yulgok was born there. The most famous food in Gangneung is potato tteok. It is soft and sweet. Come and enjoy Gangneung!

12 다음 질문에 4 단어로 이루어진 한 문장으로 답하시오.

Q: Where is Ojukheon?

➡ _____

13 According to the passage, what can we see at the beach in Gangneung? Answer in English with a full sentence.

➡ _____

14 위 글의 내용에 맞게 빈칸에 알맞은 말을 쓰시오.

A: How is potato tteok?

B: _____

➡ _____

01 다음 지도에서 나타내는 Ming's의 위치와 일치하도록 빈칸에 알맞은 말을 넣어 가는 길을 설명하시오.

> Emma: Let's try the new Chinese restaurant, Ming's. It's near the school.
> Minsu: Okay. How can I get there from the school?
> Emma: _____
> Minsu: All right. Let's meet at 12 o'clock.
> Emma: Wonderful. See you then.

➡ _____

02 주어진 단어와 지각동사를 이용하여 축제에서 볼 수 있는 다양한 사람들을 묘사해 보시오.

> children   merchants   people

(1) _____
(2) _____
(3) _____

03 주어진 단어와 가주어 It과 진주어 to부정사를 활용하여 학교생활에서 유의해야 할 점에 대해 〈보기〉와 같이 써 보시오.

> important, necessary, essential, dangerous

┌─ 보기 ───┐
│   It is important not to fall asleep during the class. │
└──┘

(1) _____
(2) _____
(3) _____
(4) _____

단원별 모의고사

01 다음 영영풀이가 가리키는 것을 고르시오.

> a small vehicle used for sliding over snow

① firework   ② sled
③ boat   ④ sail
⑤ shape

02 다음 주어진 문장의 밑줄 친 hold와 같은 의미로 쓰인 것은?

> We hold the White Nights Festival.

① Did Emily hold a large box?
② It is hard to hold a business meeting because of all this noise.
③ The girl was holding her mother's hand.
④ I'll hold the door for you.
⑤ Would you hold my place, please?

03 다음 대화의 빈칸에 들어갈 말로 어색한 것은?

> Sora: Excuse me. _____
> Tom: Oh, the library? Cross the street and go straight two blocks. Then make a left.
> Sora: Thank you very much.

① How can I get to the library?
② Where can I find the library?
③ Do you know where the library is?
④ Is there the library around here?
⑤ How long will it take to get to the library?

04 다음 우리말에 맞게 빈칸에 알맞은 말을 쓰시오.

(1) 그녀는 창문에 돌을 던졌다.
➡ She _____ stones at the window.
(2) Kate는 토론 대회에 참가했다.
➡ Kate took part in the debate _____.
(3) 마을이 거대한 시장으로 변하였다.
➡ The village was changed into the _____ market.

05 다음 문장의 빈칸에 들어갈 말을 〈보기〉에서 골라 쓰시오.

> ┤ 보기 ├
> go on / in front of / more and more / because of

(1) The festival will _____ for 5 days.
(2) _____ people are using the tablet PC.
(3) The boys couldn't go on a picnic _____ the bad weather.
(4) I felt so nervous _____ a large group of people.

06 다음 대화의 밑줄 친 우리말을 영작하시오.

> Amy: Jinho, hurry up. We're going to be late for the movie.
> Jinho: Okay. How long will it take to get to the theater?
> Amy: 버스로 약 15분 걸릴 거야.
> Jinho: All right. I'm almost ready.

➡ _____

[07~08] 다음 대화를 읽고 물음에 답하시오.

Man: Excuse me. How can I get to Suwon Hwaseong from here?

Mina: ⓐ It's easy. Do you see the bus stop over there?

Man: Yes, I do.

Mina: Take the No. 11 bus and get _____ⓑ_____ at the sixth stop.

Man: How long will it take to get there?

Mina: It will take about 20 minutes.

Man: Thank you very much.

Mina: No problem. Are you going there for the festival?

Man: Yes. I heard it's a lot of fun.

Mina: I hope you have a great time.

07 위 글의 밑줄 친 ⓐ가 가리키는 것을 우리말로 쓰시오.

➡ _____

08 위 글의 빈칸 ⓑ에 알맞은 말을 쓰시오.

➡ _____

09 다음 대화의 내용과 일치하지 <u>않는</u> 것은?

Rachel: Chris, what will you do for the class party?

Chris: I'll make sandwiches.

Rachel: Great idea. How long will it take to make them?

Chris: Maybe it'll take about an hour.

Rachel: Then, I'll decorate the classroom.

Chris: Sounds great.

① Rachel과 Chris는 학급 파티를 준비하고 있다.
② Chris는 학급 파티를 위해 샌드위치를 만들 것이다.
③ Chris는 샌드위치를 만드는 데 약 한 시간이 걸릴 것이다.
④ Rachel은 교실을 장식할 것이다.
⑤ Rachel은 교실을 장식하는 데 약 한 시간이 걸릴 것이다.

10 다음 주어진 우리말과 일치하도록 주어진 단어를 모두 배열하여 완성하시오.

(1) 너의 집에서 학교까지 가는 데 얼마나 걸리니?
(from / get / school / to / to / it / take / how / long / house / your / does)

➡ _____

(2) 은행까지 어떻게 가나요?
(the / to / I / get / can / bank / how)

➡ _____

(3) 길을 건너서 한 구역 곧장 가세요.
(street / and / the / cross / one / go / straight / block)

➡ _____

(4) 지하철로 대략 10분 정도 걸릴 거야.
(will / by / it / about / take / subway / 10 minutes)

➡ _____

11 다음 대화가 자연스럽게 이어지도록 순서대로 배열하시오.

(A) Maybe it'll take about an hour.
(B) I'll decorate the classroom.
(C) What will you do for the class party?
(D) Great idea. How long will it take to do it?

➡ _____

[12~13] 다음 대화를 읽고 물음에 답하시오.

A: How long does it take to get to school from your house?
B: It usually takes (a)about 10 minutes.
A: How do you go to school?
B: _____ (A)

12 위 대화의 빈칸 (A)에 들어갈 말로 적절한 것은?

① I walk to school.
② Go straight two blocks and you can find it on your right.
③ It will take about thirty minutes.
④ I'll decorate the classroom.
⑤ I'm almost ready.

13 위 대화의 밑줄 친 (a)와 같은 의미로 쓰인 것은?

① What is this book about?
② It is a story about wild animals.
③ My father is always worried about me.
④ We walked about five miles in the desert.
⑤ I can't understand why she's so angry about him.

14 다음 중 어법상 바르지 않은 것은?

① It is so great to be here with you.
② It is annoying to hear her to sing the same song.
③ Polly heard someone pounding on the door.
④ Christine saw her friend bounce a ball alone.
⑤ It is strange for him to be late today.

15 주어진 단어를 이용하여 다음 우리말을 영어로 쓰시오.

그녀는 비가 지붕 위로 떨어지는 소리를 들었다.
(fall on)

➡ _____

16 다음 중 빈칸에 들어갈 말이 바르게 짝지어진 것은?

• Hamilton heard Simon _____ the blackboard.
• It was really irritating to hear someone _____ the blackboard.

① to scratch – to scratch
② scratching – to scratch
③ scratch – scratch
④ scratch – to scratch
⑤ scratch – scratched

17 다음 중 빈칸에 들어갈 수 있는 말을 모두 고르시오.

Jane _____ Thomas kick the wall.

① saw   ② made
③ wanted   ④ heard
⑤ would like

18 주어진 단어를 활용하여 다음 우리말을 영어로 쓰시오.

James는 무언가가 그의 팔을 무는 것을 느꼈다.
(bite)

➡ _____

[19~20] 다음 글을 읽고 물음에 답하시오.

White Nights Festival
Victor from St. Petersburg, Russia

Have you heard of the *White Nights*? Every summer, this amazing thing happens in my hometown. The night sky does not get completely dark. (A)[While / During] that time, we hold the White Nights Festival. It usually starts in May and lasts for about a month. During the festival, there is a ballet or an opera almost every night. The most popular event is the Scarlet Sails celebration. A boat with red sails slowly (B)[appears / is appeared] on the river. Soon, fireworks begin and a water show follows. You can also hear musicians (C)[playing / to play] beautiful live music.

19 (A)~(C)에서 어법상 옳은 것끼리 바르게 짝지은 것은?

① While – appears – playing
② While – appears – to play
③ While – is appeared – to play
④ During – appears – playing
⑤ During – is appeared – playing

20 다음 중 위 글의 내용과 일치하지 <u>않는</u> 것은?

① You can experience the White Nights in Russia.
② It is hard to see something at night during the White Nights.
③ The White Nights Festival continues for about a month.
④ Musicians play live music at the festival.
⑤ You can see a ballet or an opera during the festival.

[21~23] 다음 글을 읽고 물음에 답하시오.

Kiruna Snow Festival
Ebba from Kiruna, Sweden

Winter is my favorite season (A)because of the Kiruna Snow Festival. The festival starts in the last week of January and goes on for five or six days. The largest event is the snow design competition. The artists shape huge piles of snow into animals, buildings, and other beautiful artworks. People watch the artists shaping their works from beginning to end. My favorite activity is the dog sled ride. (B)개 썰매를 타고 눈 세상을 날아가는 것은 놀라워요.

21 다음 중 밑줄 친 (A)를 대신하여 쓰일 수 있는 것은?

① because   ② due to   ③ since
④ as   ⑤ for

22 다음 중 위 글의 내용과 일치하는 것은?

① Ebba is not fond of the Kiruna Snow Festival.
② The festival lasts over a week.
③ The artists compete in the event by making something into a particular shape with snow.
④ There is only one mass of snow at the festival.
⑤ It is hard for people to watch the artists shape their works.

23 주어진 단어를 활용하여 밑줄 친 우리말 (B)를 영어로 쓰시오.

(it / through / on a dog sled)

➡ _____

_____

INSIGHT
on the textbook

교과서 파헤치기

※ 다음 영어를 우리말로 쓰시오.

01 madly

02 throw

03 definitely

04 audience

05 funny

06 giraffe

07 wall

08 hall

09 pianist

10 heal

11 meeting

12 Hungary

13 machine

14 idol

15 miss

16 fantastic

17 seat

18 liberty

19 badminton

20 invent

21 original

22 flea market

23 scream

24 zebra

25 signature

26 greeting

27 creation

28 composer

29 prepare

30 movement

31 performance

32 recent

33 face

34 unlike

35 strawberry

36 sheet music

37 paper folding

38 build up

39 cheer up

40 at once

41 press down

42 from memory

43 go wild

※ 다음 우리말을 영어로 쓰시오.

01 부드럽게, 상냥하게 ___

02 놀라운 ___

03 팬; 부채, 선풍기 ___

04 서명 ___

05 포도, 포도나무 ___

06 방학, 휴가 ___

07 인사 ___

08 북 연주자, 드러머 ___

09 단 하나의, 혼자의 ___

10 떨어지다 ___

11 딸기 ___

12 연주회, 음악회 ___

13 준비하다 ___

14 숨, 호흡 ___

15 작곡가 ___

16 움직임 ___

17 발레 ___

18 음, 음표 ___

19 공연 ___

20 최근의 ___

21 소설 ___

22 창조물, 창작 ___

23 ~와는 달리 ___

24 얼굴; ~을 향하다 ___

25 놓치다, 그리워하다 ___

26 자유 ___

27 소리치다, 괴성을 지르다 ___

28 발명하다, 창안하다 ___

29 고치다, 낫게 하다 ___

30 기계, 기계장치 ___

31 단연, 틀림없이 ___

32 미친 듯이, 열렬하게 ___

33 벼룩시장 ___

34 본래의 ___

35 악보 ___

36 청중, 관람객 ___

37 환상적인 ___

38 격려하다, 힘을 북돋우다 ___

39 숨을 참다, 숨을 죽이다 ___

40 한꺼번에 ___

41 누르다 ___

42 점점 높이다 ___

43 직접 ___

※ 다음 영영풀이에 알맞은 단어를 <보기>에서 골라 쓴 후, 우리말 뜻을 쓰시오.

1 _____ : a public performance of music: _____

2 _____ : a person who writes music: _____

3 _____ : the air that you take into your lungs and send out again: _____

4 _____ : a person who plays the piano: _____

5 _____ : an outdoor market that sells second-hand goods at low prices: _____

6 _____ : to drop down from a higher level to a lower level: _____

7 _____ : your name as you usually write it, for example at the end of a letter: _____

8 _____ : a person or thing that is loved and admired very much: _____

9 _____ : the act of performing a play, concert or some other form of entertainment: _____

10 _____ : a space or passage inside the entrance or front door of a building: _____

11 _____ : to become healthy again; to make something healthy again: _____

12 _____ : existing at the beginning of a particular period, process or activity: _____

13 _____ : to make something or somebody ready to be used or to do something: _____

14 _____ : the group of people who have gathered to watch or listen to something: _____

15 _____ : a style of dancing that tells a dramatic story with music but no talking or singing: _____

16 _____ : the act or process of making something that is new, or of causing something to exist that did not exist before: _____

보기	performance	hall	signature	audience
	creation	ballet	idol	original
	composer	flea market	breath	prepare
	heal	fall	pianist	concert

※ 다음 우리말과 일치하도록 빈칸에 알맞은 말을 쓰시오.

Listen & Speak 1 A

Jack: Hi, Sumin. _____ the book club _____?

Sumin: It's _____ . I _____ _____ _____ interesting books.

Jack: _____ _____ do you _____ _____?

Sumin: I _____ *Charlotte's Web* _____ .

Listen & Speak 1 B

Amy: Jiho, _____ _____ you _____ _____ do _____ _____?

Jiho: _____ _____ _____ Blue Sky's _____ _____ with my friends.

Amy: Wow, I'm also _____ _____ of the band.

Jiho: Really? _____ _____ do you _____ _____, Amy?

Amy: I _____ Lucy _____ . She _____ really _____ .

Jiho: I like the _____, Mike, best. He's _____! Do you _____ _____ us?

Amy: Sure, I'd _____ _____ . I _____ _____!

Listen & Speak 1 C

A: Do you _____ _____?

B: _____, I _____ .

A: _____ _____ do you _____ _____?

B: I like _____ _____ . It's so _____!

Listen & Speak 2 A

B: _____ do you have _____ _____ old clothes?

G: I'm _____ _____ _____ them at the _____ .

B: Really? I have some _____ _____, _____ .

G: Then _____ _____ _____ _____ me this Saturday?

B: Okay.

Listen & Speak 2 B

Sujin: Tom, _____ do you have so _____ _____ _____?

Tom: They're _____ my _____ _____.

Sujin: They're so _____. _____ did you _____ them?

Tom: I _____ them.

Sujin: Wow, you're really _____.

Tom: Thanks. I'm _____ these days.

Sujin: They are _____ to be _____ _____ for your mom.

Tom: I _____ so, _____.

Listen & Speak 2 C

A: _____ _____ do you _____ _____ _____ for your dream vacation?

B: I want _____ _____ _____.

A: _____ _____ _____ _____ _____ visit Canada?

B: _____ I _____ _____ _____ Niagara Falls.

Real Life Talk

Mina: Good afternoon, friends. I'm Mina _____ _____ _____. Today Mr. Smith, _____ _____, is here _____ us. Hi, Mr. Smith.

Mr. Smith: Hello, _____. I'm _____ _____ here with you.

Mina: _____ _____ about music. Mr. Smith, _____ _____ _____ _____ _____?

Mr. Smith: _____ The Beatles.

Mina: Oh, I _____ them, _____. _____ _____ do you _____ _____?

Mr. Smith: I like _____ _____ their songs, but I _____ *Hey Jude* _____.

Mina: _____ _____ _____ _____ _____ _____?

Mr. Smith: _____ the song _____ me _____ _____ when I'm _____.

Mina: That's great! _____ _____ _____ _____ the song.

Sujin: Tom, 왜 그렇게 많은 종이꽃을 가지고 있니?

Tom: 이 꽃들은 엄마 생신을 위한 거야.

Sujin: 정말 예쁘다. 그 꽃들을 어디서 구했니?

Tom: 내가 만들었어.

Sujin: 와, 너 정말 잘 만든다.

Tom: 고마워. 나 요즘 종이접기 수업을 듣고 있어.

Sujin: 그 꽃들은 너희 엄마에게 완벽한 선물이 될 거야.

Tom: 나도 그러길 바라.

A: 너는 꿈의 휴가로 어느 나라를 방문하고 싶니?

B: 나는 캐나다를 방문하고 싶어.

A: 너는 왜 캐나다를 방문하고 싶니?

B: 나는 나이아가라 폭포를 보고 싶기 때문이야.

Mina: 안녕하세요, 여러분. 저희 학교 라디오 프로그램의 미나입니다. 오늘은 영어 선생님이신 Smith 선생님과 함께 하겠습니다. 안녕하세요, Smith 선생님.

Mr. Smith: 안녕하세요, 여러분. 여러분과 함께하게 되어 기쁘군요.

Mina: 음악에 관한 이야기를 나눠 보도록 하죠. Smith 선생님, 어느 밴드를 가장 좋아하시나요?

Mr. Smith: 두말할 것도 없이 The Beatles에요.

Mina: 오, 저도 그들을 좋아해요. 어떤 노래를 가장 좋아하시나요?

Mr. Smith: 그들의 노래 대부분을 좋아하지만 'Hey Jude'를 가장 좋아하죠.

Mina: 왜 그 노래를 좋아하시나요?

Mr. Smith: 그 노래는 내가 우울할 때 기분이 나아지게 해 주기 때문이죠.

Mina: 멋지군요! 그 노래를 함께 들어 보도록 하죠.

※ 다음 우리말에 맞도록 대화를 영어로 쓰시오.

Listen & Speak 1 A

Jack: _____

Sumin: _____

Jack: _____

Sumin: _____

Jack: 안녕, 수민아. 책 동아리는 어때?
Sumin: 재미있어. 나는 흥미로운 책들을 많이 읽어.
Jack: 어느 책을 가장 좋아하니?
Sumin: 나는 'Charlotte's Web'을 가장 좋아해.

Listen & Speak 1 B

Amy: _____

Jiho: _____

Amy: _____

Jiho: _____

Amy: _____

Jiho: _____

Amy: _____

Amy: 지호야, 이번 주 토요일에 뭐 할 거니?
Jiho: 나는 친구들이랑 Blue Sky 팬 모임에 갈 거야.
Amy: 와, 나도 그 밴드의 열렬한 팬이야.
Jiho: 정말? 너는 어느 멤버를 가장 좋아하니, Amy?
Amy: 나는 Lucy를 가장 좋아해. 그녀는 노래를 정말 잘해.
Jiho: 나는 드러머인 Mike를 가장 좋아해. 그는 환상적이야. 우리와 함께 갈래?
Amy: 물론이지, 너무 좋아. 기대된다!

Listen & Speak 1 C

A: _____

B: _____

A: _____

B: _____

A: 운동을 좋아하니?
B: 응, 좋아해.
A: 어느 운동을 가장 좋아하니?
B: 나는 테니스를 가장 좋아해. 그것은 매우 흥미진진해!

Listen & Speak 2 A

B: _____

G: _____

B: _____

G: _____

B: _____

B: 너는 왜 저 모든 헌 옷들을 가지고 있니?
G: 나는 벼룩시장에 그 옷들을 팔 거야.
B: 정말? 나도 헌 옷들이 좀 있어.
G: 그러면 이번 주 토요일에 나와 함께 팔면 어때?
B: 좋아.

Listen & Speak 2 B

Sujin: _____

Tom: _____

Sujin: _____

Tom: _____

Sujin: _____

Tom: _____

Sujin: _____

Tom: _____

Sujin: Tom, 왜 그렇게 많은 종이꽃을 가지고 있니?
Tom: 이 꽃들은 엄마 생신을 위한 거야.
Sujin: 정말 예쁘다. 그 꽃들을 어디서 구했니?
Tom: 내가 만들었어.
Sujin: 와, 너 정말 잘 만든다.
Tom: 고마워. 나 요즘 종이접기 수업을 듣고 있어.
Sujin: 그 꽃들은 너희 엄마에게 완벽한 선물이 될 거야.
Tom: 나도 그러길 바라.

Listen & Speak 1 C

A: _____

B: _____

A: _____

B: _____

A: 너는 꿈의 휴가로 어느 나라를 방문하고 싶니?
B: 나는 캐나다를 방문하고 싶어.
A: 너는 왜 캐나다를 방문하고 싶니?
B: 나는 나이아가라 폭포를 보고 싶기 때문이야.

Real Life Talk

Mina: _____
_____

Mr. Smith: _____

Mina: _____

Mr. Smith: _____

Mina: _____

Mr. Smith: _____

Mina: _____

Mr. Smith: _____

Mina: _____

Mina: 안녕하세요, 여러분. 저희 학교 라디오 프로그램의 미나입니다. 오늘은 영어 선생님이신 Smith 선생님과 함께 하겠습니다. 안녕하세요, Smith 선생님.
Mr. Smith: 안녕하세요, 여러분. 여러분과 함께하게 되어 기쁘군요.
Mina: 음악에 관한 이야기를 나눠 보도록 하죠. Smith 선생님, 어느 밴드를 가장 좋아하시나요?
Mr. Smith: 두말할 것도 없이 The Beatles에요.
Mina: 오, 저도 그들을 좋아해요. 어떤 노래를 가장 좋아하시나요?
Mr. Smith: 그들의 노래 대부분을 좋아하지만 'Hey Jude'를 가장 좋아하죠.
Mina: 왜 그 노래를 좋아하시나요?
Mr. Smith: 그 노래는 내가 우울할 때 기분이 나아지게 해 주기 때문이죠.
Mina: 멋지군요! 그 노래를 함께 들어 보도록 하죠.

※ 다음 우리말과 일치하도록 빈칸에 알맞은 것을 골라 쓰시오.

1 Do you have a _____ K-pop _____? Many students _____, "Yes."

　　A. answer　　　B. idol　　　C. will　　　D. favorite

2 These students _____ _____ great love _____ their stars.

　　A. for　　　B. show　　　C. often

3 Some _____ _____ at concerts.

　　A. madly　　　B. scream

4 _____ wait _____ to _____ pictures of their stars.

　　A. take　　　B. hours　　　C. others

5 _____ students _____ travel to _____ city to see their favorite star.

　　A. another　　　B. even　　　C. some

6 Are idols a _____ _____? No _____!

　　A. way　　　B. creation　　　C. recent

7 Did idols _____ _____ The Beatles _____ the 1960's?

　　A. in　　　B. with　　　C. begin

8 They were _____ _____ many, but they were not the _____.

　　A. first　　　B. by　　　C. loved

9 How _____ Elvis Presley _____ the 1950's? Not even _____.

　　A. lose　　　B. in　　　C. about

10 To _____ the answer, _____ _____ a time machine to a concert hall in Vienna _____ 1845.

　　A. in　　　B. let's　　　C. find　　　D. take

11 _____ the seats _____ _____.

　　A. are　　　B. all　　　C. filled

12 _____ other concerts, the _____ of the piano _____ the audience.

　　A. faces　　　B. side　　　C. unlike

13 This _____, the audience _____ see the _____ 185cm pianist _____.

　　A. handsome　　　B. better　　　C. can　　　D. way

14 He doesn't have any _____ _____ with him.

　　A. music　　　B. sheet

15 He begins to _____ from _____.

　　A. memory　　　B. play

16 He starts _____ _____ softly _____ the keys.

　　A. touching　　　B. slowly　　　C. by

1 여러분은 가장 좋아하는 K팝 아이돌이 있는가? 많은 학생들이 "그렇다."라고 답할 것이다.

2 이 학생들은 종종 자신들의 스타를 향해 큰 애정을 보인다.

3 어떤 학생들은 콘서트에서 미친 듯이 괴성을 지른다.

4 어떤 학생들은 스타의 사진을 찍기 위해 몇 시간을 기다린다.

5 어떤 학생들은 심지어 가장 좋아하는 스타를 보기 위해 다른 도시로 여행을 가기까지 한다.

6 아이돌이 최근의 창조물일까? 아니다!

7 아이돌은 1960년대의 The Beatles부터 시작됐을까?

8 그들은 많은 사람들에게 사랑받았지만, 최초는 아니다.

9 1950년대의 Elvis Presley는 어떤가? 완전히 헛짚었다.

10 답을 찾기 위해서 1845년에 빈에 있는 한 콘서트홀로 타임머신을 타고 가 보자.

11 모든 좌석이 꽉 차 있다.

12 다른 연주회와는 달리 피아노의 옆면이 청중을 향해 있다.

13 이렇게 함으로써, 청중은 잘생긴 185cm의 피아니스트를 더 잘 볼 수 있다.

14 그는 어떠한 악보도 가지고 있지 않다.

15 그는 기억으로 연주하기 시작한다.

16 그는 건반을 부드럽게 누르면서 천천히 시작한다.

17 All the people _____ their _____ because they don't want to _____ a single _____.

    A. note   B. breath   C. miss   D. hold

18 He builds _____ speed, and his long fingers press _____ on many keys _____ once.

    A. down   B. up   C. at

19 This _____ the music very _____ and _____.

    A. rich   B. makes   C. powerful

20 The audience _____ _____ to his every little body _____.

    A. movement   B. attention   C. pays

21 His _____ _____ hair _____ everywhere.

    A. flies   B. beautiful   C. long

22 It's _____ _____ a piano and ballet performance _____ _____.

    A. once   B. watching   C. at   D. like

23 Time _____ and the concert _____.

    A. ends   B. flies

24 People _____ and _____ flowers and pieces of _____ onto the _____.

    A. stage   B. throw   C. clothing   D. scream

25 The concert hall _____ _____!

    A. wild   B. goes

26 Who was this _____ _____?

    A. star   B. amazing

27 _____ name was Franz Liszt and he was _____ _____ 1811 in Hungary.

    A. in   B. his   C. born

28 He _____ started _____ the piano _____ he was seven.

    A. when   B. playing   C. first

29 Liszt _____ _____ a great pianist, _____ and teacher.

    A. composer   B. became   C. later

30 But many people _____ _____ him _____ the first idol.

    A. as   B. of   C. think

31 Why _____ you _____ his music a _____?

    A. listen   B. give   C. don't

32 _____ you like _____ idols, you _____ love the _____ idol.

    A. original   B. today's   C. will   D. if

17 모든 사람들이 단 하나의 음도 놓치고 싶지 않아서 숨을 죽인다.

18 그는 속도를 점점 올리고, 그의 긴 손가락으로 많은 건반을 한 꺼번에 누른다.

19 이것은 음악을 아주 힘 있고 풍성하게 만든다.

20 청중들은 그의 모든 작은 몸짓에 주의를 집중한다.

21 그의 길고 아름다운 머리카락이 사방에 날린다.

22 이것은 마치 피아노와 발레 공연을 동시에 보는 것 같다.

23 시간은 쏜살같이 흐르고 연주회가 끝난다.

24 사람들은 소리를 지르며 꽃과 옷을 무대로 던진다.

25 콘서트홀은 열광의 도가니가 된다!

26 이 놀라운 스타는 누구였을까?

27 그의 이름은 Franz Liszt였고 그는 1811년에 헝가리에서 태어났다.

28 그는 7살에 처음 피아노를 치기 시작했다.

29 Liszt는 나중에 훌륭한 피아니스트이며 작곡가이자 선생님이 되었다.

30 그러나 많은 사람들은 그를 첫 번째 아이돌이라고 생각한다.

31 그의 음악을 한번 들어보는 게 어떤가?

32 만약 당신이 요즘의 아이돌을 좋아한다면, 원래의 아이돌도 좋아할 것이다.

※ 다음 우리말과 일치하도록 빈칸에 알맞은 말을 쓰시오.

1 Do you have a _____ K-pop _____? _____ students _____ answer, "Yes."

2 These students _____ _____ great _____ for their stars.

3 Some _____ _____ _____ concerts.

4 _____ wait hours to _____ _____ their stars.

5 Some students even _____ _____ another city _____ _____ their _____ _____.

6 Are idols a _____ _____? No _____!

7 Did idols _____ _____ The Beatles _____ the 1960's?

8 They were _____ _____ many, but they were _____ _____ _____.

9 _____ Elvis Presley _____ the 1950's? _____ even close.

10 _____ _____ the answer, _____ _____ a time machine to a concert hall _____ Vienna in 1845.

11 _____ the seats _____ _____.

12 _____ _____ _____, the side of the piano _____ the _____.

13 This _____, the audience _____ _____ the _____ 185cm pianist _____.

14 He _____ have _____ _____ _____ with him.

15 He _____ _____ play _____ _____.

16 He starts _____ _____ _____ _____ _____ the keys.

1 여러분은 가장 좋아하는 K팝 아이돌이 있는가? 많은 학생들이 "그렇다."라고 답할 것이다.

2 이 학생들은 종종 자신들의 스타를 향해 큰 애정을 보인다.

3 어떤 학생들은 콘서트에서 미친 듯이 괴성을 지른다.

4 어떤 학생들은 스타의 사진을 찍기 위해 몇 시간을 기다린다.

5 어떤 학생들은 심지어 가장 좋아하는 스타를 보기 위해 다른 도시로 여행을 가기까지 한다.

6 아이돌이 최근의 창조물일까? 아니다!

7 아이돌은 1960년대의 The Beatles부터 시작됐을까?

8 그들은 많은 사람들에게 사랑받았지만, 최초는 아니다.

9 1950년대의 Elvis Presley는 어떤가? 완전히 헛짚었다.

10 답을 찾기 위해서 1845년에 빈에 있는 한 콘서트홀로 타임머신을 타고 가 보자.

11 모든 좌석이 꽉 차 있다.

12 다른 연주회와는 달리 피아노의 옆면이 청중을 향해 있다.

13 이렇게 함으로써, 청중은 잘생긴 185cm의 피아니스트를 더 잘 볼 수 있다.

14 그는 어떠한 악보도 가지고 있지 않다.

15 그는 기억으로 연주하기 시작한다.

16 그는 건반을 부드럽게 누르면서 천천히 시작한다.

17 All the people _____ _____ _____ because they don't want _____ _____ _____ _____ _____ .

18 He _____ _____ speed, and his long fingers _____ _____ on many keys _____ _____ .

19 This _____ the music very _____ and _____ .

20 The audience _____ _____ _____ his every little _____ _____ .

21 His _____ _____ hair _____ everywhere.

22 It's _____ _____ a piano and ballet performance _____ _____ .

23 Time _____ and the concert _____ .

24 People _____ and _____ flowers and pieces of _____ _____ _____ _____ .

25 The concert hall _____ _____ !

26 _____ was this _____ _____ ?

27 His name _____ Franz Liszt and he _____ _____ _____ 1811 in Hungary.

28 He first _____ _____ the piano _____ _____ _____ .

29 Liszt _____ _____ a great pianist, _____ and teacher.

30 But many people _____ _____ him _____ the first idol.

31 _____ _____ you give his music a _____ ?

32 _____ you _____ today's _____ , you _____ _____ the _____ _____ .

17 모든 사람들이 단 하나의 음도 놓치고 싶지 않아서 숨을 죽인다.

18 그는 속도를 점점 올리고, 그의 긴 손가락으로 많은 건반을 한 꺼번에 누른다.

19 이것은 음악을 아주 힘 있고 풍성하게 만든다.

20 청중들은 그의 모든 작은 몸짓에 주의를 집중한다.

21 그의 길고 아름다운 머리카락이 사방에 날린다.

22 이것은 마치 피아노와 발레 공연을 동시에 보는 것 같다.

23 시간은 쏜살같이 흐르고 연주회가 끝난다.

24 사람들은 소리를 지르며 꽃과 옷을 무대로 던진다.

25 콘서트홀은 열광의 도가니가 된다!

26 이 놀라운 스타는 누구였을까?

27 그의 이름은 Franz Liszt였고 그는 1811년에 헝가리에서 태어났다.

28 그는 7살에 처음 피아노를 치기 시작했다.

29 Liszt는 나중에 훌륭한 피아니스트이며 작곡가이자 선생님이 되었다.

30 그러나 많은 사람들은 그를 첫 번째 아이돌이라고 생각한다.

31 그의 음악을 한번 들어보는 게 어떤가?

32 만약 당신이 요즘의 아이돌을 좋아한다면, 원래의 아이돌도 좋아할 것이다.

※ 다음 문장을 우리말로 쓰시오.

1 Do you have a favorite K-pop idol? Many students will answer, "Yes."

➡ _____

2 These students often show great love for their stars.

➡ _____

3 Some scream madly at concerts.

➡ _____

4 Others wait hours to take pictures of their stars.

➡ _____

5 Some students even travel to another city to see their favorite stars.

➡ _____

6 Are idols a recent creation? No way!

➡ _____

7 Did idols begin with The Beatles in the 1960's?

➡ _____

8 They were loved by many, but they were not the first.

➡ _____

9 How about Elvis Presley in the 1950's? Not even close.

➡ _____

10 To find the answer, let's take a time machine to a concert hall in Vienna in 1845.

➡ _____

11 All the seats are filled.

➡ _____

12 Unlike other concerts, the side of the piano faces the audience.

➡ _____

13 This way, the audience can see the handsome 185cm pianist better.

➡ _____

14 He doesn't have any sheet music with him.

➡ _____

15 He begins to play from memory.

➡ _____

16 He starts slowly by softly touching the keys.

➡ _____

17 All the people hold their breath because they don't want to miss a single note.

➡ _____

18 He builds up speed, and his long fingers press down on many keys at once.

➡ _____

19 This makes the music very powerful and rich.

➡ _____

20 The audience pays attention to his every little body movement.

➡ _____

21 His long beautiful hair flies everywhere.

➡ _____

22 It's like watching a piano and ballet performance at once.

➡ _____

23 Time flies and the concert ends.

➡ _____

24 People scream and throw flowers and pieces of clothing onto the stage.

➡ _____

25 The concert hall goes wild!

➡ _____

26 Who was this amazing star?

➡ _____

27 His name was Franz Liszt and he was born in 1811 in Hungary.

➡ _____

28 He first started playing the piano when he was seven.

➡ _____

29 Liszt later became a great pianist, composer and teacher.

➡ _____

30 But many people think of him as the first idol.

➡ _____

31 Why don't you give his music a listen?

➡ _____

32 If you like today's idols, you will love the original idol.

➡ _____

※ 다음 괄호 안의 단어들을 우리말에 맞도록 바르게 배열하시오.

1 (you / do / a / have / K-pop / favorite / idol? // students / will / many / answer, / "Yes.")
➡ ______________________

2 (students / show / these / often / love / great / stars. / their / for)
➡ ______________________

3 (scream / at / some / concerts. / madly)
➡ ______________________

4 (wait / others / to / hours / pictures / take / of / stars. / their)
➡ ______________________

5 (some / even / students / travel / another / to / city / see / to / their / stars. / favorite)
➡ ______________________

6 (idols / are / recent / a / creation? / way! / no)
➡ ______________________

7 (idols / did / with / begin / Beatles / The / in / 1960's? / the)
➡ ______________________

8 (were / they / by / loved / many, / but / were / they / first. / the / not)
➡ ______________________

9 (Elvis / Presley / about / how / the / in / 1950's? // even / close. / not)
➡ ______________________

10 (find / answer, / to / the / let's / take / machine / a / time / to / concert / a / Vienna / in / hall / 1845. / in)
➡ ______________________

____

11 (the / seats / all / filled. / are)
➡ ______________________

12 (other / unlike / concerts, / the / of / side / the / piano / audience. / the / faces)
➡ ______________________

13 (way, / this / the / audience / see / can / handsome / the / better. / pianist / 185cm)
➡ ______________________

14 (he / have / doesn't / sheet / any / with / him. / music)
➡ ______________________

15 (he / play / to / begins / memory. / from)
➡ ______________________

16 (starts / he / slowly / touching / by / keys. / the / softly)
➡ ______________________

1 여러분은 가장 좋아하는 K팝 아이돌이 있는가? 많은 학생들이 "그렇다."라고 답할 것이다.

2 이 학생들은 종종 자신들의 스타를 향해 큰 애정을 보인다.

3 어떤 학생들은 콘서트에서 미친 듯이 괴성을 지른다.

4 어떤 학생들은 스타의 사진을 찍기 위해 몇 시간을 기다린다.

5 어떤 학생들은 심지어 가장 좋아하는 스타를 보기 위해 다른 도시로 여행을 가기까지 한다.

6 아이돌이 최근의 창조물일까? 아니다!

7 아이돌은 1960년대의 The Beatles부터 시작됐을까?

8 그들은 많은 사람들에게 사랑받았지만, 최초는 아니다.

9 1950년대의 Elvis Presley는 어떤가? 완전히 헛짚었다.

10 답을 찾기 위해서 1845년에 빈에 있는 한 콘서트홀로 타임머신을 타고 가 보자.

11 모든 좌석이 꽉 차 있다.

12 다른 연주회와는 달리 피아노의 옆면이 청중을 향해 있다.

13 이렇게 함으로써, 청중은 잘생긴 185cm의 피아니스트를 더 잘 볼 수 있다.

14 그는 어떠한 악보도 가지고 있지 않다.

15 그는 기억으로 연주하기 시작한다.

16 그는 건반을 부드럽게 누르면서 천천히 시작한다.

17 (the / all / hold / people / breath / their / because / don't / they / to / want / miss / a / note. / single)
➡ _____

18 (builds / he / speed, / up / and / long / his / fingers / down / press / many / on / once. / at / keys)
➡ _____

19 (the / music / makes / this / very / rich. / and / powerful)
➡ _____

20 (audience / the / pays / to / attention / every / his / little / movement. / body)
➡ _____

21 (long / beautiful / his / everywhere. / hair / flies)
➡ _____

22 (like / it's / a / watching / piano / and / performance / once. / at / ballet)
➡ _____

23 (flies / time / and / concert / ends. / the)
➡ _____

24 (scream / people / and / flowers / throw / and / pieces / clothing / of / stage. / the / onto)
➡ _____

25 (concert / the / hall / wild! / goes)
➡ _____

26 (was / who / star? / this / amazing)
➡ _____

27 (name / his / Franz / was / Liszt / and / was / born / in / he / in / Hungary. / 1811)
➡ _____

28 (first / he / playing / started / piano / the / when / seven. / was / he)
➡ _____

29 (later / Liszt / became / pianist, / great / a / and / teacher. / composer)
➡ _____

30 (many / but / think / people / of / him / idol. / as / first / the)
➡ _____

31 (don't / why / give / you / music / his / listen? / a)
➡ _____

32 (you / like / if / idols, / today's / will / you / love / original / the / idol.)
➡ _____

17 모든 사람들이 단 하나의 음도 놓치고 싶지 않아서 숨을 죽인다.

18 그는 속도를 점점 올리고, 그의 긴 손가락으로 많은 건반을 한꺼번에 누른다.

19 이것은 음악을 아주 힘 있고 풍성하게 만든다.

20 청중들은 그의 모든 작은 몸짓에 주의를 집중한다.

21 그의 길고 아름다운 머리카락이 사방에 날린다.

22 이것은 마치 피아노와 발레 공연을 동시에 보는 것 같다.

23 시간은 쏜살같이 흐르고 연주회가 끝난다.

24 사람들은 소리를 지르며 꽃과 옷을 무대로 던진다.

25 콘서트홀은 열광의 도가니가 된다!

26 이 놀라운 스타는 누구였을까?

27 그의 이름은 Franz Liszt였고 그는 1811년에 헝가리에서 태어났다.

28 그는 7살에 처음 피아노를 치기 시작했다.

29 Liszt는 나중에 훌륭한 피아니스트이며 작곡가이자 선생님이 되었다.

30 그러나 많은 사람들은 그를 첫 번째 아이돌이라고 생각한다.

31 그의 음악을 한번 들어보는 게 어떤가?

32 만약 당신이 요즘의 아이돌을 좋아한다면, 원래의 아이돌도 좋아할 것이다.

※ 다음 우리말을 영어로 쓰시오.

1 외국어에서 유래된 영어 단어

➡ _____

2 영어는 종종 다른 문화나 언어에서 단어를 빌려왔다.

➡ _____

3 여기 재미있는 이야기가 있는 몇 개의 예가 있다.

➡ _____

shampoo 샴푸

4 shampoo라는 단어는 힌디어 *chāmpo*에서 왔고, '누르다'라는 의미이다.

➡ _____

5 인도에서 그 단어는 머리 마사지라는 의미로 쓰였다.

➡ _____

6 인도에 있는 영국 상인들은 머리 마사지를 함께하는 목욕을 경험했고 마사지를 18세기에 영국에 소개했다.

➡ _____

_____

7 *shampoo*라는 단어의 의미는 그 단어가 1762년쯤 영어에 처음으로 들어온 이후 몇 번 바뀌었다.

➡ _____

8 19세기에, *shampoo*는 '머리 감기'라는 현재의 의미를 갖게 되었다.

➡ _____

9 그 후 얼마 지나지 않아, 그 단어는 머리에 사용하는 특별한 비누에도 쓰이기 시작했다.

➡ _____

robot 로봇

10 robot이라는 단어는 "*R.U.R.*"에서 왔는데, 그 연극은 1920년 체코의 작가 Karel Čapek에 의해 쓰였다.

➡ _____

11 그 연극에서 로봇은 인간처럼 생긴 기계이다.

➡ _____

12 그들은 인간을 위해 일하도록 설계되고, 공장에서 생산된다.

➡ _____

13 robot이라는 단어를 사용하려는 생각이 Karel Čapek 자신에게서 나온 게 아니었다는 것이 흥미롭다.

➡ _____

14 그는 원래 자신의 연극에서 그 기계들을 '일'을 의미하는 라틴어에서 온 *labori*라고 불렀다.

➡ _____

15 하지만, 그의 형이 roboti를 제안했는데, roboti는 체코어로 '노예 근로자들'을 의미한다.

➡ _____

16 Karel Čapek은 그 아이디어가 마음에 들어 roboti라는 단어를 사용하기로 결정했다.

➡ _____

17 1938년에 그 연극은 영국 TV에서 공상 과학물로 만들어졌다.

➡ _____

hurricane 태풍

18 hurricane이라는 단어는 스페인어 단어 huracán에서 왔고, 그것은 마야 신의 이름에서 유래한다.

➡ _____

19 마야의 창조 신화에서, Huracán은 바람, 폭풍우, 그리고 불에 관한 날씨의 신이며, 그는 인간을 창조한 세 명의 신들 중 한 명이다.

➡ _____

20 하지만, 최초의 인간들이 신들을 화나게 해서 Huracán은 거대한 홍수를 일으켰다.

➡ _____

21 스페인이 마야 문명과 했던 첫 접촉은 1517년이었다.

➡ _____

22 카리브 제도를 지나던 스페인 탐험가들이 허리케인을 겪었고, 그 지역 사람들로부터 그것을 의미하는 단어를 듣게 되었다.

➡ _____

23 영어에서 일찍이 hurricane을 사용한 것 중 하나는 1608년 셰익스피어의 희곡에서였다.

➡ _____

hamburger 햄버거

24 hamburger라는 단어는 원래 독일에서 두 번째로 큰 도시인 함부르크에서 왔다.

➡ _____

25 hamburger는 독일어로 '함부르크 출신의 사람 또는 사물'을 의미한다.

➡ _____

26 최초의 햄버거의 기원은 분명하지 않다.

➡ _____

27 하지만 햄버거는 1885년에서 1904년 사이의 언젠가 미국 텍사스에 있는 작은 마을에서 발명되었다고 믿어진다.

➡ _____

28 한 요리사가 빵 두 조각 사이에 함부르크 스타일의 스테이크를 넣었고, 사람들은 그런 음식을 햄버거라고 부르기 시작했다.

➡ _____

※ 다음 우리말과 일치하도록 빈칸에 알맞은 말을 쓰시오.

After You Read A

1. Online _____

2. English words _____ or _____

3. shampoo: It _____ the Hindi word *chāmpo*, _____
   means "_____ _____."

4. robot: It comes from *roboti*, _____ means "_____"
   _____ _____.

5. hurricane: It comes from _____ _____, *huracán*, _____
   _____ _____ the name of a Mayan god.

6. hamburger: It comes from _____, _____
   _____ _____.

Around the World

1. 1. Many _____ about law _____.

2. Examples _____ words _____ and _____.

3. 2. _____ about music
   _____ come from Italian.

4. _____ _____, piano and violin _____.

5. 3. Many English words for _____ come from _____.

6. _____ _____, tomato _____ *tomate* and potato
   comes from *patata* _____ _____.

Think and Write Step 2

1. The _____ of the _____

2. The word *sandwich* _____ John Montagu, _____ was
   _____ of Sandwich.

3. He _____ _____ meat between _____
   _____ because he could play a card game _____
   _____.

4. People _____ _____ it was a great idea and began to call
   _____ him.

구석구석 지문 Test

※ 다음 우리말을 영어로 쓰시오.

After You Read A

1. 온라인 사전

   ➡ _____

2. 다른 문화나 언어에서 온 영어 단어들

   ➡ _____

3. 샴푸: 그것은 힌디어 chāmpo에서 왔는데, '누르다'를 의미한다.

   ➡ _____

4. 로봇: 그것은 roboti에서 왔는데, roboti는 체코어로 '노예 근로자들'을 의미한다.

   ➡ _____

5. 허리케인: 그것은 스페인어 huracán에서 왔는데, 마야 신의 이름에서 유래된다.

   ➡ _____

6. 햄버거: 그것은 독일에서 두 번째로 큰 도시인 함부르크에서 왔다

   ➡ _____

Around the World

1. 1. 법에 관한 많은 영어 단어들은 프랑스어에서 왔다.

   ➡ _____

2. judge(판사)와 justice(정의)와 같은 단어들을 예로 들 수 있다.

   ➡ _____

3. 2. 이탈리아어에서 온 음악에 관한 많은 영어 단어들이 있다.

   ➡ _____

4. 예를 들어, piano(피아노)와 violin(바이올린) 등이 있다

   ➡ _____

5. 3. 채소에 관한 많은 영어 단어들은 스페인어에서 왔다.

   ➡ _____

6. 예를 들어, tomato(토마토)는 tomate에서 왔고, potato(감자)는 patata에서 왔다.

   ➡ _____

Think and Write Step 2

1. 단어 sandwich의 유래

   ➡ _____

2. 단어 sandwich는 John Montagu에게서 유래했는데, 그는 샌드위치 백작 4세였다.

   ➡ _____

3. 그는 먹는 동안에 카드게임을 할 수 있었기 때문에 빵 두 조각 사이에 고기를 끼워서 먹는 것을 즐겼다.

   ➡ _____

4. 사람들은 그것을 좋은 생각이라고 여겼고, 그의 이름을 따서 그런 음식을 샌드위치라고 부르기 시작했다.

   ➡ _____

※ 다음 영어를 우리말로 쓰시오.

01 athlete _____

02 reach _____

03 equipment _____

04 expect _____

05 temperature _____

06 scared _____

07 amazing _____

08 scary _____

09 participant _____

10 wet _____

11 throat _____

12 freeze _____

13 limit _____

14 burn _____

15 request _____

16 protect _____

17 windy _____

18 hit _____

19 imagine _____

20 jump rope _____

21 librarian _____

22 bake _____

23 race _____

24 rock climbing _____

25 train _____

26 boiling _____

27 planet _____

28 traditional _____

29 ordinary _____

30 punch _____

31 tough _____

32 backpack _____

33 throw _____

34 hang _____

35 go on _____

36 take part in _____

37 up to _____

38 in fact _____

39 for a living _____

40 a series of _____

41 take place _____

42 be out of _____

43 take care of _____

※ 다음 우리말을 영어로 쓰시오.

01 사막 _____

02 방향 _____

03 전통적인 _____

04 결승선 _____

05 끓는, 끓어오르는 _____

06 남극대륙 _____

07 배낭 _____

08 들(판), 경기장 _____

09 던지다 _____

10 계주, 릴레이 경주 _____

11 마른, 건조한 _____

12 마라톤 _____

13 행성 _____

14 의미하다 _____

15 매달다 _____

16 힘든, 어려운 _____

17 배트, 막대기, 박쥐 _____

18 타다 _____

19 체육관 _____

20 차다 _____

21 보통의, 평범한 _____

22 타격 _____

23 거대한 _____

24 모래 _____

25 제복, 유니폼 _____

26 온도 _____

27 장비, 설비 _____

28 얼다, 얼어붙다 _____

29 보호하다 _____

30 참가자 _____

31 선수, 육상 경기 선수 _____

32 한계, 제한; 제한하다 _____

33 목구멍 _____

34 젖은, 축축한 _____

35 ~에 참가하다 _____

36 ~의 한가운데에 _____

37 일련의 _____

38 일어나다, 개최되다 _____

39 ~가 떨어지다, 바닥나다 _____

40 계속되다 _____

41 ~을 돌보다 _____

42 ~까지 _____

43 사실은, 실제로 _____

※ 다음 영영풀이에 알맞은 단어를 <보기>에서 골라 쓴 후, 우리말 뜻을 쓰시오.

1 _____ : much larger or more powerful than normal: _____

2 _____ : the continent around the South Pole: _____

3 _____ : a person who is taking part in an activity or event: _____

4 _____ : a person who is in charge of or works in a library: _____

5 _____ : a person who competes in sports: _____

6 _____ : the measurement in degrees of how hot or cold a thing or place is:

_____

7 _____ : a room or hall with equipment for doing physical exercise: _____

8 _____ : to become hard, and often turn to ice, as a result of extreme cold:

_____

9 _____ : to be heated to the point where it forms bubbles and turns to steam or

vapour: _____

10 _____ : a race in which people run a distance of 26 miles, which is about 42 km:

_____

11 _____ : being part of the beliefs, customs or way of life of a particular group of

people, that have not changed for a long time: _____

12 _____ : to make sure that somebody/something is not harmed, injured, damaged:

_____

13 _____ : a competition between people, animals, vehicles, etc. to see which one is

the faster or fastest: _____

14 _____ : a large area of land that has very little water and very few plants growing

on it: _____

15 _____ : a passage in the neck through which food and air pass on their way into

the body; the front part of the neck: _____

16 _____ : to try to make yourself stronger, faster, or better at doing something

before competing in an event or competition: _____

보기			
race	boil	librarian	traditional
freeze	throat	protect	Antarctica
train	desert	participant	giant
marathon	gym	athlete	temperature

※ 다음 우리말과 일치하도록 빈칸에 알맞은 말을 쓰시오.

Listen & Speak 1 A

Tony: Bomi, what do you do _____ _____ _____ _____?

Bomi: I _____ _____ cookies. _____ _____ you, Tony?

Tony: I _____ _____ _____.

Listen & Speak 1 B

Jean: I'm so _____. _____ Friday!

Tom: _____ _____ _____ _____ _____ _____ on the weekend, Jean?

Jean: I'm _____ _____ _____ _____.

Tom: Do you _____ badminton _____?

Jean: Yes, it's _____ _____ _____ _____ _____.

Tom: _____ do you _____ _____ _____?

Jean: My dad. _____ _____ _____ _____ _____ _____ _____ _____?

Tom: I _____ _____ to the Han River and _____ _____ _____.

Listen & Speak 1 C

Minsu: Ms. Allen, _____ do you do _____ _____ _____?

Allen: I'm a doctor.

Minsu: What do you do _____ _____ _____ _____?

Allen: _____ _____ _____ _____ _____ _____.

Listen & Speak 2 A

Mina: Tom, _____ _____ _____ _____ _____ _____ Jeju-do?

Tom: Yes, _____ _____. I _____ there last winter vacation. _____ _____ you?

Mina: _____ _____ _____ _____ _____ _____, but I'm _____ there this summer

Tom: That's great! _____ _____ you'll like it _____ _____.

Listen & Speak 2 B

Suji: Mike, _____ _____ _____ _____ _____ flying yoga?

Mike: Yeah! _____ _____ it on TV. People _____ _____ in the air!

Suji: _____ what? I'm _____ it _____ _____.

Mike: Really? It _____ _____ _____. Do you like it, Suji?

Suji: At first, I was _____ _____ _____, but now I'm _____ it.

Mike: Sounds great! I _____ I _____ _____ more, _____.

Suji: Do you _____ _____ _____ my yoga class?

Mike: No, that's too _____ _____ me. I'll just _____ _____.

Suji: Mike, 너는 플라잉 요가를 들어본 적이 있니?
Mike: 응! TV에서 본 적이 있어. 사람들이 공중에 매달려 있었어!
Suji: 그거 알아? 내가 요즘 그걸 배우고 있어.
Mike: 정말? 아주 무서워 보였는데. 그걸 좋아하니, 수지야?
Suji: 처음엔 조금 무서웠는데, 지금은 즐기고 있어.
Mike: 좋구나! 나도 운동을 더 해야 할 것 같아.
Suji: 우리 요가 수업을 함께 할래?
Mike: 아니, 그건 내게 너무 무서워. 나는 그냥 농구를 할게.

Listen & Speak 2 C

A: _____ _____ _____ _____ a horse?

B: Yes, _____ _____.

A: _____ did you _____ _____ _____?

B: _____ _____.

A: 너는 말을 타 본 적이 있니?
B: 응. 있어.
A: 언제 말을 타 보았니?
B: 지난 여름에.

Real Life Talk

Hojin: Judy, what do you do _____ _____ _____ _____?

Judy: I _____ _____ _____ _____ with my dad.

Hojin: _____ _____ do you _____ _____?

Judy: No, Hojin. I _____ _____ it at a _____ _____ my house.

Hojin: I see. _____ _____ _____ _____ it on a real mountain?

Judy: _____ _____. But I _____ _____ _____ _____ it someday.

Hojin: That's _____ _____. Can I _____ _____ you next time?

Judy: Sure. I'm _____ _____ _____ _____.

Hojin: That _____ _____.

Judy: You're _____ _____ _____ it.

Hojin: Judy, 너는 여가 시간에 무엇을 하니?
Judy: 나는 종종 아빠와 암벽 등반을 하러 가.
Hojin: 어떤 산에 가니?
Judy: 아니야, 호진아. 나는 보통 집 근처에 있는 체육관에서 그걸 해.
Hojin: 그렇구나. 실제 산에서 해 본 적이 있니?
Judy: 아직 없어. 하지만 언젠가 해 보기를 바라.
Hojin: 그거 정말 멋지다. 다음번에 내가 가서 함께 해도 될까?
Judy: 물론이야. 이번 주 토요일에 갈 거야.
Hojin: 잘됐네.
Judy: 너는 그걸 정말 좋아할 거야.

대화문 Test

※ 다음 우리말에 맞도록 대화를 영어로 쓰시오.

Listen & Speak 1 A

Tony: _____

Bomi: _____

Tony: _____

Tony: 보미야, 너는 여가 시간에 무엇을 하니?

Bomi: 나는 종종 쿠키를 구워. 너는 어때, Tony?

Tony: 나는 보통 영화를 봐.

Listen & Speak 1 B

Jean: _____

Tom: _____

Jean: _____

Tom: _____

Jean: _____

Tom: _____

Jean: _____

Tom: _____

Jean: 정말 기뻐. 금요일이야!

Tom: 주말에 무엇을 할 거니, Jean?

Jean: 나는 배드민턴을 칠 거야.

Tom: 배드민턴을 자주 치니?

Jean: 응, 그건 내가 가장 좋아하는 여가 활동이야.

Tom: 보통 누구랑 치니?

Jean: 우리 아빠랑. 너는 여가 시간에 무엇을 하니?

Tom: 나는 종종 한강에 가서 자전거를 타.

Listen & Speak 1 C

Minsu: _____

Allen: _____

Minsu: _____

Allen: _____

Minsu: Ms. Allen, 직업이 무언가요?

Allen: 의사입니다.

Minsu: 여가 시간에 무엇을 하나요?

Allen: 나는 종종 탁구를 칩니다.

Listen & Speak 2 A

Mina: _____

Tom: _____

Mina: _____

Tom: _____

Mina: Tom, 너는 제주도에 가 본 적이 있니?

Tom: 응, 가 봤어. 지난 겨울 방학에 거기에 갔어. 너는?

Mina: 나는 거기에 가 본 적이 없는데, 이번 여름에 갈 거야.

Tom: 잘됐네! 네가 아주 좋아할 거라고 확신해.

Listen & Speak 2 B

Suji: _____

Mike: _____

Suji: _____

Mike: _____

Suji: _____

Mike: _____

Suji: _____

Mike: _____

Suji: Mike, 너는 플라잉 요가를 들어본 적이 있니?

Mike: 응! TV에서 본 적이 있어. 사람들이 공중에 매달려 있었어!

Suji: 그거 알아? 내가 요즘 그걸 배우고 있어.

Mike: 정말? 아주 무서워 보였는데. 그걸 좋아하니, 수지야?

Suji: 처음엔 조금 무서웠는데, 지금은 즐기고 있어.

Mike: 좋구나! 나도 운동을 더 해야 할 것 같아.

Suji: 우리 요가 수업을 함께 할래?

Mike: 아니, 그건 내게 너무 무서워. 나는 그냥 농구를 할게.

Listen & Speak 2 C

A: _____

B: _____

A: _____

B: _____

A: 너는 말을 타 본 적이 있니?

B: 응. 있어.

A: 언제 말을 타 보았니?

B: 지난 여름에.

Real Life Talk

Hojin: _____

Judy: _____

Hojin: _____

Judy: _____

Hojin: _____

Judy: _____

Hojin: _____

Judy: _____

Hojin: _____

Judy: _____

Hojin: Judy, 너는 여가 시간에 무엇을 하니?

Judy: 나는 종종 아빠와 암벽 등반을 하러 가.

Hojin: 어떤 산에 가니?

Judy: 아니야, 호진아. 나는 보통 집 근처에 있는 체육관에서 그걸 해.

Hojin: 그렇구나. 실제 산에서 해 본 적이 있니?

Judy: 아직 없어. 하지만 언젠가 해 보기를 바라.

Hojin: 그거 정말 멋지다. 다음번에 내가 가서 함께 해도 될까?

Judy: 물론이야. 이번 주 토요일에 갈 거야.

Hojin: 잘됐네.

Judy: 너는 그걸 정말 좋아할 거야.

※ 다음 우리말과 일치하도록 빈칸에 알맞은 것을 골라 쓰시오.

1 _____ you are in the _____ of a _____ desert.
  A. middle   B. imagine   C. great

2 The sands go _____ and on in _____ _____.
  A. direction   B. on   C. every

3 The sun _____ a giant ball of _____.
  A. fire   B. like   C. feels

4 The hot wind _____ your _____ and _____.
  A. throat   B. face   C. burns

5 You _____ your _____ to _____ some water.
  A. open   B. drink   C. backpack

6 Oh, no! You're _____ _____ _____ water.
  A. of   B. almost   C. out

7 You _____ your throat with a _____ of water and _____
  _____.
  A. going   B. drop   C. wet   D. keep

8 _____ _____ a bad dream?
  A. like   B. sounds

9 Well, this is not a _____ for the people who _____ _____
  in the 4 Deserts Race.
  A. part   B. take   C. dream

10 The 4 Deserts Race is a _____ of four _____ _____ the
  world's _____ deserts.
  A. races   B. toughest   C. series   D. across

11 _____ _____ is 250 kilometers _____ and _____ seven
  days.
  A. takes   B. race   C. each   D. long

12 The first race _____ _____ in the Atacama Desert _____
  Chile.
  A. in   B. place   C. takes

13 It is _____ _____ desert _____ the world.
  A. in   B. driest   C. the

14 In _____, it _____ _____ in some parts of the Atacama
  Desert _____ 400 years!
  A. for   B. hasn't   C. fact   D. rained

15 The next race _____ _____ the Gobi Desert _____
  China.
  A. to   B. in   C. goes

16 It is _____ _____ _____ on earth.
  A. desert   B. windiest   C. the

1 당신이 아주 큰 사막의 한 가운데에 있다고 상상해 봐라.

2 모래 벌판이 사면팔방으로 계속 이어진다.

3 태양은 거대한 불덩이 같다.

4 뜨거운 바람이 당신의 얼굴과 목구멍을 태운다.

5 당신은 물을 좀 마시려고 배낭을 연다.

6 오. 이런! 물이 거의 떨어져 간다.

7 당신은 물 한 방울로 목을 적시고 계속 간다.

8 나쁜 꿈인 것 같은가?

9 글쎄, '4 Deserts Race'에 참가하는 사람들에게 이것은 꿈이 아니다.

10 '4 Deserts Race'는 세계에서 가장 험한 사막들을 가로지르는 연속된 4개의 경주이다.

11 각 경주는 250킬로미터이고 7일이 걸린다.

12 첫 번째 경주는 칠레에 있는 아타카마 사막에서 열린다.

13 그곳은 세계에서 가장 건조한 사막이다.

14 실제로 아타카마 사막의 어떤 곳에는 400년간 비가 내리지 않았다!

15 다음 경주는 중국에 있는 고비 사막으로 이어진다.

16 그곳은 세상에서 가장 바람이 많이 부는 사막이다.

17 The _____ race _____ _____ the Sahara Desert _____ Egypt.

    A. in   B. to   C. heads   D. third

18 It is _____ _____ of the four _____.

    A. hottest   B. deserts   C. the

19 Temperatures can _____ _____ _____ 50°C.

    A. reach   B. to   C. up

20 Finally, the race _____ to the _____ desert on _____, Antarctica.

    A. coldest   B. earth   C. travels

21 If you _____ _____ water into the air here, it _____!

    A. freezes   B. boiling   C. throw

22 Only _____ _____ runners on the planet can _____ _____ in 4 Deserts Race, right?

    A. part   B. greatest   C. take   D. the

23 _____ _____.

    A. exactly   B. not

24 Many of the _____ are _____ people _____ you and me.

    A. like   B. ordinary   C. participants

25 _____ _____ do they _____ it?

    A. why   B. do   C. so

26 Adrianna, a _____ _____ France, _____,

    A. from   B. librarian   C. says

27 "It's a _____ to test your _____ and make your _____ history.

    A. own   B. chance   C. limits

28 _____ e who _____ the finish line can do _____."

    A. anything   B. crosses   C. anyone

---

17 세 번째 경주는 이집트에 있는 사하라 사막으로 향한다.

18 그곳은 네 개의 사막 중 가장 뜨겁다.

19 온도가 섭씨 50도까지 올라갈 수 있다.

20 마지막으로 경주는 세상에서 가장 추운 사막인 남극 대륙으로 향한다.

21 이곳에서 끓는 물을 공중에 던지면, 그것은 얼어버린다!

22 세상에서 가장 훌륭한 달리기 주자들만 '4 Deserts Race'에 참가할 수 있다. 맞는가?

23 꼭 그렇진 않다.

24 많은 참가자들은 당신과 나와 같은 평범한 사람들이다.

25 그러면 그들은 왜 그것을 하는가?

26 프랑스 출신의 사서인 Adrianna는 말한다.

27 "그것은 당신의 한계를 시험하고 당신만의 역사를 만들 기회예요.

28 결승선을 넘는 사람은 어떤 것이든 할 수 있어요."

※ 다음 우리말과 일치하도록 빈칸에 알맞은 말을 쓰시오.

1 _____ you are _____ _____ _____ _____ a great desert.

2 The sands _____ _____ _____ _____ in every direction.

3 The sun _____ _____ a _____ ball of _____.

4 The hot wind _____ _____ _____ and _____.

5 You _____ _____ _____ _____ some water.

6 Oh, no! You're _____ _____ _____ _____.

7 You _____ your throat _____ _____ _____ _____ water and _____ _____.

8 _____ _____ a _____ _____?

9 Well, this is not a dream for the people _____ _____ _____ _____ the 4 Deserts Race.

10 The 4 Deserts Race is _____ _____ _____ _____ _____ the world's _____ _____.

11 _____ _____ _____ 250 kilometers _____ and _____ seven days.

12 The first race _____ _____ in the Atacama Desert _____ Chile.

13 It is _____ _____ desert in the world.

14 _____ _____, it _____ _____ in some parts of the Atacama Desert _____ 400 years!

15 The next race _____ _____ the Gobi Desert _____ China.

16 It is _____ _____ _____ _____ _____ _____.

1 당신이 아주 큰 사막의 한 가운데에 있다고 상상해 봐라.

2 모래 벌판이 사면팔방으로 계속 이어진다.

3 태양은 거대한 불덩이 같다.

4 뜨거운 바람이 당신의 얼굴과 목구멍을 태운다.

5 당신은 물을 좀 마시려고 배낭을 연다.

6 오, 이런! 물이 거의 떨어져 간다.

7 당신은 물 한 방울로 목을 적시고 계속 간다.

8 나쁜 꿈인 것 같은가?

9 글쎄, '4 Deserts Race'에 참가하는 사람들에게 이것은 꿈이 아니다.

10 '4 Deserts Race'는 세계에서 가장 험한 사막들을 가로지르는 연속된 4개의 경주이다.

11 각 경주는 250킬로미터이고 7일이 걸린다.

12 첫 번째 경주는 칠레에 있는 아타카마 사막에서 열린다.

13 그곳은 세계에서 가장 건조한 사막이다.

14 실제로 아타카마 사막의 어떤 곳에는 400년간 비가 내리지 않았다!

15 다음 경주는 중국에 있는 고비 사막으로 이어진다.

16 그곳은 세상에서 가장 바람이 많이 부는 사막이다.

17 The third race _____ _____ the Sahara Desert in Egypt.

18 It is _____ _____ the _____ _____ .

19 Temperatures can _____ _____ _____ 50°C.

20 _____ , the race _____

on earth, Antarctica.

21 If you _____ the air here, it _____ !

22 Only _____ _____ _____ on the planet can _____

_____ _____ 4 Deserts Race, _____ ?

23 _____ _____ .

24 Many of _____ _____ _____ _____ people _____

you and me.

25 So _____ do they _____ _____ ?

26 Adrianna, _____ _____ _____ _____ _____ , says,

27 "It's _____ _____ _____ _____ _____

and _____ your own history.

28 Anyone _____ _____ the finish line _____ _____

_____ ."

17 세 번째 경주는 이집트에 있는 사하라 사막으로 향한다.

18 그곳은 네 개의 사막 중 가장 뜨 겁다.

19 온도가 섭씨 50도까지 올라갈 수 있다.

20 마지막으로 경주는 세상에서 가 장 추운 사막인 남극 대륙으로 향한다.

21 이곳에서 끓는 물을 공중에 던 지면, 그것은 얼어버린다!

22 세상에서 가장 훌륭한 달리기 주자들만 '4 Deserts Race'에 참가할 수 있다. 맞는가?

23 꼭 그렇진 않다.

24 많은 참가자들은 당신과 나와 같은 평범한 사람들이다.

25 그러면 그들은 왜 그것을 하는 가?

26 프랑스 출신의 사서인 Adrianna 는 말한다.

27 "그것은 당신의 한계를 시험하 고 당신만의 역사를 만들 기회 예요.

28 결승선을 넘는 사람은 어떤 것 이든 할 수 있어요."

※ 다음 문장을 우리말로 쓰시오.

1 ▸ Imagine you are in the middle of a great desert.

➡ _____

2 ▸ The sands go on and on in every direction.

➡ _____

3 ▸ The sun feels like a giant ball of fire.

➡ _____

4 ▸ The hot wind burns your face and throat.

➡ _____

5 ▸ You open your backpack to drink some water.

➡ _____

6 ▸ Oh, no! You're almost out of water.

➡ _____

7 ▸ You wet your throat with a drop of water and keep going.

➡ _____

8 ▸ Sounds like a bad dream?

➡ _____

9 ▸ Well, this is not a dream for the people who take part in the 4 Deserts Race.

➡ _____

10 ▸ The 4 Deserts Race is a series of four races across the world's toughest deserts.

➡ _____

11 ▸ Each race is 250 kilometers long and takes seven days.

➡ _____

12 ▸ The first race takes place in the Atacama Desert in Chile.

➡ _____

13 ▸ It is the driest desert in the world.

➡ _____

14 ▸ In fact, it hasn't rained in some parts of the Atacama Desert for 400 years!

➡ _____

15 ▸ The next race goes to the Gobi Desert in China.

➡ _____

16 ▸ It is the windiest desert on earth.

➡ _____

17 The third race heads to the Sahara Desert in Egypt.

➡ _____

18 It is the hottest of the four deserts.

➡ _____

19 Temperatures can reach up to 50℃.

➡ _____

20 Finally, the race travels to the coldest desert on earth, Antarctica.

➡ _____

21 If you throw boiling water into the air here, it freezes!

➡ _____

22 Only the greatest runners on the planet can take part in 4 Deserts Race, right?

➡ _____

23 Not exactly.

➡ _____

24 Many of the participants are ordinary people like you and me.

➡ _____

25 So why do they do it?

➡ _____

26 Adrianna, a librarian from France, says,

➡ _____

27 "It's a chance to test your limits and make your own history.

➡ _____

28 Anyone who crosses the finish line can do anything."

➡ _____

※ 다음 괄호 안의 단어들을 우리말에 맞도록 바르게 배열하시오.

1 (you / imagine / in / are / middle / the / of / desert. / great / a)
➡ _____

2 (sands / the / on / go / and / on / in / direction. / every)
➡ _____

3 (sun / the / feels / like / giant / a / fire. / of / ball)
➡ _____

4 (hot / the / wind / your / burns / throat. / and / face)
➡ _____

5 (open / you / backpack / your / drink / to / water. / some)
➡ _____

6 (no! / oh, / almost / you're / water. / of / out)
➡ _____

7 (wet / you / throat / with / your / a / of / drop / and / going. / keep / water)
➡ _____

8 (like / bad / sounds / dream? / a)
➡ _____

9 (well, / is / this / not / dream / a / for / people / the / take / who / in / part / the / Race. / Deserts / 4)
➡ _____

10 (the / Race / 4 / Deserts / is / series / of / a / four / across / races / world's / the / deserts. / toughest)
➡ _____

11 (race / each / 250 / is / long / kilometers / takes / and / days. / seven)
➡ _____

12 (first / the / race / place / takes / the / in / Desert / Chile. / in / Atacama)
➡ _____

13 (is / the / it / driest / world. / the / in / desert)
➡ _____

14 (fact, / in / hasn't / it / rained / some / in / parts / the / of / Desert / Atacama / year! / 400 / for)
➡ _____

15 (next / the / goes / race / to / Gobi / the / China. / Desert / in)
➡ _____

16 (is / it / the / desert / earth. / on / windiest)
➡ _____

1 당신이 아주 큰 사막의 한 가운데에 있다고 상상해 봐라.

2 모래 벌판이 사면팔방으로 계속 이어진다.

3 태양은 거대한 불덩이 같다.

4 뜨거운 바람이 당신의 얼굴과 목구멍을 태운다.

5 당신은 물을 좀 마시려고 배낭을 연다.

6 오, 이런! 물이 거의 떨어져 간다.

7 당신은 물 한 방울로 목을 적시고 계속 간다.

8 나쁜 꿈인 것 같은가?

9 글쎄. '4 Deserts Race'에 참가하는 사람들에게 이것은 꿈이 아니다.

10 '4 Deserts Race'는 세계에서 가장 험한 사막들을 가로지르는 연속된 4개의 경주이다.

11 각 경주는 250킬로미터이고 7일이 걸린다.

12 첫 번째 경주는 칠레에 있는 아타카마 사막에서 열린다.

13 그곳은 세계에서 가장 건조한 사막이다.

14 실제로 아타카마 사막의 어떤 곳에는 400년간 비가 내리지 않았다!

15 다음 경주는 중국에 있는 고비 사막으로 이어진다.

16 그곳은 세상에서 가장 바람이 많이 부는 사막이다.

17 ▸ (third / the / heads / race / the / to / in / Desert / Egypt. / Sahara)

➡ _____

18 ▸ (is / the / it / of / hottest / the / deserts. / four)

➡ _____

19 ▸ (can / reach / temperatures / 50℃ / to / up)

➡ _____

20 ▸ (finally, / race / the / to / travels / coldest / the / on / desert / Antarctica. / earth,)

➡ _____

21 ▸ (you / if / boiling / throw / into / water / air / the / here, / freezes! / it)

➡ _____

22 ▸ (the / only / runners / greatest / on / planet / the / take / can / in / part / Deserts / 4 / right? / Race,)

➡ _____

➡ _____

23 ▸ (exactly. / not)

➡ _____

24 ▸ (of / many / participants / the / ordinary / are / like / people / me. / and / you)

➡ _____

25 ▸ (why / so / do / they / it? / do)

➡ _____

26 ▸ (a / Adrianna, / from / librarian / say, / France,)

➡ _____

27 ▸ (a / "It's / to / chance / your / test / limits / and / your / history. / own / make)

➡ _____

28 ▸ (who / anyone / crosses / finish / the / can / line / anything." / do)

➡ _____

17 세 번째 경주는 이집트에 있는 사하라 사막으로 향한다.

18 그곳은 네 개의 사막 중 가장 뜨겁다.

19 온도가 섭씨 50도까지 올라갈 수 있다.

20 마지막으로 경주는 세상에서 가장 추운 사막인 남극 대륙으로 향한다.

21 이곳에서 끓는 물을 공중에 던지면, 그것은 얼어버린다!

22 세상에서 가장 훌륭한 달리기 주자들만 '4 Deserts Race'에 참가할 수 있다. 맞는가?

23 꼭 그렇진 않다.

24 많은 참가자들은 당신과 나와 같은 평범한 사람들이다.

25 그러면 그들은 왜 그것을 하는가?

26 프랑스 출신의 사서인 Adrianna는 말한다.

27 "그것은 당신의 한계를 시험하고 당신만의 역사를 만들 기회예요.

28 결승선을 넘는 사람은 어떤 것이든 할 수 있어요."

※ 다음 우리말을 영어로 쓰시오.

1 당신이 아주 큰 사막의 한 가운데에 있다고 상상해 봐라.

➡ _____

2 모래 벌판이 사면팔방으로 계속 이어진다.

➡ _____

3 태양은 거대한 불덩이 같다.

➡ _____

4 뜨거운 바람이 당신의 얼굴과 목구멍을 태운다.

➡ _____

5 당신은 물을 좀 마시려고 배낭을 연다.

➡ _____

6 오, 이런! 물이 거의 떨어져 간다.

➡ _____

7 당신은 물 한 방울로 목을 적시고 계속 간다.

➡ _____

8 나쁜 꿈인 것 같은가?

➡ _____

9 글쎄, '4 Deserts Race'에 참가하는 사람들에게 이것은 꿈이 아니다.

➡ _____

10 '4 Deserts Race'는 세계에서 가장 험한 사막들을 가로지르는 연속된 4개의 경주이다.

➡ _____

11 각 경주는 250킬로미터이고 7일이 걸린다.

➡ _____

12 첫 번째 경주는 칠레에 있는 아타카마 사막에서 열린다.

➡ _____

13 그곳은 세계에서 가장 건조한 사막이다.

➡ _____

14 실제로 아타카마 사막의 어떤 곳에는 400년간 비가 내리지 않았다!

➡ _____

15 다음 경주는 중국에 있는 고비 사막으로 이어진다.

➡ _____

16 그곳은 세상에서 가장 바람이 많이 부는 사막이다.

➡ _____

17 세 번째 경주는 이집트에 있는 사하라 사막으로 향한다.

➡ _____

18 그곳은 네 개의 사막 중 가장 뜨겁다.

➡ _____

19 온도가 섭씨 50도까지 올라갈 수 있다.

➡ _____

20 마지막으로 경주는 세상에서 가장 추운 사막인 남극 대륙으로 향한다.

➡ _____

21 이곳에서 끓는 물을 공중에 던지면, 그것은 얼어버린다!

➡ _____

22 세상에서 가장 훌륭한 달리기 주자들만 '4 Deserts Race'에 참가할 수 있다. 맞는가?

➡ _____

23 꼭 그렇진 않다.

➡ _____

24 많은 참가자들은 당신과 나와 같은 평범한 사람들이다.

➡ _____

25 그러면 그들은 왜 그것을 하는가?

➡ _____

26 프랑스 출신의 사서인 Adrianna는 말한다.

➡ _____

27 "그것은 당신의 한계를 시험하고 당신만의 역사를 만들 기회예요.

➡ _____

28 결승선을 넘는 사람은 어떤 것이든 할 수 있어요."

➡ _____

※ 다음 우리말과 일치하도록 빈칸에 알맞은 말을 쓰시오.

Real Life Talk - Step 2

1. G: What do you do _____ _____ _____ _____?

2. B: I _____ _____ sports.

3. G: _____ you ever _____ table tennis?

4. B: No, I _____.

5. G: _____ you ever _____ baseball?

6. B: _____, _____ _____.

7. G: Have you ever _____ _____ _____ _____?

8. B: Yes, I _____.

1. G: 너는 여가 시간에 무엇을 하니?
2. B: 나는 종종 운동을 해.
3. G: 탁구를 쳐 본 적이 있니?
4. B: 아니, 없어.
5. G: 야구를 해 본 적이 있니?
6. B: 응, 있어.
7. G: 홈런을 쳐 본 적이 있니?
8. B: 응, 있어.

Think and Write

1. A Happy _____ for _____ 3

2. The school sports day _____ _____ _____ May 14th.

3. It was very _____.

4. Students _____ _____ and did group _____ _____.

5. They also _____ _____ _____ _____ and a 100m race.

6. Class 2 won the group _____ _____, and Class 1 won the _____ _____.

7. Class 3 _____ the basketball game and the _____ _____.

8. They _____ the _____ and _____ the _____ winner.

9. _____ _____ _____ had great fun.

1. 3반을 위한 행복한 날
2. 학교 운동회는 5월 14일에 개최되었다.
3. 그것은 매우 신났다.
4. 학생들은 농구를 하고 단체 줄넘기를 했다.
5. 그들은 또한 릴레이 경주를 했고 100 미터 달리기도 했다.
6. 2반은 단체 줄넘기에서 우승을 했고, 1반은 릴레이 경주에서 우승을 했다.
7. 3반은 농구 경기와 100미터 경주에서 우승을 차지했다.
8. 그들은 가장 높은 점수를 얻어서 전체 우승자가 되었다.
9. 모든 반은 재미있는 시간을 보냈다.

※ 다음 우리말을 영어로 쓰시오.

Real Life Talk - Step 2

1. G: 너는 여가 시간에 무엇을 하니?
   ➡ _____

2. B: 나는 종종 운동을 해.
   ➡ _____

3. G: 탁구를 쳐 본 적이 있니?
   ➡ _____

4. B: 아니, 없어.
   ➡ _____

5. G: 야구를 해 본 적이 있니?
   ➡ _____

6. B: 응, 있어.
   ➡ _____

7. G: 홈런을 쳐 본 적이 있니?
   ➡ _____

8. B: 응, 있어.
   ➡ _____

Think and Write

1. 3반을 위한 행복한 날
   ➡ _____

2. 학교 운동회는 5월 14일에 개최되었다.
   ➡ _____

3. 그것은 매우 신났다.
   ➡ _____

4. 학생들은 농구를 하고 단체 줄넘기를 했다.
   ➡ _____

5. 그들은 또한 릴레이 경주를 했고 100미터 달리기도 했다.
   ➡ _____

6. 2반은 단체 줄넘기에서 우승을 했고, 1반은 릴레이 경주에서 우승을 했다.
   ➡ _____

7. 3반은 농구 경기와 100미터 경주에서 우승을 차지했다.
   ➡ _____

8. 그들은 가장 높은 점수를 얻어서 전체 우승자가 되었다.
   ➡ _____

9. 모든 반은 재미있는 시간을 보냈다.
   ➡ _____

※ 다음 영어를 우리말로 쓰시오.

01 piece _____

02 cool _____

03 cold _____

04 cut _____

05 step _____

06 pineapple _____

07 peel _____

08 blender _____

09 freezer _____

10 source _____

11 about _____

12 tip _____

13 smooth _____

14 blend _____

15 stay _____

16 try _____

17 add _____

18 slice _____

19 vitamin _____

20 share _____

21 health _____

22 mix _____

23 excellent _____

24 pour _____

25 finish _____

26 strawberry _____

27 until _____

28 stick _____

29 need _____

30 maker _____

31 pretty _____

32 own _____

33 close _____

34 ice pop _____

35 apple juice _____

36 stay cool _____

37 have a cold _____

38 put A into B _____

39 a half(=one half) _____

40 cut A into B _____

41 mix up _____

42 pour A into B _____

43 a cup of ~ _____

※ 다음 우리말을 영어로 쓰시오.

01	사과 주스	
02	나누다, 공유하다	
03	딸기	
04	즐기다	
05	우수한, 훌륭한	
06	끝내다	
07	(문, 가게를) 닫다	
08	막대기, 지팡이	
09	건강	
10	혼합(물); 섞다	
11	막대 아이스크림	
12	키위	
13	~을 만드는 기계(사람)	
14	필요하다	
15	붓다, 따르다	
16	오렌지	
17	예쁜; 꽤	
18	~까지	
19	자기 자신의	
20	껍질을 벗기다; 껍질	
21	냉동고	

22	얇게 썰다; 얇은 조각	
23	매끄러운, 부드러운	
24	섞다, 혼합하다	
25	조각, 일부, 부분	
26	더하다, 추가하다	
27	원천, 근원	
28	믹서	
29	조언, 비결	
30	자르다	
31	시도하다, 해보다	
32	~인 채로 있다, 머무르다	
33	시원한, 냉정한	
34	파인애플	
35	단계	
36	조각, 일부, 부분	
37	A를 B에 붓다	
38	2분의 1	
39	시원함을 유지하다	
40	A를 B(상태)로 자르다	
41	감기에 걸리다	
42	~을 섞다	
43	A를 B에 넣다	

※ 다음 영영풀이에 알맞은 단어를 <보기>에서 골라 쓴 후, 우리말 뜻을 쓰시오.

1   _____ : extremely good: _____

2   _____ : to have or use something with others: _____

3   _____ : to take the outer layer off fruit, vegetables, etc.: _____

4   _____ : an electric machine for mixing soft food or liquid: _____

5   _____ : completely flat and even, without any lumps, holes or rough areas:
    _____

6   _____ : a thin piece of wood that has fallen or been broken from a tree:
    _____

7   _____ : one of a series of things that you do in order to achieve something:
    _____

8   _____ : a small piece of advice about something practical: _____

9   _____ : to divide something into two or more pieces with a knife, etc.: _____

10 _____ : a thin flat piece of food that has been cut off a larger piece: _____

11 _____ : a combination of things that you need to make something: _____

12 _____ : a natural substance found in food that is an essential part of what humans
    and animals eat to help them grow and stay healthy: _____

13 _____ : a large tropical fruit with thick rough skin, sweet yellow flesh with a lot
    of juice and stiff leaves on top: _____

14 _____ : to make a liquid or other substance flow from a container in a continuous
    stream: _____

15 _____ : to put something together with something else so as to increase the size,
    number, amount, etc.: _____

16 _____ : a soft red fruit with very small yellow seeds on the surface, that grows
    on a low plant: _____

보기			
peel	cut	mix	add
tip	step	share	vitamin
pour	slice	excellent	stick
strawberry	pineapple	blender	smooth

※ 다음 우리말과 일치하도록 빈칸에 알맞은 것을 골라 쓰시오.

1 The _____ _____ of summer _____ here.
A. hot   B. are   C. days

2 How _____ we _____ _____?
A. stay   B. can   C. cool

3 _____ _____ ice pops _____!
A. together   B. make   C. let's

4 You _____: 1/2 pineapple, 2 kiwis, 1 cup _____ apple juice, ice pop _____
A. of   B. need   C. makers

5 Steps: _____ the pineapple _____ small _____.
A. into   B. cut   C. pieces

6 _____ the kiwis and _____ _____.
A. them   B. slice   C. peel

7 _____ the pineapple _____ _____ the blender.
A. pieces   B. into   C. put

8 _____ the apple _____.
A. juice   B. add

9 _____ _____ the mix is _____.
A. until   B. smooth   C. blend

10 _____ the mix _____ the ice pop _____.
A. makers   B. pour   C. into

11 _____ the kiwi _____.
A. slices   B. add

12 _____ the ice _____ makers.
A. pop   B. close

13 _____ them _____ the freezer _____ _____ three hours.
A. in   B. about   C. put   D. for

1 더운 여름날이 왔어요.

2 우리는 어떻게 시원하게 지낼 수 있을까요?

3 막대 아이스크림을 함께 만들어 봐요!

4 여러분은 필요해요: 파인애플 1/2개. 키위 2개, 사과 주스 1컵, 막대 아이스크림 틀

5 단계: 파인애플을 작은 조각으로 자르세요.

6 키위의 껍질을 벗기고 얇게 자르세요.

7 파인애플 조각들을 믹서에 넣으세요.

8 사과 주스를 첨가하세요.

9 혼합물이 덩어리 없이 골고루 잘 섞일 때까지 섞으세요.

10 혼합물을 막대 아이스크림 틀에 부으세요.

11 키위 조각을 추가하세요.

12 막대 아이스크림 틀을 닫으세요.

13 약 세 시간 동안 그것들을 냉동고에 넣으세요.

14 _____! _____ your summer _____ a _____!

A. stick   B. enjoy   C. on   D. finished

15 _____ _____

A. Tips   B. Health

16 Pineapples are an _____ _____ of _____ C.

A. source   B. excellent   B. vitamin

17 They have _____ _____ C _____ oranges.

A. vitamin   B. than   C. more

18 So _____ you have a _____, _____ pineapples.

A. try   B. when   C. cold

19 _____ Your _____!

A. Ideas   B. Share

20 How _____ you make _____ _____ ice pops?

A. own   B. your   C. will

21 _____ _____ ideas!

A. your   B. share

22 I _____ _____ kiwis and _____.

A. use   B. strawberries   C. will

23 I will _____ them _____ big _____.

A. into   B. cut   C. pieces

24 I will _____ them _____ the ice pop makers _____ apple juice.

A. into   B. with   C. put

25 I _____ my ice pops _____ pretty.

A. be   B. think   C. will

14 끝났어요! 막대 위의 여름을 맛보세요!

15 건강 조언들

16 파인애플은 비타민 C의 훌륭한 원천이에요.

17 파인애플에는 비타민 C가 오렌지보다 더 많이 들어 있어요.

18 그러니 감기에 걸리면 파인애플을 먹어 보세요.

19 여러분의 생각을 나누세요!

20 여러분은 어떻게 막대 아이스크림을 만들 건가요?

21 여러분의 생각을 나누세요!

22 저는 키위와 딸기를 사용할 거예요.

23 저는 그것들을 크게 자를 거예요.

24 그것들을 사과 주스와 함께 막대 아이스크림 틀에 넣을 거예요.

25 제 막대 아이스크림은 예쁠 것 같아요.

※ 다음 우리말과 일치하도록 빈칸에 알맞은 말을 쓰시오.

1 The _____ _____ _____ summer _____ here.

2 _____ _____ we _____ _____ ?

3 _____ _____ ice pops _____ !

4 You _____ :

   1/2 _____

   2 _____

   1 _____ of apple juice

   ice pop _____

5 _____

6 _____ the pineapple _____ _____ _____ .

7 _____ the kiwis and _____ _____ .

8 _____ the pineapple _____ _____ _____ _____ .

9 _____ the _____ _____ .

10 _____ _____ the mix is _____ .

11 _____ the mix _____ the _____ _____ _____ .

12 _____ the kiwi _____ .

13 _____ the _____ _____ _____ .

14 _____ _____ in the freezer _____ _____ three hours.

1 더운 여름날이 왔어요.

2 우리는 어떻게 시원하게 지낼 수 있을까요?

3 막대 아이스크림을 함께 만들어 봐요!

4 여러분은 필요해요:

   파인애플 1/2개

   키위 2개

   사과 주스 1컵

   막대 아이스크림 틀

5 단계

6 파인애플을 작은 조각으로 자르세요.

7 키위의 껍질을 벗기고 얇게 자르세요.

8 파인애플 조각들을 믹서에 넣으세요.

9 사과 주스를 첨가하세요.

10 혼합물이 덩어리 없이 골고루 잘 섞일 때까지 섞으세요.

11 혼합물을 막대 아이스크림 틀에 부으세요.

12 키위 조각을 추가하세요.

13 막대 아이스크림 틀을 닫으세요.

14 약 세 시간 동안 그것들을 냉동고에 넣으세요.

15 _____!

16 _____ your summer _____ _____ _____!

17 _____ _____

18 Pineapples _____ _____ _____ _____ _____ _____ C.

19 They have _____ _____ _____ _____ _____.

20 So _____ you _____ _____ _____, _____ pineapples.

21 _____ Your _____!

22 _____ _____ you _____ _____ _____ ice pops?

23 _____ _____ _____!

24 I will _____ kiwis and _____.

25 I will _____ _____ _____ _____.

26 I will _____ _____ _____ the ice pop makers _____ _____ _____.

27 _____ _____ my ice pops _____ _____ _____.

15 끝났어요!

16 막대 위의 여름을 맛보세요!

17 건강 조언들

18 파인애플은 비타민 C의 훌륭한 원천이에요.

19 파인애플에는 비타민 C가 오렌지보다 더 많이 들어 있어요.

20 그러니 감기에 걸리면 파인애플을 먹어 보세요.

21 여러분의 생각을 나누세요!

22 여러분은 어떻게 막대 아이스크림을 만들 건가요?

23 여러분의 생각을 나누세요!

24 저는 키위와 딸기를 사용할 거예요.

25 저는 그것들을 크게 자를 거예요.

26 그것들을 사과 주스와 함께 막대 아이스크림 틀에 넣을 거예요.

27 제 막대 아이스크림은 예쁠 것 같아요.

※ 다음 문장을 우리말로 쓰시오.

1 The hot days of summer are here.

➡ _____

2 How can we stay cool?

➡ _____

3 Let's make ice pops together!

➡ _____

4 You need: 1/2 pineapple, 2 kiwis, 1 cup of apple juice, ice pop makers

➡ _____

5 Steps

➡ _____

6 Cut the pineapple into small pieces.

➡ _____

7 Peel the kiwis and slice them.

➡ _____

8 Put the pineapple pieces into the blender.

➡ _____

9 Add the apple juice.

➡ _____

10 Blend until the mix is smooth.

➡ _____

11 Pour the mix into the ice pop makers.

➡ _____

12 Add the kiwi slices.

➡ _____

13 Close the ice pop makers.

➡ _____

14 Put them in the freezer for about three hours.

➡ _____

15 Finished!

➡ _____

16 Enjoy your summer on a stick!

➡ _____

17 Health Tips

➡ _____

18 Pineapples are an excellent source of vitamin C.

➡ _____

19 They have more vitamin C than oranges.

➡ _____

20 So when you have a cold, try pineapples.

➡ _____

21 Share Your Ideas!

➡ _____

22 How will you make your own ice pops?

➡ _____

23 Share your ideas!

➡ _____

24 I will use kiwis and strawberries.

➡ _____

25 I will cut them into big pieces.

➡ _____

26 I will put them into the ice pop makers with apple juice.

➡ _____

27 I think my ice pops will be pretty.

➡ _____

※ 다음 괄호 안의 단어들을 우리말에 맞도록 바르게 배열하시오.

1 (hot / the / of / days / here. / are / summer)

➡ _____

2 (can / how / cool? / stay / we)

➡ _____

3 (make / let's / pops / together! / ice)

➡ _____

4 (need: / you / pineapple, / 1/2 / kiwis, / 2 / of / cup / 1 / juice, / apple / makers / pop / ice)

➡ _____

5 (steps: / the / cut / into / pineapple / pieces. / small)

➡ _____

6 (the / peel / and / kiwis / them. / slice)

➡ _____

7 (the / put / pieces / pineapple / blender. / the / into)

➡ _____

8 (the / juice. / apple / add)

➡ _____

9 (the / until / blend / mix / smooth. / is)

➡ _____

10 (the / pour / into / mix / ice / the / makers. / pop)

➡ _____

11 (the / add / slices. / kiwi)

➡ _____

12 (the / close / pop / makers. / ice)

➡ _____

13 (them / put / the / in / freezer / about / for / hours. / three)

➡ _____

1 더운 여름날이 왔어요.

2 우리는 어떻게 시원하게 지낼 수 있을까요?

3 막대 아이스크림을 함께 만들어 봐요!

4 여러분은 필요해요: 파인애플 1/2개, 키위 2개, 사과 주스 1컵, 막대 아이스크림 틀

5 단계: 파인애플을 작은 조각으로 자르세요.

6 키위의 껍질을 벗기고 얇게 자르세요.

7 파인애플 조각들을 믹서에 넣으세요.

8 사과 주스를 첨가하세요.

9 혼합물이 덩어리 없이 골고루 잘 섞일 때까지 섞으세요.

10 혼합물을 막대 아이스크림 틀에 부으세요.

11 키위 조각을 추가하세요.

12 막대 아이스크림 틀을 닫으세요.

13 약 세 시간 동안 그것들을 냉동고에 넣으세요.

14 (finished! // your / enjoy / on / summer / stick! / a)

➡ _____

15 (Tips / Health)

➡ _____

16 (are / pineapples / excellent / an / source / C. / of / vitamin)

➡ _____

17 (have / they / vitamin / more / oranges. / than / C)

➡ _____

18 (when / so / have / you / cold, / a / pineapples. / try)

➡ _____

19 (Ideas! / Your / Share)

➡ _____

20 (will / how / you / make / own / your / pops? / ice)

➡ _____

21 (your / share / ideas!)

➡ _____

22 (will / I / use / kiwis / strawberries. / and)

➡ _____

23 (will / I / cut / into / them / pieces. / big)

➡ _____

24 (will / I / them / put / the / into / pop / ice / with / makers / juice. / apple)

➡ _____

25 (think / I / ice / my / pops / pretty. / be / will)

➡ _____

14 끝났어요! 막대 위의 여름을 맛보세요!

15 건강 조언들

16 파인애플은 비타민 C의 훌륭한 원천이에요.

17 파인애플에는 비타민 C가 오렌지보다 더 많이 들어 있어요.

18 그러니 감기에 걸리면 파인애플을 먹어 보세요.

19 여러분의 생각을 나누세요!

20 여러분은 어떻게 막대 아이스크림을 만들 건가요?

21 여러분의 생각을 나누세요!

22 저는 키위와 딸기를 사용할 거예요.

23 저는 그것들을 크게 자를 거예요.

24 그것들을 사과 주스와 함께 막대 아이스크림 틀에 넣을 거예요.

25 제 막대 아이스크림은 예쁠 것 같아요.

※ 다음 우리말을 영어로 쓰시오.

1 더운 여름날이 왔어요.

➡ _____

2 우리는 어떻게 시원하게 지낼 수 있을까요?

➡ _____

3 막대 아이스크림을 함께 만들어 봐요!

➡ _____

4 여러분은 필요해요: 파인애플 1/2개, 키위 2개, 사과 주스 1컵, 막대 아이스크림 틀

➡ _____

5 단계: 파인애플을 작은 조각으로 자르세요.

➡ _____

6 키위의 껍질을 벗기고 얇게 자르세요.

➡ _____

7 파인애플 조각들을 믹서에 넣으세요.

➡ _____

8 사과 주스를 첨가하세요.

➡ _____

9 혼합물이 덩어리 없이 골고루 잘 섞일 때까지 섞으세요.

➡ _____

10 혼합물을 막대 아이스크림 틀에 부으세요.

➡ _____

11 키위 조각을 추가하세요.

➡ _____

12 막대 아이스크림 틀을 닫으세요.

➡ _____

13 약 세 시간 동안 그것들을 냉동고에 넣으세요.

➡ _____

14 끝났어요! 막대 위의 여름을 맛보세요!

➡ _____

15 건강 조언들

➡ _____

16 파인애플은 비타민 C의 훌륭한 원천이에요.

➡ _____

17 파인애플에는 비타민 C가 오렌지보다 더 많이 들어 있어요.

➡ _____

18 그러니 감기에 걸리면 파인애플을 먹어 보세요.

➡ _____

19 여러분의 생각을 나누세요!

➡ _____

20 여러분은 어떻게 막대 아이스크림을 만들 건가요?

➡ _____

21 여러분의 생각을 나누세요!

➡ _____

22 저는 키위와 딸기를 사용할 거예요.

➡ _____

23 저는 그것들을 크게 자를 거예요.

➡ _____

24 그것들을 사과 주스와 함께 막대 아이스크림 틀에 넣을 거예요.

➡ _____

25 제 막대 아이스크림은 예쁠 것 같아요.

➡ _____

※ 다음 영어를 우리말로 쓰시오.

01 arrow

02 neighborhood

03 appear

04 dark

05 solve

06 decorate

07 far

08 firework

09 follow

10 gather

11 shape

12 amazing

13 huge

14 last

15 advertise

16 competition

17 festival

18 sled

19 almost

20 completely

21 post

22 musician

23 celebrate

24 outdoor

25 chase

26 pile

27 artwork

28 powder

29 adult

30 colorful

31 hold

32 throw

33 hometown

34 bakery

35 each other

36 out of hand

37 from beginning to end

38 between A and B

39 go on

40 because of

41 more and more

42 on one's right

43 in front of

※ 다음 우리말을 영어로 쓰시오.

01 빵집, 제과점		22 장식하다
02 축하하다, 기념하다		23 모이다, 모으다
03 형형색색의		24 광고하다
04 퍼레이드, 행진		25 해결하다
05 (시간이) 걸리다		26 지속하다
06 ~ 동안		27 나타나다
07 돛		28 근처, 이웃, 인근
08 예술 작품		29 대회, 시합, 경쟁
09 뒤쫓다		30 불꽃놀이
10 개최하다		31 거대한
11 고향		32 화살
12 배, 선박		33 완전히
13 가로지르다		34 따르다
14 라이브의, 실황인		35 더욱 더
15 가까운, 가까이에 있는		36 내리다
16 가루		37 서로
17 야외의		38 ~ 앞에
18 블록, 구획		39 ~ 때문에
19 더미		40 ~ 옆에
20 성인, 어른		41 지속되다, 계속되다
21 던지다		42 A와 B 사이에
		43 처음부터 끝까지

※ 다음 영영풀이에 알맞은 단어를 <보기>에서 골라 쓴 후, 우리말 뜻을 쓰시오.

1 _____ : to move something or someone to a higher position: _____

2 _____ : a fully grown person: _____

3 _____ : to follow and try to catch: _____

4 _____ : objects produced by artists: _____

5 _____ : an event or contest in which people compete: _____

6 _____ : a day or period of celebration: _____

7 _____ : a small vehicle used for sliding over snow: _____

8 _____ : to continue in time: _____

9 _____ : the city or town where you were born or grew up: _____

10 _____ : to come together to form a group: _____

11 _____ : to have a meeting, competition, conversation, etc.: _____

12 _____ : a mass of something that has been placed somewhere: _____

13 _____ : to tell the public about goods to make people buy them: _____

14 _____ : to make something into a particular shape: _____

15 _____ : to do something special for an important event, holiday, etc.: _____

16 _____ : to make something look more beautiful by putting things on it:

_____

보기			
sled	chase	artwork	lift
decorate	pile	hometown	competition
adult	celebrate	advertise	last
shape	hold	gather	festival

※ 다음 우리말과 일치하도록 빈칸에 알맞은 말을 쓰시오.

Listen and Speak 1-A

Sora: Excuse me. _____ _____ _____ _____ _____

_____ _____?

Tom: Oh, the library? _____ the street and _____ _____ two

blocks. Then _____ _____ _____.

Sora: _____ _____ very much.

Sora: 실례합니다. 도서관까지 어떻게
가나요?
Tom: 아, 도서관이요? 길을 건너서 두
구역을 곧장 가세요. 그런 다음 왼
쪽으로 도세요.
Sora: 정말 고마워요.

Listen and Speak 1-B

(*A phone rings.*)

Minsu: Hi, Emma. _____ _____?

Emma: Hey, Minsu. _____ you _____ _____ _____?

Minsu: Yes. _____ _____ you _____?

Emma: Well, how _____ _____ _____ together?

Minsu: Sure.

Emma: _____ _____ the new _____ _____, Ming's. It's

_____ the school.

Minsu: Okay. _____ _____ _____ _____ _____

_____ _____?

Emma: _____ _____ from the school and _____ _____ to

Green Street. _____ _____ _____, and the restaurant

will _____ _____ _____ _____ _____.

Minsu: _____ _____. _____ _____ _____ 12 o'clock.

Emma: Wonderful. _____ _____ _____.

(전화벨이 울린다.)
Minsu: 안녕, Emma. 잘 지내니?
Emma: 안녕, 민수야. 이번 토요일에 한
가하니?
Minsu: 응. 왜 묻는 거니?
Emma: 음, 함께 점심 먹는 게 어떠니?
Minsu: 좋아.
Emma: Ming's라는 새로 생긴 중국 음
식점에 가 보자. 학교 근처에 있어.
Minsu: 좋아. 학교에서 거기까지 어떻게
가니?
Emma: 학교에서 나와서 Green Street
까지 곧장 가. 왼쪽으로 돌면 음
식점이 네 왼쪽에 있을 거야.
Minsu: 알겠어. 12시에 만나자.
Emma: 좋아. 그때 보자.

Listen and Speak 1-C

A: _____ _____. How _____ I _____ _____ the post office?

B: _____ _____ to 1st Street and _____ _____ _____. It

_____ _____ _____ _____ _____ _____.

A: _____ it _____ _____ here?

B: _____, it's _____.

A: _____ _____ very much.

A: 실례합니다. 우체국에 어떻게 갈 수
있나요?
B: 1st Street까지 곧장 가서 오른쪽으로
도세요. 그것은 오른쪽에 있을 거예요.
A: 여기서 먼가요?
B: 아니요, 멀지 않아요.
A: 정말 고마워요.

Listen and Speak 2-A

Amy: Jinho, _____ _____. We're _____ _____ _____ _____ _____ the movie.

Jinho: Okay. _____ _____ _____ _____ _____ _____ _____ _____ _____ _____?

Amy: It will _____ _____ 15 minutes _____ _____.

Jinho: All right. I'm _____ _____.

Amy: 진호야, 서둘러. 우리 영화 시간에 늦겠어.
Jinho: 응. 영화관까지 가는 데 시간이 얼마나 걸릴까?
Amy: 버스로 대략 15분 정도 걸릴 거야.
Jinho: 알겠어. 나 거의 준비됐어.

Listen and Speak 2-B

Andy: I'm so _____ _____ the school festival _____ _____.

Mike: _____, _____. What _____ we _____ it, Andy?

Andy: How _____ _____ posters?

Mike: Great idea. We _____ _____ _____ _____ in our _____.

Andy: Right. _____ _____ make them?

Mike: Well, it will _____ _____ _____ _____ _____.

Andy: Okay, _____ _____ many people _____ _____ _____.

Andy: 나는 이번 금요일 학교 축제가 정말 기대돼.
Mike: 나도. 축제를 광고하기 위해 무엇을 할 수 있을까, Andy?
Andy: 포스터를 만들면 어떨까?
Mike: 좋은 생각이야. 이 근방에 포스터를 붙일 수 있겠다.
Andy: 맞아. 포스터를 만드는 데 시간이 얼마나 걸릴까?
Mike: 음, 대략 세 시간 정도 걸릴 거야.
Andy: 좋아, 많은 사람들이 축제에 왔으면 좋겠다.

Real Life Talk

Man: _____ me. _____ _____ I _____ _____ _____ Suwon Hwaseong from here?

Mina: It's _____. Do you see the bus stop _____ _____?

Man: Yes, _____ _____.

Mina: _____ the No. 11 bus and _____ _____ at the sixth stop.

Man: _____ _____ _____ _____ _____ _____?

Mina: It will _____ _____ _____ _____ _____.

Man: Thank you _____ _____.

Mina: No _____. _____ you _____ there for _____ _____?

Man: Yes. I heard _____ _____ _____ _____ _____.

Mina: _____ _____ you _____ _____ _____.

Man: 실례합니다. 여기에서 수원 화성까지 어떻게 가나요?
Mina: 쉬워요. 저쪽에 버스 정류장 보이세요?
Man: 네, 보여요.
Mina: 11번 버스를 타서 여섯 번째 정류장에서 내리세요.
Man: 그곳까지 가는 데 시간이 얼마나 걸릴까요?
Mina: 대략 20분 정도 걸릴 거예요.
Man: 정말 고마워요.
Mina: 별말씀을요. 그곳에 축제 때문에 가시는 건가요?
Man: 네. 그 축제가 무척 재미있다고 들었어요.
Mina: 즐거운 시간 보내길 바라요.

※ 다음 우리말에 맞도록 대화를 영어로 쓰시오.

Listen and Speak 1-A

Sora: _____

Tom: _____

Sora: _____

Sora: 실례합니다. 도서관까지 어떻게 가나요?
Tom: 아, 도서관이요? 길을 건너서 두 구역을 곧장 가세요. 그런 다음 왼쪽으로 도세요.
Sora: 정말 고마워요.

Listen and Speak 1-B

(*A phone rings.*)

Minsu: _____

Emma: _____

Minsu: _____

Emma: _____

Minsu: _____

Emma: _____

Minsu: _____

Emma: _____

_____

Minsu: _____

Emma: _____

(전화벨이 울린다.)
Minsu: 안녕, Emma. 잘 지내니?
Emma: 안녕, 민수야. 이번 토요일에 한가하니?
Minsu: 응. 왜 묻는 거니?
Emma: 음, 함께 점심 먹는 게 어떠니?
Minsu: 좋아.
Emma: Ming's라는 새로 생긴 중국 음식점에 가 보자. 학교 근처에 있어.
Minsu: 좋아. 학교에서 거기까지 어떻게 가니?
Emma: 학교에서 나와서 Green Street까지 곧장 가. 왼쪽으로 돌면 음식점이 네 왼쪽에 있을 거야.
Minsu: 알겠어. 12시에 만나자.
Emma: 좋아. 그때 보자.

Listen and Speak 1-C

A: _____

B: _____

A: _____

B: _____

A: _____

A: 실례합니다. 우체국에 어떻게 갈 수 있나요?
B: 1st Street까지 곧장 가서 오른쪽으로 도세요. 그것은 오른쪽에 있을 거예요.
A: 여기서 먼가요?
B: 아니요, 멀지 않아요.
A: 정말 고마워요.

Listen and Speak 2-A

Amy: _____

Jinho: _____

Amy: _____

Jinho: _____

Amy: 진호야, 서둘러. 우리 영화 시간에 늦겠어.
Jinho: 응. 영화관까지 가는 데 시간이 얼마나 걸릴까?
Amy: 버스로 대략 15분 정도 걸릴 거야.
Jinho: 알겠어. 나 거의 준비됐어.

Listen and Speak 2-B

Andy: _____

Mike: _____

Andy: _____

Mike: _____

Andy: _____

Mike: _____

Andy: _____

Andy: 나는 이번 금요일 학교 축제가 정말 기대돼.
Mike: 나도. 축제를 광고하기 위해 무엇을 할 수 있을까, Andy?
Andy: 포스터를 만들면 어떨까?
Mike: 좋은 생각이야. 이 근방에 포스터를 붙일 수 있겠다.
Andy: 맞아. 포스터를 만드는 데 시간이 얼마나 걸릴까?
Mike: 음, 대략 세 시간 정도 걸릴 거야.
Andy: 좋아, 많은 사람들이 축제에 왔으면 좋겠다.

Real Life Talk

Man: _____

Mina: _____

Man: _____

Mina: _____

Man: _____

Mina: _____

Man: _____

Mina: _____

Man: _____

Mina: _____

Man: 실례합니다. 여기에서 수원 화성까지 어떻게 가나요?
Mina: 쉬워요. 저쪽에 버스 정류장 보이세요?
Man: 네, 보여요.
Mina: 11번 버스를 타서 여섯 번째 정류장에서 내리세요.
Man: 그곳까지 가는 데 시간이 얼마나 걸릴까요?
Mina: 대략 20분 정도 걸릴 거에요.
Man: 정말 고마워요.
Mina: 별말씀을요. 그곳에 축제 때문에 가시는 건가요?
Man: 네. 그 축제가 무척 재미있다고 들었어요.
Mina: 즐거운 시간 보내길 바라요.

※ 다음 우리말과 일치하도록 빈칸에 알맞은 것을 골라 쓰시오.

1 Holi, the _____ of _____
A. Colors   B. Festival

2 Amala _____ _____, India
A. from   B. Delhi

3 Holi is the _____ _____ festival in _____ country.
A. popular   B. my   C. most

4 It _____ _____ _____ March.
A. usually   B. is   C. in

5 _____ the festival, we _____ goodbye to cold winter and _____ to warm spring.
A. say   B. during   C. hello

6 We _____ the festival _____ _____ two days.
A. everywhere   B. for   C. celebrate

7 _____ the first day, people _____ _____ a big fire _____ night and sing and dance.
A. around   B. at   C. on   D. gather

8 The _____ event _____ the _____ day.
A. next   B. main   C. begins

9 Children and adults _____ _____ _____ with *gulal*.
A. each   B. chase   C. other

10 _____ is *gulal*? It is blue, yellow, _____ and pink _____.
A. powder   B. what   C. green

11 It's a lot of fun to _____ _____ and _____ colorful powder _____ everyone.
A. throw   B. run   C. at   D. around

12 We _____ _____ street _____!
A. join   B. parades   C. also

13 _____ _____ Festival
A. Nights   B. White

14 Victor _____ St. _____, _____
A. Russia   B. Petersburg   C. from

15 _____ you _____ _____ the *White Nights*?
A. heard   B. have   C. of

16 _____ summer, this _____ thing _____ in my hometown.
A. amazing   B. every   C. happens

---

1 홀리, 색의 축제

2 인도, 델리의 Amala

3 '홀리'는 우리나라에서 가장 인기 있는 축제예요.

4 그것은 보통 3월에 있어요.

5 축제 기간 동안에, 우리는 추운 겨울에게 작별 인사를 하고 따뜻한 봄을 맞는 인사를 해요.

6 우리는 이틀 동안 어디서든 축제를 기념해요.

7 첫째 날, 사람들은 밤에 큰 모닥불 주변에 모여 노래하고 춤을 춰요.

8 주요 행사는 다음 날에 시작돼요.

9 어린이들과 어른들이 'gulal'을 지니고 서로를 쫓아다녀요.

10 'gulal'이 무엇이냐고요? 그것은 파랑, 노랑, 초록, 분홍의 가루예요.

11 주변을 뛰어다니며 형형색색의 가루를 모든 사람들에게 던지는 것은 정말 재미있어요.

12 우리는 거리 행진에도 참가해요!

13 백야 축제

14 러시아, 상트페테르부르크의 Victor

15 '백야'에 대해 들어 봤나요?

16 매년 여름, 이 놀라운 일이 나의 고향에서 벌어져요.

17 The night sky does not _____ _____ _____.
A. completely   B. get   C. dark

18 _____ that time, we _____ the White Nights Festival.
A. hold   B. during

19 It usually starts _____ May and _____ for _____ a month.
A. lasts   B. about   C. in

20 During the festival, _____ is a ballet or an opera _____ night.
A. every   B. there   C. almost

21 The _____ _____ event is the Scarlet Sails _____.
A. celebration   B. popular   C. most

22 A boat _____ red sails slowly _____ the river.
A. appears   B. with   C. on

23 Soon, fireworks _____ and a water show _____.
A. follows   B. begin

24 You can _____ musicians _____ beautiful live music.
A. playing   B. hear   C. also

25 _____ Snow _____
A. Festival   B. Kiruna

26 Ebba _____ _____, Sweden
A. Kiruna   B. from

27 Winter is my _____ season _____ the Kiruna Snow Festival.
A. because   B. favorite   C. of

28 The festival _____ in the _____ week of January and _____ _____ for five or six days.
A. on   B. last   C. goes   D. starts

29 The _____ _____ is the snow design _____.
A. competition   B. event   C. largest

30 The artists _____ huge piles of snow _____ animals, buildings, and _____ beautiful artworks.
A. shape   B. other   C. into

31 People _____ the artists _____ their works _____ beginning _____ end.
A. shaping   B. to   C. from   D. watch

32 My favorite _____ is the dog _____ _____.
A. sled   B. activity   C. ride

33 It is amazing _____ fly _____ a world of snow _____ a dog sled.
A. on   B. through   C. to

---

17 밤하늘이 완전히 어두워지지 않아요.

18 그 시기 동안, 우리는 백야 축제를 열어요.

19 축제는 보통 5월에 시작되고 약 한 달 동안 지속돼요.

20 축제 기간 동안 거의 매일 밤 발레나 오페라 공연이 있어요.

21 가장 인기 있는 행사는 '붉은 돛 축하 행사'예요.

22 빨간 돛을 단 배가 강 위에 서서히 나타나요.

23 곧 불꽃놀이가 시작되고 물 쇼가 이어져요.

24 또한 여러분은 음악가들이 아름다운 라이브 음악을 연주하는 것을 들을 수 있어요.

25 키루나 눈 축제

26 스웨덴, 키루나의 Ebba

27 겨울은 키루나 눈 축제 때문에 내가 가장 좋아하는 계절이에요.

28 축제는 1월 마지막 주에 시작해서 5일이나 6일 동안 계속돼요.

29 가장 큰 행사는 '눈 디자인 대회'예요.

30 미술가들이 거대한 눈 덩어리를 동물, 건물, 다른 아름다운 작품의 모양으로 만들어요.

31 사람들은 미술가들이 그들의 작품을 만드는 것을 처음부터 끝까지 지켜봐요.

32 내가 가장 좋아하는 활동은 개썰매 타기예요.

33 개썰매를 타고 눈 세상을 날아가는 것은 정말 놀라워요.

※ 다음 우리말과 일치하도록 빈칸에 알맞은 말을 쓰시오.

1 Holi, the _____ _____ _____

2 Amala _____ _____ , _____

3 Holi is _____ _____ _____ _____ in my country.

4 It _____ _____ _____ _____ .

5 _____ the festival, we _____ _____ to cold winter and _____ to _____ _____ .

6 We _____ the festival everywhere _____ _____ _____ .

7 _____ the first day, people _____ _____ a big fire _____ and _____ _____ .

8 The _____ event _____ _____ _____ _____ .

9 Children and adults _____ _____ _____ _____ *gulal*.

10 _____ is *gulal*? It is blue, yellow, green and pink _____ .

11 It's a lot of fun _____ _____ _____ and _____ colorful powder _____ _____ .

12 We _____ _____ _____ _____ !

13 _____ _____ Festival

14 Victor _____ St. Petersburg, _____

15 _____ _____ _____ _____ the *White Nights*?

16 Every summer, this _____ thing _____ in my hometown.

---

1 홀리, 색의 축제

2 인도, 델리의 Amala

3 '홀리'는 우리나라에서 가장 인기 있는 축제예요.

4 그것은 보통 3월에 있어요.

5 축제 기간 동안에, 우리는 추운 겨울에게 작별 인사를 하고 따뜻한 봄을 맞는 인사를 해요.

6 우리는 이틀 동안 어디서든 축제를 기념해요.

7 첫째 날, 사람들은 밤에 큰 모닥불 주변에 모여 노래하고 춤을 춰요.

8 주요 행사는 다음 날에 시작돼요.

9 어린이들과 어른들이 'gulal'을 지니고 서로를 쫓아다녀요.

10 'gulal'이 무엇이냐고요? 그것은 파랑, 노랑, 초록, 분홍의 가루예요.

11 주변을 뛰어다니며 형형색색의 가루를 모든 사람들에게 던지는 것은 정말 재미있어요.

12 우리는 거리 행진에도 참가해요!

13 백야 축제

14 러시아, 상트페테르부르크의 Victor

15 '백야'에 대해 들어 봤나요?

16 매년 여름, 이 놀라운 일이 나의 고향에서 벌어져요.

17 The night sky _____ _____ _____ _____ _____ .

18 _____ that time, we _____ the White Nights Festival.

19 It _____ _____ _____ May and _____ _____ _____ a month.

20 _____ the festival, _____ _____ a ballet or an opera _____ _____ _____ .

21 The _____ _____ event is the Scarlet Sails _____ .

22 A boat with red sails slowly _____ _____ _____ .

23 Soon, _____ _____ and a water show _____ .

24 You can _____ musicians _____ beautiful live music.

25 Kiruna _____ _____

26 Ebba _____ _____ , _____

27 Winter is _____ _____ _____ _____ _____ the Kiruna Snow Festival.

28 The festival _____ _____ _____ _____ _____ of January and _____ _____ _____ five or six days.

29 _____ _____ is the snow design _____ .

30 The artists _____ _____ of snow _____ animals, buildings, and _____ beautiful artworks.

31 People _____ the artists _____ their works _____ _____ _____ .

32 My _____ is the _____ _____ .

33 _____ is _____ _____ a world of snow _____ a dog sled.

17	밤하늘이 완전히 어두워지지 않아요.
18	그 시기 동안, 우리는 백야 축제를 열어요.
19	축제는 보통 5월에 시작되고 약 한 달 동안 지속돼요.
20	축제 기간 동안 거의 매일 밤 발레나 오페라 공연이 있어요.
21	가장 인기 있는 행사는 '붉은 돛 축하 행사'예요.
22	빨간 돛을 단 배가 강 위에 서서히 나타나요.
23	곧 불꽃놀이가 시작되고 물 쇼가 이어져요.
24	또한 여러분은 음악가들이 아름다운 라이브 음악을 연주하는 것을 들을 수 있어요.
25	키루나 눈 축제
26	스웨덴, 키루나의 Ebba
27	겨울은 키루나 눈 축제 때문에 내가 가장 좋아하는 계절이에요.
28	축제는 1월 마지막 주에 시작해서 5일이나 6일 동안 계속돼요.
29	가장 큰 행사는 '눈 디자인 대회'예요.
30	미술가들이 거대한 눈 덩어리를 동물, 건물, 다른 아름다운 작품의 모양으로 만들어요.
31	사람들은 미술가들이 그들의 작품을 만드는 것을 처음부터 끝까지 지켜봐요.
32	내가 가장 좋아하는 활동은 개썰매 타기예요.
33	개썰매를 타고 눈 세상을 날아가는 것은 정말 놀라워요.

※ 다음 문장을 우리말로 쓰시오.

1 Holi, the Festival of Colors

➡ _____

2 Amala from Delhi, India

➡ _____

3 Holi is the most popular festival in my country.

➡ _____

4 It is usually in March.

➡ _____

5 During the festival, we say goodbye to cold winter and hello to warm spring.

➡ _____

6 We celebrate the festival everywhere for two days.

➡ _____

7 On the first day, people gather around a big fire at night and sing and dance.

➡ _____

8 The main event begins the next day.

➡ _____

9 Children and adults chase each other with *gulal*.

➡ _____

10 What is *gulal*? It is blue, yellow, green and pink powder.

➡ _____

11 It's a lot of fun to run around and throw colorful powder at everyone.

➡ _____

12 We also join street parades!

➡ _____

13 White Nights Festival

➡ _____

14 Victor from St. Petersburg, Russia

➡ _____

15 Have you heard of the *White Nights*?

➡ _____

16 Every summer, this amazing thing happens in my hometown.

➡ _____

17 The night sky does not get completely dark.

➡ _____

18 During that time, we hold the White Nights Festival.

➡ _____

19 It usually starts in May and lasts for about a month.

➡ _____

20 During the festival, there is a ballet or an opera almost every night.

➡ _____

21 The most popular event is the Scarlet Sails celebration.

➡ _____

22 A boat with red sails slowly appears on the river.

➡ _____

23 Soon, fireworks begin and a water show follows.

➡ _____

24 You can also hear musicians playing beautiful live music.

➡ _____

25 Kiruna Snow Festival

➡ _____

26 Ebba from Kiruna, Sweden

➡ _____

27 Winter is my favorite season because of the Kiruna Snow Festival.

➡ _____

28 The festival starts in the last week of January and goes on for five or six days.

➡ _____

29 The largest event is the snow design competition.

➡ _____

30 The artists shape huge piles of snow into animals, buildings, and other beautiful artworks.

➡ _____

31 People watch the artists shaping their works from beginning to end.

➡ _____

32 My favorite activity is the dog sled ride.

➡ _____

33 It is amazing to fly through a world of snow on a dog sled.

➡ _____

※ 다음 괄호 안의 단어들을 우리말에 맞도록 바르게 배열하시오.

1 (the / Colors / Holi, / of / Festival)
➡ _____

2 (from / Amala / India / Delhi,)
➡ _____

3 (is / Holi / most / the / festival / popular / country. / my / in)
➡ _____

4 (is / it / usually / March. / in)
➡ _____

5 (the / during / festival, / say / we / to / goodbye / cold / and / winter / spring. / warm / to / hello)
➡ _____

6 (celebrate / we / festival / the / for / everywhere / days. / two)
➡ _____

7 (the / day, / on / first / people / around / gather / fire / big / a / night / at / and / dance. / and / sing)
➡ _____

8 (main / the / begins / event / day. / next / the)
➡ _____

9 (and / children / chase / adults / other / each / *gulal*. / with)
➡ _____

10 (*gulal*? / is / what // is / it / blue, / green / yellow, / and / powder. / pink)
➡ _____

11 (a / it's / of / lot / fun / run / to / around / and / colorful / throw / everyone. / at / powder)
➡ _____

12 (join / also / we / parades! / street)
➡ _____

13 (Nights / White / Festival)
➡ _____

14 (from / Victor / Russia / St. Petersburg)
➡ _____

15 (you / have / of / heard / *Nights*? / *White* / the)
➡ _____

16 (summer, / every / amazing / this / happens / thing / hometown. / my / in)
➡ _____

1 홀리, 색의 축제

2 인도, 델리의 Amala

3 '홀리'는 우리나라에서 가장 인기 있는 축제예요.

4 그것은 보통 3월에 있어요.

5 축제 기간 동안에, 우리는 추운 겨울에게 작별 인사를 하고 따뜻한 봄을 맞는 인사를 해요.

6 우리는 이틀 동안 어디서든 축제를 기념해요.

7 첫째 날, 사람들은 밤에 큰 모닥불 주변에 모여 노래하고 춤을 춰요.

8 주요 행사는 다음 날에 시작돼요.

9 어린이들과 어른들이 'gulal'을 지니고 서로를 쫓아다녀요.

10 'gulal'이 무엇이냐고요? 그것은 파랑, 노랑, 초록, 분홍의 가루예요.

11 주변을 뛰어다니며 형형색색의 가루를 모든 사람들에게 던지는 것은 정말 재미있어요.

12 우리는 거리 행진에도 참가해요!

13 백야 축제

14 러시아, 상트페테르부르크의 Victor

15 '백야'에 대해 들어 봤나요?

16 매년 여름, 이 놀라운 일이 나의 고향에서 벌어져요.

17 (night / sky / the / not / does / completely / dark. / get)

➡ _____

18 (that / during / time, / hold / we / the / White / Festival. / Nights)

➡ _____

19 (usually / it / in / starts / May / and / for / lasts / about / month. / a)

➡ _____

20 (the / festival, / during / is / there / ballet / a / or / opera / an / night. / every / almost)

➡ _____

21 (most / the / is / event / popular / Scarlet / the / celebration. / Sails)

➡ _____

22 (boat / a / red / with / sails / appears / slowly / river. / the / on)

➡ _____

23 (fireworks / soon, / begin / and / water / a / follows. / show)

➡ _____

24 (can / you / hear / also / playing / musicians / music. / live / beautiful)

➡ _____

25 (Festival / Snow / Kiruna)

➡ _____

26 (from / Sweden / Ebba / Kiruna,)

➡ _____

27 (is / winter / favorite / season / my / of / because / the / Festival. / Snow / Kiruna)

➡ _____

28 (festival / starts / the / in / last / the / week / January / of / and / on / goes / for / days. / six / or / five)

➡ _____

_____

29 (largest / the / event / is / snow / the / competition. / design)

➡ _____

30 (artists / shape / the / piles / huge / snow / of / animals, / into / buildings, / and / artworks. / beautiful / other)

➡ _____

_____

31 (watch / people / artists / the / shaping / works / their / from / end. / to / beginning)

➡ _____

32 (favorite / my / activity / is / dog / the / ride. / sled)

➡ _____

33 (is / it / amazing / fly / to / a / through / world / snow / of / on / sled. / dog / a)

➡ _____

17 밤하늘이 완전히 어두워지지 않아요.

18 그 시기 동안, 우리는 백야 축제를 열어요.

19 축제는 보통 5월에 시작되고 약한 달 동안 지속돼요.

20 축제 기간 동안 거의 매일 밤 발레나 오페라 공연이 있어요.

21 가장 인기 있는 행사는 '붉은 돛 축하 행사'예요.

22 빨간 돛을 단 배가 강 위에 서서히 나타나요.

23 곧 불꽃놀이가 시작되고 물 쇼가 이어져요.

24 또한 여러분은 음악가들이 아름다운 라이브 음악을 연주하는 것을 들을 수 있어요.

25 키루나 눈 축제

26 스웨덴, 키루나의 Ebba

27 겨울은 키루나 눈 축제 때문에 내가 가장 좋아하는 계절이에요.

28 축제는 1월 마지막 주에 시작해서 5일이나 6일 동안 계속돼요.

29 가장 큰 행사는 '눈 디자인 대회'예요.

30 미술가들이 거대한 눈 덩어리를 동물, 건물, 다른 아름다운 작품의 모양으로 만들어요.

31 사람들은 미술가들이 그들의 작품을 만드는 것을 처음부터 끝까지 지켜봐요.

32 내가 가장 좋아하는 활동은 개썰매 타기예요.

33 개썰매를 타고 눈 세상을 날아가는 것은 정말 놀라워요.

※ 다음 우리말을 영어로 쓰시오.

1 홀리, 색의 축제

➡ _____

2 인도, 델리의 Amala

➡ _____

3 '홀리'는 우리나라에서 가장 인기 있는 축제예요.

➡ _____

4 그것은 보통 3월에 있어요.

➡ _____

5 축제 기간 동안에, 우리는 추운 겨울에게 작별 인사를 하고 따뜻한 봄을 맞는 인사를 해요.

➡ _____

6 우리는 이틀 동안 어디서든 축제를 기념해요.

➡ _____

7 첫째 날, 사람들은 밤에 큰 모닥불 주변에 모여 노래하고 춤을 춰요.

➡ _____

8 주요 행사는 다음 날에 시작돼요.

➡ _____

9 어린이들과 어른들이 'gulal'을 지니고 서로를 쫓아다녀요.

➡ _____

10 'gulal'이 무엇이냐고요? 그것은 파랑, 노랑, 초록, 분홍의 가루예요.

➡ _____

11 주변을 뛰어다니며 형형색색의 가루를 모든 사람들에게 던지는 것은 정말 재미있어요.

➡ _____

12 우리는 거리 행진에도 참가해요!

➡ _____

13 백야 축제

➡ _____

14 러시아, 상트페테르부르크의 Victor

➡ _____

15 '백야'에 대해 들어 봤나요?

➡ _____

16 매년 여름, 이 놀라운 일이 나의 고향에서 벌어져요.

➡ _____

17 밤하늘이 완전히 어두워지지 않아요.

➡ _____

18 그 시기 동안, 우리는 백야 축제를 열어요.

➡ _____

19 축제는 보통 5월에 시작되고 약 한 달 동안 지속돼요.

➡ _____

20 축제 기간 동안 거의 매일 밤 발레나 오페라 공연이 있어요.

➡ _____

21 가장 인기 있는 행사는 '붉은 돛 축하 행사'예요.

➡ _____

22 빨간 돛을 단 배가 강 위에 서서히 나타나요.

➡ _____

23 곧 불꽃놀이가 시작되고 물 쇼가 이어져요.

➡ _____

24 또한 여러분은 음악가들이 아름다운 라이브 음악을 연주하는 것을 들을 수 있어요.

➡ _____

25 키루나 눈 축제

➡ _____

26 스웨덴, 키루나의 Ebba

➡ _____

27 겨울은 키루나 눈 축제 때문에 내가 가장 좋아하는 계절이에요.

➡ _____

28 축제는 1월 마지막 주에 시작해서 5일이나 6일 동안 계속돼요.

➡ _____

29 가장 큰 행사는 '눈 디자인 대회'예요.

➡ _____

30 미술가들이 거대한 눈 덩어리를 동물, 건물, 다른 아름다운 작품의 모양으로 만들어요.

➡ _____

31 사람들은 미술가들이 그들의 작품을 만드는 것을 처음부터 끝까지 지켜봐요.

➡ _____

32 내가 가장 좋아하는 활동은 개썰매 타기예요.

➡ _____

33 개썰매를 타고 눈 세상을 날아가는 것은 정말 놀라워요.

➡ _____

※ 다음 우리말과 일치하도록 빈칸에 알맞은 말을 쓰시오.

Listen and Speak 2 - C

1. A: Chris, what _____ you _____ for the _____ _____?

2. B: I'll _____ _____.

3. A: Great idea. _____ _____ will it _____ _____ make them?

4. B: _____ it'll _____ _____ _____ _____.

1. A: Chris, 학급 파티를 위해 무엇을 할 거니?
2. B: 나는 샌드위치를 만들 거야.
3. A: 좋은 생각이야. 그것들을 만드는 데 얼마가 걸릴까?
4. B: 아마도 약 한 시간 정도 걸릴 거야.

Think and Write

1. I _____ Gangneung

2. I _____ _____ Gangneung.

3. _____ _____ beautiful beaches in my _____.

4. It's _____ _____ _____ fun _____ _____ at the beach.

5. There is a _____ _____ _____ _____ Gangneung.

6. It _____ _____ Ojukheon. Yulgok _____ _____ there.

7. _____ _____ _____ _____ in Gangneung is potato tteok.

8. It is soft and sweet. _____ _____ _____ Gangneung!

1. 강릉이 정말 좋아요
2. 저는 강릉에 살아요.
3. 나의 이웃에는 아름다운 해변들이 있어요.
4. 해변에서 수영하는 것은 정말 재미있어요.
5. 강릉에는 유명한 한옥이 있어요.
6. 그것은 오죽헌이라고 불려요. 율곡이 거기에서 태어났어요.
7. 강릉에서 가장 유명한 음식은 감자떡이에요.
8. 그것은 부드럽고 달콤해요. 와서 강릉을 즐기세요!

Project Culture

1. I want _____ _____ Boryeong Mud Festival.

2. It _____ _____ _____ Daecheon Beach _____ _____.

3. There are _____ _____ _____ in the festival.

4. First, you can _____ _____ _____ Ssireum in mud.

5. Also _____ is fun _____ colorful mud body _____ on your body.

6. _____, there is an _____ _____.

7. You can _____ _____ _____ beautiful musics.

1. 나는 보령 진흙 축제를 소개하고 싶어요.
2. 그것은 7월에 대천 해수욕장에서 열립니다.
3. 축제에는 많은 흥미로운 행사가 있습니다.
4. 우선, 당신은 사람들이 진흙 속에서 씨름하는 것을 볼 수 있어요.
5. 또한 당신의 몸에 형형색색의 진흙을 바르는 것은 재미있어요.
6. 마지막으로, 실외 콘서트가 있습니다.
7. 당신은 음악가들이 아름다운 음악을 연주하는 것을 들을 수 있습니다.

※ 다음 우리말을 영어로 쓰시오.

Listen and Speak 2 - C

1. A: Chris, 학급 파티를 위해 무엇을 할 거니?
➡ _____

2. B: 나는 샌드위치를 만들 거야.
➡ _____

3. A: 좋은 생각이야. 그것들을 만드는 데 얼마가 걸릴까?
➡ _____

4. B: 아마도 약 한 시간 정도 걸릴 거야.
➡ _____

Think and Write

1. 강릉이 정말 좋아요
➡ _____

2. 저는 강릉에 살아요.
➡ _____

3. 나의 이웃에는 아름다운 해변들이 있어요.
➡ _____

4. 해변에서 수영하는 것은 정말 재미있어요.
➡ _____

5. 강릉에는 유명한 한옥이 있어요.
➡ _____

6. 그것은 오죽헌이라고 불려요. 율곡이 거기에서 태어났어요.
➡ _____

7. 강릉에서 가장 유명한 음식은 감자떡이에요.
➡ _____

8. 그것은 부드럽고 달콤해요. 와서 강릉을 즐기세요!
➡ _____

Project Culture

1. 나는 보령 진흙 축제를 소개하고 싶어요.
➡ _____

2. 그것은 7월에 대천 해수욕장에서 열립니다.
➡ _____

3. 그 축제에는 많은 흥미로운 행사가 있습니다.
➡ _____

4. 우선, 당신은 사람들이 진흙 속에서 씨름하는 것을 볼 수 있어요.
➡ _____

5. 또한 당신의 몸에 형형색색의 진흙을 바르는 것은 재미있어요.
➡ _____

6. 마지막으로, 실외 콘서트가 있습니다.
➡ _____

7. 당신은 음악가들이 아름다운 음악을 연주하는 것을 들을 수 있습니다.
➡ _____

MEMO

영어 기출 문제집

적중 100

1학기

정답 및 해설

동아 | 이병민

중 2

영어 기출 문제집

적중100

1학기

정답 및 해설

동아 | 이병민

중 2

Lesson 3

The Music Goes On

시험대비 실력평가   p.08

01 single   02 breath   03 flea market
04 composer   05 ④   06 ①   07 ⑤
08 My favorite book is *Charlotte's Web.*

01 주어진 단어는 반의어 관계를 나타낸다. multiple: 다수의,
    single: 단 하나의
02 당신이 폐로 들이마시고 다시 내뱉는 공기를 가리키는 말은
    breath(숨, 호흡)이다.
03 중고 물건들을 낮은 가격에 판매하는 야외 시장을 가리키는 말
    은 flea market(벼룩시장)이다.
04 곡을 쓰는 사람을 가리키는 말은 composer(작곡가)이다.
05 ④번의 face는 동사로 '~을 향하다'를 의미한다.
06 주어진 문장에서 fan은 '팬, 열렬한 애호가'를 가리킨다. ②, ③
    번의 fan은 '부채', ④, ⑤번은 '선풍기'를 의미한다.
07 • 나는 수표에 당신의 서명이 필요합니다. • 당신은 계약서 두 장
    에 당신의 서명을 적어야 합니다. • 그는 종이 밑에 그의 서명을
    하고 있었다.
08 favorite: 가장 좋아하는

서술형 시험대비   p.09

01 composer   02 creation   03 audience
04 (1) down   (2) breath   (3) audience
05 (1) The flea market will be held in the park.
     (2) She played the piano without sheet music
06 (1) press down   (2) build up speed   (3) at once
06 (A) at   (B) up   (C) in

01 teach: 가르치다, teacher: 교사, compose: 작곡하다,
    composer: 작곡가
02 새롭거나 전에 존재하지 않았던 무언가를 만들어 내는 과정이나
    행위를 가리키는 말은 creation(창조)이다.
03 무언가를 보거나 듣기 위해 모인 사람들의 무리를 가리키는 말은
    audience(관객, 청중)이다.
04 down: 우울한, breath: 숨, 호흡, audience: 관객, 청중
06 press down: ~을 누르다, build up speed: 속도를 높이다,

at once: 한꺼번에
07 at once: 한꺼번에, build up: 점점 높이다, in person: 직접

[교과서] Conversation

핵심 Check   p.10~11

1 (1) Which animal   (2) favorite subject   (3) love
2 (1) Why / Because
   (2) the reason why / The reason I want to visit it
   (3) the reason why you want to move / because of

교과서 대화문 익히기

Check(√) True or False   p.12

1 T   2 T   3 T   4 F

교과서 확인학습   p.14~15

Listen & Speak 1 A
How's / Which book / best
Listen & Speak 1 B
what are you going to do / a big fan / Which member
/ drummer / I can't wait
Listen & Speak 1 C
Which sport / tennis, exciting
Listen & Speak 2 A
Why / flea market / why don't you
Listen & Speak 2 B
why / for / Where / a paper folding class / the
perfect gift
Listen & Speak 2 C
Which country / Why do you want to / Because
Real Life Talk
with the school radio show / what's your favorite
band / Definitely / Which song do you like best /
Why do you like it / Because, when I'm down

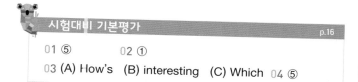
01 ⑤   02 ①
03 (A) How's   (B) interesting   (C) Which   04 ⑤

01 ①번~④번 모두 선호하는 것을 나타내지만, ⑤번의 'I would like to ~'는 '~하고 싶다'는 의미를 나타낸다.

02 이어지는 대답으로 이유를 설명하고 있으므로 'Why'가 적절하다.

03 (A) '독서 동아리는 어때?'라고 안부를 묻는 질문으로 How가 적절하다. (B) interested: 흥미를 갖고 있는, interesting: 흥미로운. (C) 가장 좋아하는 책이 어느 것인지를 묻고 있으므로 Which가 적절하다.

04 *Charlotte's Web*은 Sumin이 가장 좋아하는 책의 이름이다.

시험대비 실력평가   p.17~18

01 I like tennis best.   02 ⑤
03 drummer   04 ②   05 ①   06 Then why don't you join me this Saturday?   07 He is going to bring some old clothes to the flea market.
08 ②   09 ③   10 ⓒ → Definitely, ⓔ → Because   11 Hey Jude   12 ⑤

01 어느 스포츠를 가장 좋아하는지 질문하고 있으므로 이에 대한 대답으로 테니스를 가장 좋아한다는 답변이 이어져야 한다.

02 ⑤번을 제외한 나머지는 이번 주 토요일 계획에 대해 질문하는 표현이다.

03 드럼을 연주하는 사람을 가리키는 말은 drummer이다.

04 ⓒ는 기대감을 표현하고 있으므로 ②와 바꾸어 쓸 수 있다. look forward to: ~을 고대하다, 기대하다

05 ① Jiho와 Amy가 Blue Sky의 팬 모임에서 무엇을 할지는 알 수 없다.

07 소년은 벼룩시장에 그의 헌옷들을 가져올 것이다.

08 주어진 문장 다음에 이어지는 말로 종이꽃을 직접 만들었다는 말이 와야 자연스러우므로 (B)가 적절하다.

09 ③ Tom이 꽃을 만들기 위해 교실에서 종이를 가져왔다는 설명은 바르지 않다.

10 ⓒ는 '단연, 틀림없이'를 의미하는 부사 Definitely가 적절하다. ⓔ는 뒤에 절이 이어지므로 Because가 적절하다.

11 Mina와 Mr. Smith는 Hey Jude를 들을 것이다.

12 Mina가 Hey Jude를 들을 때 어떻게 느끼는지는 알 수 없다.

서술형 시험대비   p.19

01 Which sport do you like best?
02 Because I want to visit my friend.

---

03 (1) Mr. Smith   (2) music
   (3) The Beatles   (4) *Hey Jude*
   (5) it makes him feel better when he is down
04 He made them for his mom's birthday
05 I'm taking a paper folding class these days.

03 오늘 라디오 쇼를 들었니? 라디오 쇼에 특별한 손님이 있었다. 그는 우리 영어 선생님인 Mr. Smith였다. Mina와 Mr. Smith는 음악에 대해 이야기했다. Mr. Smith는 그가 가장 좋아하는 밴드는 The Beatles라고 하셨다. 그들의 노래들 중, 그는 Hey Jude를 가장 좋아했다. 왜냐하면 기분이 안 좋을 때 기분을 좋게 만들어주기 때문이다. 그 노래는 아름다웠다. 나도 그 노래가 매우 좋았다.

04 Tom은 그의 어머니의 생일을 위해서 많은 종이 꽃을 만들었다.

교과서
Grammar

핵심 Check   p.20~21

1 (1) is covered   (2) was asked
2 (1) arrive, will call   (2) come, will be   (3) if, will go

---

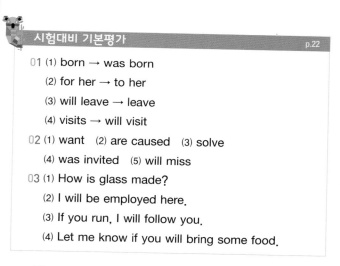
시험대비 기본평가   p.22

01 (1) born → was born
   (2) for her → to her
   (3) will leave → leave
   (4) visits → will visit
02 (1) want   (2) are caused   (3) solve
   (4) was invited   (5) will miss
03 (1) How is glass made?
   (2) I will be employed here.
   (3) If you run, I will follow you.
   (4) Let me know if you will bring some food.

01 (1) 태어나다는 'be born'으로 표현한다. (2) 직접목적어를 주어로 한 4형식 수동태는 간접목적어에 특정 전치사를 부여한다. send는 전치사 to를 사용한다. (3) 조건의 부사절에서 현재시제로 미래를 표현한다. (4) if가 명사절을 이끌고 있으므로 내용에 맞게 시제를 바꾸어 주는 것이 옳다.

02 (1) 조건절에서는 현재형으로 미래를 나타낸다. (2) 사고는 유발되는 것이므로 수동태를 쓰는 것이 옳다. (3) 문제를 해결하는 주체가 You이므로 능동태를 쓴다. (4) 파티에 초대되었지만 가지 않았다는 의미이므로 수동태가 옳다. (5) 조건절은 현재형

으로 미래를 나타내지만 주절은 미래를 나타낼 경우 미래시제를 써야 한다.

03 (1) is made: 만들어지다 (2) employ: 고용하다 (3) follow: 따라가다 (4) let+목적어+원형부정사: 목적어가 ~하게 하다

---

01 ④　　02 ④　　03 ③　　04 If you are invited to the party, will you go there? 05 ②
06 ④　　07 ③　　08 I don't know what we will do if we don't find the way.　09 ③
10 ⓐⓑⓓ, ⓒⓔ　　11 Unless　12 ③
13 ④　　14 I wasn't told about the class meeting by anybody.　15 ⑤　　16 ②, ④
17 If a bike is given to you, what will you do?
18 ④　　19 ②　　20 ④　　21 was invented by King Sejong　22 If I meet you in person, I will ask you many questions.　23 is not[isn't] used (by you), will not get clean　24 will hold → will be held

---

01 지난주에 부쳐진 것이므로 과거시제 수동태를 쓰는 것이 옳다.

02 ④ 구동사의 수동태에서 'by+행위자'를 생략하기 쉬우므로 이에 유의한다. brought up by my grandparents라고 써야 한다.

03 ③번은 '~인지 아닌지'로 해석되는 명사절을 이끄는 접속사 if이다. 나머지는 모두 조건절을 이끄는 if이다.

04 초대받는다는 것을 조건으로 하는 문장이므로 if절은 현재시제로 쓰고, 주절은 미래시제를 사용한다.

05 ① be filled with: ~으로 가득 차 있다 ③ 내일 계획이 있는지를 묻는 명사절이므로 내용과 시제를 일치시켜 will meet으로 써야 한다. ④ 5형식 동사의 목적격보어가 원형부정사인 경우 수동태를 만들 때 to부정사로 쓴다. 따라서 made to do가 옳다. ⑤ make는 직접목적어를 주어로 한 수동태에서 간접목적어에 전치사 for를 쓰는 동사이므로 for me로 쓰는 것이 옳다.

06 ④ 현재시제로 미래를 표현하는 조건의 부사절이므로 give를 쓰는 것이 옳다.

07 by 이외에 다른 전치사를 쓰는 수동태 문제이다. be covered with: ~로 덮이다 be pleased with: ~에 기뻐하다

08 부사절 if는 현재시제로 미래를 표현한다.

09 주어진 문장을 수동태로 만드는 문제이다. The child는 단수 주어이고, 본 문장의 시제가 과거형 saw이므로 수동태를 만들 때 was seen으로 쓰고, 목적격보어 playing은 그대로 써주면 된다.

10 ⓐ, ⓑ, ⓓ는 부사절을 이끄는 if이고 ⓒ, ⓔ는 명사절을 이끄는 if이다.

11 if ... not은 unless와 같다.

12 ③ 건물이 디자인된 것이냐고 묻고 있으므로 수동태를 써야 한다. 따라서 Did가 아닌 Was를 쓰는 것이 옳다.

13 ④번의 빈칸에는 about이 들어가고, 나머지는 모두 with가 공통으로 들어간다. ⑤ fill A with B: A를 B로 채우다

14 주어진 문장의 의미는 '누구도 나에게 학급회의에 관하여 말하지 않았다'이므로 '나는 학급회의에 관하여 듣지 못했다'로 쓰면 된다.

15 빈칸이 이끄는 절은 현재형이지만, 주절은 미래이므로 빈칸에는 시간이나 조건의 부사절이 들어가야 한다. 따라서 양보절 접속사인 ⑤번은 적절하지 않다.

16 밑줄 친 offer는 4형식 동사로 직접목적어를 주어로 한 수동태에서는 간접목적어에 전치사 to를 부여하는 동사이다. 따라서 ②, ④번이 옳다.

17 전치사 to를 활용해야 하므로 직접목적어를 주어로 한 수동태를 써야 한다.

18 직접목적어를 주어로 할 때 간접목적어에 전치사 for를 부여하는 동사는 ④번이다. 나머지 동사들은 모두 to를 사용한다.

19 Harry에 의하여 사진이 찍힌 것이므로 ②번이 옳다.

20 ④ 시간이나 조건의 부사절에서는 현재시제가 미래를 대신하지만, 주절에서는 미래시제로 표현하는 것이 옳다. 따라서 do가 아닌 will이 옳다. ⑤ go (and) see 또는 go (to) see

21 한글을 누가 발명했는지 말해달라고 하였으므로 한글은 세종대왕에 의해 발명되었다고 답하면 된다.

22 in person: 직접, 몸소

23 조건절을 수동태로 만드는 문제이다. soap은 단수 주어이고, 조건절은 현재가 미래를 대신하므로 is not used를 쓰는 것이 내용과 일치한다.

24 파티는 개최되는 것이므로 수동태를 써야 옳다.

---

01 If the machine is used by people, they will be happy.
02 was written by
03 was made to feel comfortable by his sister
04 (1) get up　(2) will plant　(3) was stung
05 The police were given the important evidence. / The important evidence was given to the police.
06 If you need money, I will lend you some. / If you want those pictures, you can have them. / If you are busy now, I will call you later.
07 I was really moved by Liszt's music.
08 ⓐ it rains　ⓑ will take　ⓒ was brought for me
09 was invented / was surprised / is surrounded / was divided / will build
10 If there is a fire, the alarm will ring. / If you want

---

me to help you. I will help you. / If I don't feel well tomorrow, I will stay at home.

11 arrives, will see

12 Unless, will miss / will be very surprised / is crowded with / will go

01 기계가 사용되는 것이므로 수동태로 쓰는 것이 옳으며, 조건절은 현재시제로, 주절은 미래시제로 표현하면 된다.

02 로미오와 줄리엣은 누가 썼는지에 관한 질문이므로 셰익스피어에 의해 쓰여진 것이라고 답하면 된다.

03 목적어를 주어로 하고 있으므로 수동태로 만들어 준다. 목적격보어가 원형부정사이므로 to부정사가 되는 것을 잊지 말자.

04 (1) 조건절이므로 현재시제 (2) 명사절 접속사 if가 이끄는 절이므로 내용과 시점을 일치시켜 미래시제 (3) 별에 의해 쓰인 것이므로 수동태를 쓴다.

05 4형식 동사의 수동태를 묻는 문제이다. 동사 give는 직접목적어를 주어로 하는 수동태에서 간접목적어에 전치사 to를 붙인다. the police는 복수 취급하므로 be동사는 were가 된다. by somebody는 생략할 수 있다.

06 네가 돈이 필요하다면 내가 좀 빌려줄게. / 네가 저 그림들을 원한다면, 가져도 좋아. / 네가 지금 바쁘다면 내가 나중에 전화할게.

07 move: 감동을 주다

08 ⓐ 조건절의 동사는 현재시제로 미래를 나타낼 수 있으므로 it rains를 쓰는 것이 옳다. ⓑ 내일 우산을 가지고 갈 것이라는 의미이므로 주절은 미래형을 쓴다. ⓒ 주어가 우산이므로 수동태를 쓰며, 4형식 수동태이므로 간접목적어에 for를 붙인다.

09 전구는 1879년 Thomas Edison에 의해 발명되었다. / 나는 어제 Jane이 회의에 올 것이라고 기대하지 않았지만 그녀가 그곳에 있었다. 나는 그녀를 보고 놀랐다. / 섬은 물에 의해 둘러싸여 있다. / 지난 학기에 그 수업 규모가 너무 커서 수업이 두 개로 나뉘었다. / 건설 비용이 비싸지 않으면 그들은 새 기숙사를 지을 것이다.

10 feel well: 건강하다

11 시간이나 조건의 부사절에서 현재가 미래를 대신하므로 다음 주에 파리에 도착하는 조건은 현재형으로 표현하고, 만나게 될 것이라는 주절은 미래형으로 표현한다.

12 miss: 놓치다 be surprised: 놀라다 be crowded with: ~으로 붐비다

Reading

확인문제   p.28

1 T   2 F   3 T   4 T   5 F

확인문제   p.29

1 T   2 T   3 F   4 T   5 T   6 F

교과서 확인학습 A   p.30~31

01 a favorite, idol, will answer
02 often show, for
03 scream madly at
04 Others, hours to take
05 even travel to, to see
06 a recent creation
07 Did, begin with
08 were loved by, the first   09 How about, in
10 To find, let's take, to, in, in   11 are filled
12 Unlike, the side, faces
13 can see, better
14 any sheet music
15 to play from memory
16 by softly touching the keys
17 hold their breath because, a single note
18 builds up, press down on, at once
19 makes, powerful, rich
20 pays attention to, body movement
21 long beautiful hair flies
22 like watching, performance at once
23 flies, ends   24 throw flowers, onto the stage
25 goes wild   26 this amazing star
27 was, was born in
28 playing the piano when
29 later became, composer, teacher
30 think of, as   31 Why don't you give
32 like, will love, original

교과서 확인학습 B   p.32~33

1 Do you have a favorite K-pop idol? Many students will answer, "Yes."
2 These students often show great love for their stars.
3 Some scream madly at concerts.
4 Others wait hours to take pictures of their stars.
5 Some students even travel to another city to see their favorite stars.
6 Are idols a recent creation? No way!
7 Did idols begin with The Beatles in the 1960's?
8 They were loved by many, but they were not the first.

9 How about Elvis Presley in the 1950's? Not even close.

10 To find the answer, let's take a time machine to a concert hall in Vienna in 1845.

11 All the seats are filled

12 Unlike other concerts, the side of the piano faces the audience.

13 This way, the audience can see the handsome 185cm pianist better.

14 He doesn't have any sheet music with him.

15 He begins to play from memory.

16 He starts slowly by softly touching the keys.

17 All the people hold their breath because they don't want to miss a single note.

18 He builds up speed, and his long fingers press down on many keys at once.

19 This makes the music very powerful and rich.

20 The audience pays attention to his every little body movement.

21 His long beautiful hair flies everywhere.

22 It's like watching a piano and ballet performance at once.

23 Time flies and the concert ends.

24 People scream and throw flowers and pieces of clothing onto the stage.

25 The concert hall goes wild!

26 Who was this amazing star?

27 His name was Franz Liszt and he was born in 1811 in Hungary.

28 He first started playing the piano when he was seven.

29 Liszt later became a great pianist, composer and teacher.

30 But many people think of him as the first idol.

31 Why don't you give his music a listen?

32 If you like today's idols, you will love the original idol.

시험대비 실력평가　　　　　　　p.34~37

01 ③　　02 ③　　03 are asked, will answer　04 were loved by　05 ③　06 ②　07 The writer wants to go to a concert hall in Vienna in 1845.　08 ①　09 ③　10 He begins to play from memory.　11 ④　12 ④　13 They were loved by many people.　14 ②　15 All the seats are filled.　16 The

side of the piano faces the audience.　17 ③　18 ③　　19 ②　　20 ④　　21 ④　22 are thrown　　23 Great love for their stars is often showed by these students.　24 ③

01 ③ 몇몇 학생들이 콘서트에서 마구 소리를 지르는 것일 뿐, 미치는 것은 아니다.

02 ①, ④, ⑤번은 목적격보어로, ②번은 a book을 수식하는 형용사로 사용된 to부정사이다. 밑줄 친 ⓐ는 '~하기 위해서'로 해석되는 부사로 쓰인 to부정사이므로 ③번이 옳다.

03 학생들이 가장 좋아하는 K-pop 아이돌이 있느냐는 질문을 받으면 "네"라고 대답할 것이다.

04 많은 사람들에게 사랑을 받았던 것이므로 수동태를 쓰는 것이 옳다.

05 최초의 아이돌이 누구인지에 관하여 이야기하고 있다.

06 최초의 아이돌을 알아보기 위하여 타임머신을 타고 가보자고 하였으므로 뒤에 이어질 내용으로는 ②가 옳다.

07 글쓴이는 타임머신을 타고 어디로 가기를 원하나요?

08 ①번 뒤 문장에 이어지는 This way는 주어진 문장을 가리킨다.

09 연도 앞에는 전치사 in을 쓴다.

10 from memory: 외워서, 기억을 더듬어

11 어떤 종류의 대답을 찾기를 원하는지는 알 수 없다.

12 당신이 자물쇠에 꽂는 특수한 모양의 금속 조각은 '열쇠'이다. ⓓ는 '건반'으로 사용된 key이다.

13 수동태로 바꾸기 위해서는 능동태의 목적어인 them을 주격으로 바꾸고, 시제가 과거이므로 were loved로 고친 후, by 이하에 행위자를 넣어 만들면 된다.

14 최초의 아이돌이 언제 시작되었는지에 관한 질문이므로 ②번이 옳다.

15 밑줄 친 문장은 모든 좌석이 찼다는 의미이므로 fill을 수동태로 하여 같은 문장을 만들 수 있다.

16 질문: 콘서트는 다른 콘서트들과 어떻게 다른가요?

17 연주 속도를 점점 올리면서 강력하고 풍부한 음악을 만들었다고 하였으므로 ③번은 옳지 않다.

18 ③번 이후에 나오는 This가 가리키는 것은 피아니스트가 연주 속도를 점점 올리면서 모든 건반을 한 번에 누르는 것을 의미한다. 따라서 ③번에 들어가는 것이 옳다.

19 청중들은 꽃과 옷을 던지며 연주자를 향해 열광하고 있다. '열광하다'는 go wild이다.

20 발레 공연과 피아노 연주를 한 번에 보는 것 같다는 말이 나와 있을 뿐, 발레 공연을 본다는 것은 어디에도 없다.

21 연주자의 사소한 움직임에도 주의를 기울인다고 하였으므로 ④번은 옳지 않다.

22 청중들이 꽃을 던졌다고 했으므로 꽃이 주어로 올 경우 수동태를 쓰는 것이 옳다.

23 목적어인 great love for their stars를 주어로 두고, 이 주어부

의 핵심 명사가 great love로 단수이므로 be동사를 is로 하여 수동태를 만들면 된다.

24 최초의 아이돌이 누구인지 알아보기 위해 타임머신을 탈 것을 권하고 있다. 따라서 ③번이 가장 옳다.

🦉 **서술형 시험대비**   p.38~39

01 Some scream madly at concerts. 02 waiting for their stars to take pictures of them 03 Idols were not[weren't] created recently. 04 the first idol 05 let's take a time machine 06 다른 콘서트들과는 달리 피아노 측면이 청중을 향해 있는 것 07 they don't want to miss a single note. 08 He plays from memory. 09 This makes the music very powerful and rich. 10 Vienna, different, faced, see, played, memory, powerful 11 Flowers and pieces of clothing are thrown onto the stage. 12 ⓓ → movement 13 (A) touching (B) watching (C) goes 14 is held at the concert hall / sounds powerful and rich

01 madly: 미친 듯이, 마구

02 몇몇 학생들은 그들의 스타 사진을 찍기 위해서 스타를 기다리느라 몇 시간을 소비한다.

03 아이돌은 최근 창작물이 아니라고 하였으므로 create의 수동태를 쓰면 된다.

04 최초의 아이돌이라는 의미이다.

06 다른 콘서트들과는 달리 피아노가 청중을 향해 있는 것을 의미한다.

07 청중들이 숨죽이는 이유는 단 하나의 음도 놓치기를 원치 않아서이다.

08 피아니스트는 악보 없이 어떻게 연주하는가?

09 make를 'make+목적어+목적격보어'로 이루어진 5형식으로 사용하였다.

10 어제 공연에 대한 기사이므로 시제에 유의하여 빈칸을 채운다. face: ~을 마주보다

11 질문은 '무대 위로 무엇이 던져지고 있는가?'이다.

12 every 뒤에는 단수명사가 온다.

13 (A), (B)는 각각 전치사의 목적어로 사용되어야 하므로 동명사 형태로 빈칸을 채우는 것이 옳으며, the concert hall은 단수이므로 (C)는 goes를 쓰는 것이 옳다.

14 피아노 콘서트는 콘서트홀에서 개최되며, 음악은 강력하고 풍부하게 들린다.

🦉 **영역별 핵심문제**   p.41~45

01 ⑤   02 signature   03 ②   04 (1) sheet music (2) went wild (3) in person   05 ④   06 It cheers me up.   07 Which book do you like best?   08 ⑤   09 He plays the drums.   10 flea market   11 They are going to sell old clothes at the flea market.   12 ③   13 ③   14 ③, ⑤   15 ②   16 ②   17 didn't play, was canceled[cancelled]   18 ③   19 ④   20 ④   21 is taken care of by you   22 ③   23 ④   24 I was not allowed to go to the park alone by my mom.   25 ④   26 ④   27 ⑤   28 ③   29 ②   30 연주 속도를 점점 올리고, 많은 건반을 한 번에 누르는 것   31 at once   32 ④

01 보기와 ① ~ ④번까지의 단어들은 형용사와 부사의 관계를 나타내지만 ⑤번은 명사와 형용사의 관계를 나타낸다.

02 예를 들어, 편지 끝에 당신이 보통 적는 당신의 이름을 가리키는 말은 signature(서명)이다.

03 unlike: ~와 달리

04 sheet music: 악보, go wild: 열광하다, in person: 직접

05 주어진 문장에서 miss는 '놓치다'를 의미하며 이와 같은 의미로 쓰인 것은 ④번이다. ①번은 '이해하지 못하다', ②, ③, ⑤번은 '그리워하다'를 의미한다.

06 cheer up: 힘을 북돋우다

08 주어진 문장은 '우리와 함께 가고 싶니?'라고 질문하고 있으므로 이에 대한 대답이 이어지는 (E)번이 적절하다.

09 Mike는 Blue Sky 밴드에서 드럼을 연주한다.

10 flea market: 벼룩시장

11 그들은 함께 이번 주 토요일에 벼룩시장에서 헌 옷을 팔 예정이다.

12 (A)는 기분이 좋지 않음을 뜻한다. ③ satisfied: 만족스러운

13 The Beatles의 대부분의 노래를 좋아하는 사람은 Mina가 아닌 Mr. Smith이다.

14 빈칸이 이끄는 절은 현재시제이지만 주절은 미래이므로, 빈칸에는 시간이나 조건의 부사절이 들어가야 한다.

15 disappear는 자동사이므로 수동태가 될 수 없다.

16 오늘 밤에 늦게 온다면 기다리지 않을 것이라는 의미로. 조건의 부사절이므로 현재형으로 미래를 나타낼 수 있다. 따라서 ②번이 가장 적절하다.

17 축구를 하는 주체는 we이므로 능동태를 써야 하며, 경기는 취소가 되는 것이므로 수동태를 쓰는 것이 옳다.

18 ③ 능동태 동사의 시제가 과거이므로 was recorded를 쓰는 것이 옳다.

19 be broken: 고장 나다 repair: 수리하다

20 happen은 자동사이므로 수동태로 쓰일 수 없다.

7

21 relieved: 안도한 take care of: ~을 돌보다

22 ③번은 명사절을 이끄는 접속사 if이다.

23 be known to: ~에게 알려지다 be known as: ~로 알려져 있다

24 엄마는 내가 혼자 공원에 가는 것을 허락하지 않으셨다.

25 스타의 사진을 찍기 위하여 몇 시간을 기다린다고 하였으므로 ④는 옳지 않다.

26 ① (형) 고른, 반반한 ② (형) 차분한 ③ (비교급 강조 부사) 한층, 훨씬 ④ (부) 심지어 ~하기도 ⑤ (형) 공정한, 공평한

27 (A) 앞에서 Some으로 불특정한 학생들을 지칭하였고, 스타 사진을 찍기 위해 몇 시간씩 기다리는 학생들 외에도, 스타를 보기 위해 다른 도시로 이동하는 학생들의 사례도 제시되고 있으므로 the others가 아닌 others를 쓰는 것이 옳다. (B) 단수 명사 city를 수식할 수 있는 것은 another이다.

28 아이돌은 최근에 만들어진 것이 아니고, 비틀즈는 세계 최초의 아이돌이 아니다. 엘비스 프레슬리가 비틀즈를 좋아했는지는 알 수 없으며 1960년대에 아이돌이 매우 인기 있었는지도 알 수 없다.

29 밑줄 친 ⓐ는 to부정사가 부사로 쓰였으며 '~하기 위해서'라는 의미의 목적을 나타낸다. 따라서 ②가 옳다.

30 This는 지시대명사로 앞 문장을 가리킨다.

31 피아노와 발레 공연을 한 번에 보는 것 같았다는 표현이 가장 적절하다.

32 청중들이 연주자의 몸짓에도 집중했다고 나와 있을 뿐, 어떻게 움직였는지는 나와 있지 않다.

단원별 예상문제
p.46~49

01 ③　　02 I'm very fond of tennis.　03 (1) pay attention to　(2) paper folding　(3) from memory
04 (1) I bought the shoes in the flea market.
　(2) The last runner began to build up the speed.
　(3) The driver pressed down on the brake.
05 ④　　06 ⑤　　07 Which fruit do you like best?　08 (C) → (E) → (B) → (D) → (A)　09 She thought it was fun.　10 Her favorite book is *Charlotte's Web*.　11 ③　　12 will disappoint, will be disappointed with[in, at]
13 ④　　14 If it snows, the roads will be closed.
15 ③　　16 ④　　17 is blocked / will call
18 ④　　19 ④　　20 ②　　21 ④
22 The audience pays attention to his every little body movement.　　23 performance
24 ③　　25 other concerts, the side of the piano faced the audience

01 • 정부는 같은 위험을 마주할 것이다. • 모나리자의 얼굴에는 눈썹이 없다. • 왜 너는 울상이니?

---

02 be fond of: ~을 좋아하다

03 pay attention to: ~에 주의를 기울이다, paper folding: 종이 접기, from memory: 기억해서, 외워서

05 이어지는 대답으로 가장 좋아하는 노래에 대한 설명이 이어져야 하므로 (D)가 적절하다.

06 ⑤번을 제외한 나머지는 모두 노래를 함께 들을 것을 제안하는 표현이다.

08 (C) 이번 주 토요일의 계획 질문 → (E) Blue Sky 팬모임에 갈 계획을 설명 → (B) 반응 및 본인도 팬임을 설명 → (D) 가장 좋아하는 멤버 질문 → (A) 대답

09 Sumin은 독서 동아리에 대해 재미있어 한다.

10 Sumin의 가장 좋아하는 책은 *Charlotte's Web*이다.

11 ① he → him,
　② did → was,
　④ locking → locked,
　⑤ will not change → will not be changed

12 disappoint는 '실망시키다'는 의미로, '네가 포기하면 너는 나를 실망시킬 것이다', '네가 포기하면 나는 너에게 실망할 것이다'로 각각 능동태와 수동태를 활용하여 쓰면 된다.

13 시간 • 조건의 부사절에서 현재시제로 미래를 나타낸다. 따라서 rains로 쓰는 것이 옳다.

15 ⓑ '길을 잃다'는 be lost로 표현한다. ⓓ 누군가와 결혼한 상태임을 표현할 때에는 'be married to'라고 쓰는 것이 옳다.

16 ①번은 목적격보어가 원형부정사인 5형식 동사의 수동태이므로 to clean으로 고쳐야 하며, ②번은 아버지에 의해 강아지라고 불리는 것이므로 수동태 was called, ③번은 불이 꺼졌는지를 물어보는 수동태 의문문이므로 주어 the lights에 맞추어 Were, ⑤번 조건절 시제는 현재형으로 미래를 나타내므로 throw를 쓰는 것이 옳다.

17 block: ~을 막다 drain: 배수관 plumber: 배관공

18 단 하나의 음도 놓치기를 원치 않기 때문에 숨죽이고 있다고 보는 것이 옳다. 따라서 ⓓ는 don't want이다.

19 연주자는 천천히 연주를 시작했다. 따라서 ④번은 옳지 않다.

20 밑줄 친 (A)는 5형식으로 쓰였다. 5형식은 '동사+목적어+목적격보어'의 형태로 목적격보어가 목적어를 설명한다. ①, ④, ⑤번은 3형식, ③번은 4형식으로 쓰였다.

21 breathe는 '호흡하다'라는 의미의 동사이다. 명사형 breath를 써야 한다.

23 누군가가 노래를 부르거나 춤을 추거나 악기를 연주함으로써 청중을 즐겁게 할 때 사용되는 단어는 '공연'이다.

24 ① 다른 콘서트들과는 달리 피아노 측면이 청중을 향해 있다고 하였다. ② 연주자는 악보 없이 연주하고 있다. ④ 시간이 빠르게 흘러간다고 하였으므로 청중들이 지루함을 느꼈다고 볼 수 없다. ⑤ 발레 공연은 보여주지 않는다.

01 Definitely   02 They are going to listen to *Hey Jude.*
03 Which song do you like best?   04 Some mistakes were made by her. / Lots of cookies were made for me by my friends. / I am always made to laugh by Jason.   05 find, will tell
06 don't have any homework to do, will go to a movie   07 I have enough apples, I wll bake / is located   08 were not written by   09 It's like watching a piano and ballet performance at once.
10 He is thought of as the first idol by many people.
11 will like → like   12 other concerts
13 be seen better by them

01 무언가가 진실이거나 이에 대해 의심이 없다는 것을 강조하는 방식을 가리키는 말은 'definitely(단연, 틀림없이)'이다.

02 그들은 함께 Hey Jude를 들을 것이다.

04 3, 4, 5형식으로 쓰일 수 있는 동사 make를 수동태로 만드는 문제이다. 첫 번째 문장은 3형식 동사로 쓰인 make이고, 두 번째 문장은 4형식 동사로 쓰인 make이다. 직접목적어를 주어로 한 수동태를 만들어 간접목적어에 for를 붙인다. 마지막 문장은 목적격보어로 원형부정사를 취하는 5형식 make로, 수동태를 만들 때 목적격보어를 to부정사화 하는 것을 유의해야 한다.

05 시간 • 조건의 부사절에서 현재시제가 미래를 대신한다는 것에 유의하여 빈칸을 채운다.

06 영화 보러 갈 시간이 있느냐는 물음에 아직 숙제가 있는지 없는지 모른다며, 만약 할 숙제가 없다면 함께 가겠다고 답할 수 있다.

07 be located in: ~에 위치하다

08 수동태의 핵심 주어가 복수명사인 the letters이므로 복수 동사 were를 써서 수동태를 만드는 것에 유의한다.

09 like는 전치사이므로 watch를 동명사 형태로 만들어야 한다.

10 think of A as B: A를 B라고 여기다

11 조건의 부사절에서 현재가 미래를 대신한다.

12 others는 other concerts를 대신하는 대명사이다.

13 조동사의 수동태를 묻고 있다. 조동사 뒤의 be동사는 원형으로 써야 한다.

|모범답안|
01 (1) so many paper flowers   (2) beautiful
     (3) a paper folding class   (4) how
02 (1) The cake was baked by Tom yesterday.
     (2) This book was read by me many times.
     (3) The picture was drawn by my brother three years ago.
     (4) The bread was passed to my dad by me.

     (5) The doll was made for the girl by him.
03 (1) If it is sunny tomorrow, I will go on a picnic.
     (2) If it is windy tomorrow, I'll wear my coat.
     (3) If it rains tomorrow, I will stay at home and watch a movie.
     (4) If it is hot tomorrow, I will have lots of ice cream.

01 오늘 나는 Tom의 선물을 받았을 때 매우 행복했다. 그는 나를 위해 매우 많은 종이꽃을 만들어 주었다. 매우 아름다워 보였다. 요즘 그는 종이접기 수업을 듣고 있다. 그는 수업에서 그것들을 어떻게 만드는지 배운 것 같다. 나는 그가 매우 자랑스러웠다.

01 Which country do you want to visit?
02 (1) Which novel is the most popular?
     (2) How did you prepare for your role?
     (3) Why did King Sejong invent Hangeul?
03 (1) faced   (2) performance   (3) throw   (4) invented
04 ②   05 (D) → (B) → (E) → (C) → (A)
06 Why do you want to visit Canada?   07 ⓓ → these   08 ③   09 Which member do you like best?   10 ⑤   11 (B) → (D) → (C) → (E) → (A)   12 ④   13 ①
14 ④   15 you lend me, I will pay, back
16 ⑤   17 was seen to stop (by us)
18 ③   19 ②   20 ⑤   21 you hold your breath, you won't miss a single note
22 ④   23 ⑤   24 ⑤   25 Why don't you give his music a listen?   26 ②

01 want to~: ~하고 싶다

03 throw: 던지다, performance: 공연, invent: 발명하다, face: 직면하다

04 (A)는 어느 나라를 선호하는지 질문하고 있으므로 which, (B)는 이어지는 대답으로 이유를 설명하고 있으므로 why가 적절하다.

05 (D) 가장 좋아하는 가수 대답 → (B) 이유 질문 → (E) 이유 설명 → (C) 가장 좋아하는 곡 질문 → (A) 가장 좋아하는 곡 대답

06 이어지는 대화가 이유를 설명하고 있으므로 Why로 시작하는 의문문이 적절하다.

07 those days: 그때, 그 당시에, these days: 요즘

08 나머지는 모두 '선물'을 뜻하지만 ③번은 '재능'을 뜻한다.

09 best: 가장

10 ⑤ Jiho와 Amy는 이번 주 Blue Sky의 팬 미팅에 함께 갈 것이다.

11 (B) 헌 옷을 가지고 있는 이유 질문 → (D) 헌 옷을 가지고 있는
   이유 설명 → (C) 본인도 헌 옷을 가지고 있음을 설명 → (E) 토
   요일 계획 제안 → (A) 제안 수락

12 ① 유익한, ② 인상 깊은, ③ 매력적인, ④ 지루한, ⑤ 재미있는

13 가장 선호하는 책이 무엇인지 질문하고 있으므로 ①번과 바꾸어
   쓸 수 있다. favorite: 가장 좋아하는

14 주어는 복수명사인 The keys이므로 복수 동사를 쓰는 것이 옳
   다. 따라서 are이다.

15 pay somebody back: (빌린 돈을) 갚다, 돌려주다

16 by 이외의 다른 전치사를 사용하는 수동태 및 구동사의 수동태
   를 묻는 문제이다. ① pay attention to: ~에 관심을 기울이
   다 ② be married to: ~와 결혼한 상태이다 ③ be exposed
   to: ~에 노출되다 ④ be accustomed to: ~에 익숙하다
   ⑤ be composed of: ~으로 구성되어 있다 oxygen: 산소
   hydrogen: 수소

17 목적격보어로 원형부정사를 쓰는 동사는 수동태로 전환할 때 목
   적격보어를 to부정사화 한다.

18 4형식 동사의 수동태에서 간접목적어가 주어로 사용될 경우 직
   접목적어는 전치사 없이 쓴다. 따라서 'Tom was given some
   bad advice about studying English.'가 옳다.

19 주어진 문장의 This way가 가리키는 것은 타 콘서트와는 달리
   피아노 측면을 청중과 마주보게 하여 청중이 연주자의 모습을
   더 잘 볼 수 있게 만든 것을 말한다.

20 at once: 한 번에 one at a time: 차례로, 한 번에 하나씩

21 사람들은 단 하나의 음도 놓치기를 원치 않아서 숨죽이고 있다
   고 하였다.

22 콘서트가 끝난 후 사람들은 소리를 지르며 꽃을 던지고 있으므로
   '흥분한' 반응을 보이고 있다고 하는 것이 옳다.

23 'think of A as B'는 'A를 B로 여기다'라는 의미이다. ⓐ the
   audience는 집합명사로 단수 취급하며, ⓑ once는 '한 때, 한
   번'의 의미로 사용되므로 글에 맞게 고치기 위해서 at once를
   쓰는 것이 적절하다. ⓒ 시간은 흘러가는 것이 아니라 저절로
   흐르는 것이므로 수동태가 아닌 자동사로써 flies를 쓰는 것이
   옳다. ⓓ 놀라움을 유발하는 스타이므로 amazing으로 고치는
   것이 맞다.

24 많은 사람들이 Franz Liszt를 최초의 아이돌이라고 여긴다고 하
   고, 글쓴이 역시 오늘날의 아이돌을 좋아한다면 최초의 아이돌도
   좋아하게 될 것이라고 글을 마무리하고 있으므로 ⑤는 옳지 않다.

25 give는 두 개의 목적어를 취하는 4형식 동사이다.

26 Franz Liszt의 콘서트에 관한 기사로 그가 사람들의 환호 속에
   성황리에 공연을 마쳤다는 내용이다. 따라서 ②번이 가장 적절
   하다.

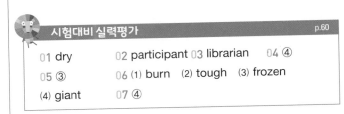

Go for It!

시험대비 실력평가   p.60

01 dry   02 participant 03 librarian   04 ④
05 ③   06 (1) burn (2) tough (3) frozen
(4) giant   07 ④

01 주어진 단어는 반의어 관계를 나타낸다. dry: 마른, 건조한,
   wet: 젖은

02 어떤 활동이나 행사에 참가하는 사람을 가리키는 말은
   participant(참가자)이다.

03 도서관을 담당하거나 도서관에서 일하는 사람을 가리키는 말은
   librarian(사서)이다.

04 ordinary: 보통의, 평범한

05 주어진 문장의 bat은 '배트, 막대기'를 의미한다. ③번을 제외한
   나머지는 모두 '박쥐'를 뜻한다.

06 tough: 힘든, burn: 태우다, frozen: 얼은, giant: 거대한

07 field: 분야, 들판, 매장지[산지]

서술형 시험대비   p.61

01 melt   02 traditional
03 desert   04 (A) In (B) out (C) in
05 (1) in the middle of (2) takes place
   (3) go on (4) are out of
06 No, I've never been there.
07 (1) Have you ever tried yoga?
   (2) In fact, we are out of salt.
   (3) I want to take part in the rock climbing contest.

01 주어진 단어는 반의어 관계를 나타낸다. freeze: 얼다, melt: 녹다

02 '오랫동안 변하지 않은 특정 그룹의 사람들의 삶의 양식, 믿음,
   관습의 일부인' 것은 traditional(전통적인)이다.

03 '물이 거의 없고 이곳에서 자라는 식물도 거의 없는 넓은 땅'은
   desert(사막)이다.

04 in fact: 사실은, 실은 be out of: ~이 떨어지다 take part in:
   ~에 참가하다

05 in the middle of: ~의 한 가운데에 take place: 발생하다, 일어
   나다 go on: 계속되다 be out of: ~이 바닥나다, ~이 떨어지다

Conversation

핵심 Check
p.62~63

1 (1) What do you do in your free[leisure] time
(2) favorite free time activity / doing yoga
(3) I often bake cookies
2 (1) Have you ever run
(2) visited Canada / Yes, I have, Have you
(3) made / never

교과서 대화문 익히기

Check(√) True or False
p.64

1 F　2 T　3 T　4 F

교과서 확인학습
p.66~67

Listen & Speak 1 A
in your free time / often / usually watch movies

Listen & Speak 1 B
What are you going to do / play badminton / my favorite free time activity / Who / What do you do in your free time / ride my bike

Listen & Speak 1 C
for a living / I often play table tennis

Listen & Speak 2 A
have you ever been to / I have / I've never been there

Listen & Speak 2 B
have you ever heard of / I've seen / these days / scary / scared / exercise / join / scary, play basketball

Listen & Speak 1 C
Have you ever ridden / When

Real Life Talk
often go rock climbing / What mountain / gym / Have you ever done / Not yet / come and join / this Saturday / sounds / going to

시험대비 기본평가
p.68

01 what do you do for a living
02 Have you ever ridden a horse?
03 ③　　　04 (B) → (D) → (C) → (A)

---

01 for a living: 생계를 위하여
02 ride - rode - ridden
03 여가 활동을 묻고 있으므로 '나는 소방관이야.'라는 대답은 어색하다.
04 (B) 경험 질문 → (D) 대답 및 상대방에게 경험 질문 → (C) 대답 및 계획 설명 → (A) 반응 및 확신 표현

시험대비 실력평가
p.69~70

01 ⑤　　　02 ②
03 I usually watch movies.　04 ⑤　　　05 ⑤
06 (E) → (A) → (C) → (B) → (D)
07 He thinks (that) it is too scary for him.
08 He is going to play basketball.
09 (1) she often goes rock climbing with her dad
(2) a gym near her house
(3) she has never done it
(4) I could come and join her next time
10 (D) → (B) → (C) → (A)

---

01 이어지는 대답으로 보아 빈칸에는 직업을 묻는 질문이 적절하다. occupation: 직업
02 '너는 여가 시간에 무엇을 하니?' '너는 어때?'라고 각각 묻고 있으므로 빈칸에 공통으로 들어가기에 적절한 말은 what이다.
04 ⑤번은 '직업이 무엇인가요?'라는 의미이다.
05 주어진 질문에 대한 대답으로 여가 시간에 무엇을 하는지에 대한 대답이 이어져야 하므로 (E)가 적절하다.
06 (E) 대답 및 추가 설명 → (A) 자신이 플라잉 요가를 배우고 있음을 이야기함 → (C) 놀람 표현 및 선호 여부 질문 → (B) 선호 대답 → (D) 반응 및 다짐
07 Mike는 플라잉 요가가 너무 무섭다고 생각한다.
08 Mike는 요가 수업에 참여하는 대신 농구를 할 것이다.
09 오늘 나는 Judy와 여가 활동에 대해 이야기를 했다. 그녀는 여가 시간에 종종 아빠와 암벽 등반을 간다고 했다. 그녀는 보통 집 근처 체육관에서 그걸 한다. 그러나 그녀는 실제로 산에서는 한 번도 해본 적이 없으며 언젠가는 그렇게 하고 싶어 한다. 나는 암벽 등반에 흥미가 생겨 내가 그녀와 다음에 함께 할 수 있을지 물어 보았다. 우리는 그걸 이번 주 토요일에 할 것이다. 나는 정말 그것이 기대가 된다.
10 (D) 경험 질문 → (B) 경험 여부 대답 → (C) 언제 경험했는지 질문 → (A) 대답

서술형 시험대비
p.71

01 what do you do in your free time?
02 I usually play with my dad.

03 favorite

04 (1) plays badminton   (2) goes to the Han River
   (3) ride his bike

05 I often go rock climbing with my dad.

06 She usually does it at a gym near her house.

07 They are going to go rock climbing this Saturday.

02 '보통 누구와 함께 운동하니?'라는 질문에 '나는 보통 아빠와 함께 운동한다.'는 대답이 이어져야 한다.

03 '같은 종류의 다른 것들보다 더 좋아하는'은 favorite(가장 좋아하는)이다.

06 Judy는 주로 집 근처의 체육관에서 암벽 등반을 한다.

07 Judy와 Hojin은 이번 주 토요일에 암벽 등반을 하러 갈 것이다.

교과서 Grammar

핵심 Check
p.72~73

1 (1) the cheapest, all   (2) the most interesting

2 (1) who   (2) whose bicycle

시험대비 기본평가
p.74

01 (1) I have a friend who studies abroad.
   (2) We stayed in the hotel which had a beautiful lounge.
   (3) Do you want to see the pictures which the photographer took?
   (4) Jenny took care of the dog whose leg was hurt.

02 (1) the hottest   (2) taller than
   (3) is   (4) the most diligent

03 (1) Did you read the book that I lent to you?
   (2) Is there anything that you want to ask?
   (3) Do you know the longest river in the world?
   (4) Time is the most precious of all.

01 (1) She가 사람이고 주격이므로 주격 관계대명사 who. (2) 선행사가 사물인 the hotel이고, 대명사 It이 주격으로 쓰였으므로 관계대명사 which. (3) them이 목적격으로 쓰인 사물이므로 관계대명사 which. (4) Its가 소유격으로 쓰이고 있고 개를 가리키므로 관계대명사 whose를 쓴다.

02 (1) 내용상 최상급을 쓰는 것이 가장 옳다. (2) 비교급을 이용한 최상급 표현이다. (3) 관계대명사의 수의 일치 문제이다. 선행사에 수의 일치를 시켜야 하므로 the girl에 맞도록 be동사를 쓰

는 것이 옳다. (4) 3음절 이상의 단어이므로 the most를 이용하여 최상급을 만든다.

03 (1) '빌려준 책'이므로 the book을 수식하는 관계절을 만든다. (2) 의문문이나 부정문에서는 anything을 쓴다. (3) long은 -est를 붙여서 최상급을 만든다. (4) precious는 -ous로 끝나는 형용사이므로 the most를 이용하여 최상급을 만든다.

시험대비 실력평가
p.75~77

01 ①   02 ④   03 ④   04 Where is the cheese which(또는 that) was in the refrigerator?
05 ③   06 ②, ③, ⑤   07 ⑤   08 more comfortable than   09 ⑤   10 ⑤
11 which(또는 that), higher than   12 ③
13 ③   14 that[which], whose, that[which]
15 The woman who(또는 that 또는 whom) I spoke to gave me good advice.   16 What is the most popular sport in your country?   17 ④
18 ④   19 The eldest daughter   20 I liked the woman whom I met at the party last night.
21 ③   22 ②

01 healthy는 -est를 붙여서 최상급을 만들고 나머지는 모두 the most를 이용해서 최상급을 만드는 형용사이다.

02 모두 주격 혹은 목적격으로 사용되는 관계대명사 who를 쓰지만 ④번은 소유격 관계대명사 whose의 자리이다.

03 의미상 B가 여지껏 본 영화 중 가장 지루한 영화라는 의미가 되어야 하므로 the most boring이라고 쓰는 것이 옳다.

04 냉장고 안에 있던 치즈가 어디 있는지를 묻는 문장으로 쓰면 된다.

05 비교급과 원급으로 최상급의 의미를 표현하는 문장을 찾는 것이다. '비교급+than any other+단수명사', 최상급, 'as 원급 as'를 써서 빈칸을 채운다.

06 목적격 관계대명사 whom의 자리이다. 따라서 who가 가능하며 that이 쓰여도 무방하다.

07 ⑤번은 돌고래가 다른 모든 동물들만큼 영리하다는 의미가 되므로 다른 문장과 의미가 다르다.

08 비교급으로 최상급의 의미를 갖는 표현이다. the+최상급은 '비교급+than all the other+복수명사'와 같다.

09 '가장 ~한 사람들 중 한 사람'이란 표현은 'one of the 최상급+복수명사'를 쓴다. 따라서 men으로 쓰는 것이 옳다.

10 모두 최상급의 의미를 갖지만 ⑤번은 '이것은 다른 모든 그림들만큼 가치 있다.'는 뜻이므로 다른 문장과 의미가 다르다.

11 세계에서 가장 높은 빌딩은 두바이에 있는 Burj Khalifa이다.

12 ③번은 비교급으로 최상급을 나타내는 것으로 the most가 아닌 more로 쓰는 것이 옳다.

13 ⓐ 주격 관계대명사가 빠져 있다. people who don't have a

car로 쓰는 것이 옳다. ⓑ 목적격 관계대명사가 생략되어 있다. ⓒ that은 전치사의 목적어였던 the music을 받는 관계대명사이다. ⓓ 목적격 관계대명사가 생략된 채로 두 문장이 이어지고 있으므로 대명사 it을 빼는 것이 옳다.

14 첫 번째 문장의 빈칸은 목적격 관계대명사 자리이므로 that이나 which를 쓰는 것이 옳다. 두 번째 문장에는 eyes를 받아주는 소유격 관계대명사가 들어가는 것이 옳으며 마지막 문장의 빈칸에는 목적격 관계대명사 that 혹은 which를 쓰면 된다.

15 give someone advice: ~에게 조언을 해 주다

17 ④번은 명사절을 이끄는 접속사 that이다. 명사절을 이끄는 접속사 that은 완전한 문장을 이끌며, 관계대명사 that은 불완전한 문장을 이끈다.

18 빈칸 뒤에 명사가 나오므로 소유격 관계대명사가 오는 것이 옳다.

19 서열상 가장 연장자를 나타낼 때에는 the eldest로 표현한다.

20 whom을 대신하여 who, that을 써도 무방하다.

21 bad의 최상급으로 the worst를 써야 하며 내가 저질러온 실수 중에서 최악이라고 하였으므로 ③번이 옳다.

22 ② the prettiest로 쓰는 것이 옳다. the most와 최상급은 함께 쓰지 않는다.

서술형 시험대비
p.78~79

01 the highest, higher than
02 (1) that cannot be explained
   (2) which(또는 that) were on the wall
   (3) who are never on time
03 The man who[that] examined the sick children is the kindest doctor in this hospital.
04 (1) Sydney is the largest
   (2) Jupiter is larger than
   (3) The Nile is the longest river
05 He is the most boring person that I have ever met.
06 (1) shorter than   (2) shorter than all
   (3) the longest   (4) longer than
07 A customer is someone who buys something from a store. / The boy who was injured in the accident is now in the hospital. / The bus which goes to the airport runs every half hour. / A dictionary is a book which gives you the meanings of words. / I met somebody whose mother is a famous writer.
08 (1) the people whom
   (2) their children everything that
   (3) whose menu
09 the most patient person that I have ever met
10 (1) I know the boy. / His bicycle was stolen.
   (2) Daisy lectured on a topic. /

She knew very little about the topic.
11 (1) No other river / longer than
   (2) the longest river in

01 에베레스트 산은 세계에서 가장 높은 산이다. 산의 높이는 high를 써서 나타낸다.

02 (1) 선행사가 something이므로 관계대명사 that이나 which를 쓰는 것이 옳다. (2) 선행사가 사물이므로 which나 that을 써서 문장을 하나로 만든다. (3) 사람이 선행사이므로 관계대명사 who나 that을 이용한다.

03 examine: 검사하다, 진찰하다

04 시드니는 호주에서 가장 큰 도시이며, 목성은 태양계에서 가장 큰 행성이다. 나일 강은 세계에서 가장 긴 강이다.

05 지루함을 유발하는 사람에게는 boring을 쓴다.

06 밧줄의 길이를 비교하는 문제이다. 밧줄 D는 다른 모든 밧줄 중에서 가장 짧고 밧줄 A는 가장 긴 밧줄이다. 문장의 형태를 살펴가며 빈칸을 채우는 것이 좋다.

07 customer: 고객 be injured: 부상을 입다

08 (1) who나 that을 써도 무방하다.

09 Jason은 이제껏 만나본 사람 중에서 Kelly가 가장 인내심 있다고 말하는 것이 적절하다.

10 lecture: 강의하다 topic: 주제 little: 그다지[별로] ~하지 않다

11 비교급을 이용하여 최상급의 의미를 나타내는 표현들이다. the Mississippi River: 미시시피 강

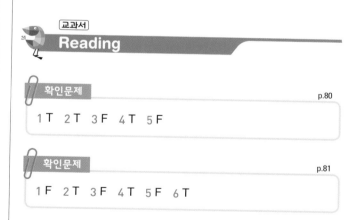

교과서
Reading

확인문제
p.80

1 T   2 T   3 F   4 T   5 F

확인문제
p.81

1 F   2 T   3 F   4 T   5 F   6 T

교과서 확인학습 A
p.82~83

01 Imagine, in the middle of   02 go on and on
03 feels like, fire   04 burns your face, throat
05 your backpack to drink   06 out of water
07 wet, with a drop of, keep going
08 Sounds like   09 who take part in
10 a series of four races, toughest deserts

13

11 Each race is, takes   12 takes place, in

13 the driest desert

14 hasn't rained, for   15 goes to, in

16 the windiest desert

17 heads to

18 the hottest   19 reach up to

20 travels to the coldest desert

21 boiling water, freezes

22 the greatest runners, take part in

23 exactly   24 the participants are ordinary

25 do it   26 a librarian from

27 a chance to test, make

28 who crosses, can do anything

23 Not exactly.

24 Many of the participants are ordinary people like you and me.

25 So why do they do it?

26 Adrianna, a librarian from France, says,

27 "It's a chance to test your limits and make your own history.

28 Anyone who crosses the finish line can do anything."

교과서 확인학습 B
p.84~85

1 Imagine you are in the middle of a great desert.

2 The sands go on and on in every direction.

3 The sun feels like a giant ball of fire.

4 The hot wind burns your face and throat.

5 You open your backpack to drink some water.

6 Oh, no! You're almost out of water.

7 You wet your throat with a drop of water and keep going.

8 Sounds like a bad dream?

9 Well, this is not a dream for the people who take part in the 4 Deserts Race.

10 The 4 Deserts Race is a series of four races across the world's toughest deserts.

11 Each race is 250 kilometers long and takes seven days.

12 The first race takes place in the Atacama Desert in Chile.

13 It is the driest desert in the world.

14 In fact, it hasn't rained in some parts of the Atacama Desert for 400 years!

15 The next race goes to the Gobi Desert in China.

16 It is the windiest desert on earth.

17 The third race heads to the Sahara Desert in Egypt.

18 It is the hottest of the four deserts.

19 Temperatures can reach up to 50℃.

20 Finally, the race travels to the coldest desert on earth, Antarctica.

21 If you throw boiling water into the air here, it freezes!

22 Only the greatest runners on the planet can take part in 4 Deserts Race, right?

시험대비 실력평가
p.86~89

01 Imagine   02 ④   03 ③   04 ⑤

05 ④   06 ④   07 ②   08 the people who take part in the 4 Deserts Race

09 Each race is 250km long. 10 ②   11 ④

12 ⑤   13 boiling water

14 Antarctica, is the coldest on earth   15 limit

16 ③   17 take part in 4 Deserts Race

18 ③, ④   19 ②   20 How many deserts have you run through?   21 tougher than, deserts

22 ④   23 temperature   24 ⑤

25 ④   26 ②   27 which(혹은 that), toughest deserts

01 당신이 무언가에 관하여 생각할 때 마음속에서 그것에 관한 그림이나 아이디어를 형성할 경우 이 단어가 사용된다.

02 물이 거의 떨어져 간다고 하였으므로 ④번은 옳지 않다.

03 '거대한'이라는 의미이므로 ③번이 옳다.

04 ⓒ '물을 마시기 위해서'라는 의미가 적합하므로 to부정사를 이용하여 부사를 만들어 준다. ⓓ keep+Ving: 계속해서 V하다

05 carry on은 '계속해서 ~하다, 계속 가다'는 의미이다. in the middle of는 in the heart of를, on and on은 continuously를, bad는 terrible을, a series of는 a chain of로 대신하여 쓸 수 있다.

06 태양이 거대한 불의 공 같다는 것은 매우 뜨겁다는 의미이다.

07 밑줄 친 (B)는 부사로 쓰인 to부정사로 목적을 나타내며 '~하기 위해서'라는 의미로 해석된다. ① 목적격 보어로 쓰인 to부정사 ③ 형용사로 쓰인 to부정사 ④ would like의 목적어로 쓰인 to부정사 ⑤ 진주어로 쓰인 to부정사

08 take part in: ~에 참가하다

09 각 사막 경주의 길이를 묻고 있다. 각각 250km씩이라고 하였다.

10 Atacama 사막이 세계에서 가장 건조한 곳이라고 말하며 400년 동안 비가 내리지 않은 곳도 있다는 말로 앞 문장을 강조하는 말이 들어가는 것이 옳다.

11 지구상에서 가장 작은 사막이 어디에 있는지는 알 수 없다.

12 ⑤번은 최상급을 나타내는 문장이 아니다.

13 끓는 물을 던지면 언다고 하였다.

14 사막 레이스의 최종 목적지는 지구상에서 가장 추운 남극이다.

15 '가능한 최대의 양, 범위 혹은 정도'는 한계(limit)이다.

16 특별한 사람만이 참가하는 것이 아니라 너와 나 같은 평범한 사람들이라고 말하는 것이 글의 흐름에 맞다.

17 4 Deserts Race에 참가하는 것을 가리킨다.

18 빈칸은 주격 관계대명사의 자리이며 선행사가 사람이므로 who 혹은 that을 쓰는 것이 옳다.

19 위 글은 평범한 사람들이 '4 Deserts Race'에 참가하는 이유이다.

20 답변으로 미루어 보아 얼마나 많은 사막을 뛰었는지를 묻는 질문이 들어가는 것이 옳다.

21 '비교급 than all the other+복수명사'는 최상급의 의미를 갖는다.

22 ④ 참가자들과 좋은 친구가 되었다고 하였으므로 ④번은 옳지 않다.

23 어떤 것이 얼마나 뜨거운지 혹은 얼마나 차가운지에 대한 척도

24 가장 추운 사막이므로 끓는 물을 던지면 언다고 볼 수 있다. 따라서 ⑤번에 들어가는 것이 가장 적합하다.

25 다른 지역보다 고비 사막에 바람이 더 많이 부는 이유는 위 글을 읽고 알 수 없다.

26 ⓐ는 인칭대명사 it으로 ②번이 그 쓰임과 같다. ① 가주어 it, ③, ⑤ 날씨, 날짜, 거리, 명암 등을 말할 때 쓰는 비인칭 주어 it, ④ 가목적어 it으로 각각 쓰였다.

27 선행사가 사물인 four deserts이며 동사를 이끌고 있으므로 주격 관계대명사를 써야 옳다.

서술형 시험대비 p.90~91

01 Imagine that you are in the middle of a great desert.

02 The hot wind makes my face and throat burn.

03 I'm almost out of water

04 in order to drink some water (혹은 so as to drink some water)

05 Well, this is not a dream for the people who[that] take part in the 4 Deserts Race.

06 toughest   07 freezes

08 The Sahara Desert is hotter than all the other deserts.

09 The second race takes place in the Gobi Desert in China.

10 colder than   11 who[that] are ordinary

12 who[that] is a librarian from France

01 '네가 거대한 사막의 한 가운데에 있다고 상상해 보아라.'는 의미이다.

02 얼굴을 뜨겁게 하고 목이 마르게 만드는 것은 뜨거운 바람이다.

03 왜 물을 조금만 마시는지를 묻고 있으므로 물이 거의 떨어져서라고 답하면 된다.

04 부사 중에서 목적을 나타내는 to부정사는 in order to나 so as to로 쓸 수 있다.

06 문맥상 가장 힘든 사막이라는 의미이다.

07 낮은 온도로 인하여 어떤 것이 고체화되는 것을 '얼다'라고 한다. 따라서 수의 일치에 유의하여 freezes를 빈칸에 쓴다.

08 비교급을 이용하여 최상급의 의미를 표현하는 문제이다.

09 두 번째 경주는 어디에서 열리나요?

10 남극이 가장 춥다. 비교급을 이용한 최상급 표현이다.

11 they는 평범한 사람들을 가리키는 말이므로 관계대명사를 이용하여 '우리와 같은 평범한 사람들'이라는 의미의 문장을 만들어 주면 된다.

12 Adrianna는 프랑스에서 온 사서이다.

영역별 핵심문제 p.93~97

01 marathon   02 ⑤   03 (1) a series of
(2) take part in (3) for a living   04 ④
05 (1) Have you ever hit a home run?
   (2) I often play table tennis in my free time.
   (3) What does he do for a living?
06 Who do you usually play with?
07 She plays badminton with her dad.   08 ③
09 ⓒ scaring → scared   10 ⑤   11 ⑤
12 rock climbing
13 What mountain do you go to?
14 ④   15 (B) → (D) → (C) → (A)   16 ③
17 The lake which you swam in today is the deepest lake in our country.   18 ④   19 ⑤
20 ④   21 bigger than any other   22 as heavy as   23 ③   24 the most famous, that   25 ③   26 ④   27 ③, ④
28 burning   29 who[that] takes part in   30 ②
31 ④

01 26마일, 약 42km의 거리를 달리는 경주를 나타내는 말은 marathon(마라톤)이다.

02 throat: 목구멍

03 a series of: 일련의, take part in: ~에 참가하다, for a living: 생계를 위해

04 주어진 문장에서 go on은 '계속하다'라는 의미를 나타내므로 이와 같이 쓰인 것은 ④번이다. ①번은 '넘어가다' ②번은 '일어나다, 발생하다' ③ go on a picnic: 소풍가다, ⑤ go on a diet:

식이요법을 하다

07 Jean은 여가 시간에 아빠와 함께 배드민턴을 친다.

08 두 사람은 여가 활동(leisure activity)에 대해 이야기하고 있다.

09 scaring: 위협하는, scared: 무서운, 겁먹은

10 나머지는 상대방의 말에 대한 만족감을 나타내지만, ⑤는 '괜찮아요.'라고 격려할 때 쓰는 말이다.

11 왜 Suji가 요즘 요가하는 것을 좋아하는지는 알 수 없다.

12 가파른 바위 표면을 오르는 활동이나 스포츠를 가리키는 말은 rock climbing(암벽 등반)이다.

14 ④ Judy는 언젠가 실제 산에서 암벽 등반을 하기를 희망하지만 이번 주 토요일에 암벽 등반을 하러 산에 간다는 설명은 바르지 않다.

15 (B) 경험 질문 → (D) 대답 및 상대방에게 경험 질문 → (C) 대답 및 계획 설명 → (A) 반응 및 확신 표현

16 ③번은 선행사가 사람이므로 who를 쓰는 것이 옳다.

17 swim in: ~에서 수영하다

18 ④번의 위 문장은 '내 지갑을 발견한 여자가 나에게 전화했다.'이고 아래 문장은 '내가 발견한 지갑의 주인에게 내가 전화를 걸었다.'는 의미이다.

19 one of the 최상급+복수명사: 가장 ~한 사람들 중 하나

20 ④번은 주격 관계대명사로 생략이 불가능하다. 생략 가능한 관계대명사는 목적격 관계대명사이다.

21~22 박스 A, B, C 중에서 A의 크기가 가장 작지만 무게는 가장 무거우며, C의 크기가 가장 크지만 무게는 가장 가볍다. 따라서 가장 큰 박스와 가장 무거운 박스를 묻는 질문에 조건에 맞도록 답하면 된다.

23 주어진 문장의 빈칸에는 주격 관계대명사 who가 들어간다. ③번에는 목적격 관계대명사 whom이 들어가야 하며 whom을 대신하여 who를 써도 무방하다. ① whose ② which ④ whose ⑤ that

24 선행사에 최상급이 있으므로 that을 쓰는 것이 보통이지만 who[whom]를 쓰기도 한다.

25 첫 번째 문장은 소녀의 꿈이 가수가 되는 것이므로 소유격 관계대명사가 들어가는 자리이다. 두 번째 문장의 빈칸은 동사를 이끌고 있으므로 주격 관계대명사 자리이다.

26 full of가 들어갈 곳은 없다. ⓐ in the middle of ⓑ feels like ⓒ out of ⓓ a drop of

27 ③ 물은 호주머니가 아닌 배낭에 있었다. ④ 물은 거의 떨어졌다.

28 뜨거운 바람이 얼굴을 태운다고 하였다.

29 참가자는 행사에 참가하는 사람을 의미한다.

30 ⓐ 사막 레이스에 참가하는 것을 가리키므로 복수명사를 지칭하는 them이 아니라 it, ⓑ 내용상 to test와 연결되는 것이므로 make, ⓒ anyone은 단수 취급하는 부정대명사이므로 crosses가 옳다.

31 Adrianna는 프랑스에서 온 사서라고 하였다. 따라서 도서관에서 일한다고 말한 ④번이 옳다.

01 freeze 02 ①

03 ⓒ → Who[Whom] 04 ⑤

05 (1) I often draw pictures in my free time.
(2) Have you ever been to Japan?
(3) I've never been to China.

06 what do you do in your free time?

07 I've never been there. 08 ①

09 Tom has been to Jeju-do.

10 have you ever heard of flying yoga?

11 ⑤ 12 ③ 13 ③, ⑤ 14 ③

15 ⑤ 16 It was the most painful moment of my life. 17 Kelly bought a book whose cover looked familiar to him. 18 the most diligent, as[so] diligent as (혹은 more diligent than) 19 ③

20 ③ 21 The Gobi Desert which[that] is in China is the windiest desert on earth. 22 ③

23 ④ 24 ④ 25 the greatest runners, ordinary people 26 Anyone who crosses the finish line can do anything.

01 주어진 단어는 반의어 관계를 나타낸다. melt: 녹다, freeze: 얼다

02 주어진 문장과 ①번에서는 '힘든', ②와 ③번에서는 '거친', ④번에서는 '질긴', ⑤번에서는 '건강한'을 의미한다.

03 이어지는 대화에서 '아빠'와 함께 배드민턴을 친다는 것으로 보아 'Who[Whom]'가 적절하다.

04 Jean이 이번 주 토요일에 Tom과 자전거를 탈 것이라는 설명은 바르지 않다.

08 확신을 표현하는 말로 certain(확신하는, 자신하는)과 바꾸어 쓸 수 있다.

09 제주도에 가 본 사람은 Tom이다.

11 No라는 대답으로 보아 (E)가 적절하다.

12 각각 지시부사, 관계대명사, 접속사 that이 들어가야 한다.

13 'She has long hair.' 혹은 'Her hair is long.'으로 머리가 길다는 표현을 할 수 있다.

14 late은 순서상 나중을 나타내는 의미로 사용될 때 최상급으로 last를 쓴다. You are the last person I want to talk with. '너는 내가 가장 대화하고 싶지 않은 사람이야.'라는 의미이다.

15 ⑤번은 '정직보다 덜 중요한 것은 아무것도 없다.'는 의미로 정직이 가장 중요하다는 의미의 다른 문장과 의미가 다르다.

16 painful: 고통스러운

17 look familiar to ~: ~에게 익숙해 보이다

18 diligent: 부지런한, 근면한

19 온도가 50도까지 올라가므로 가장 더운 곳과 어울리는 문장이다.

20 밑줄 친 ⓐ는 현재완료의 계속적 용법이다. ① 완료, ② 경험, ④, ⑤ 결과적 용법으로 쓰였다. 따라서 계속을 나타내는 ③번이 옳다.

21 관계대명사를 적절하게 이용하여 문장을 만든다. '중국에 있

는 고비사막'이므로 The Gobi Desert를 which[that] is in China가 수식하도록 한다.

22 take: ~만큼의 시간이 걸리다, take place: 개최되다

23 down이 아닌 up이라고 쓰는 것이 옳다.

24 (D) 평범한 사람들로만 이루어진 것은 아니다.

25 '4 Deserts Race'에 참가하는 사람들은 최고의 경주자들이 아니다.

26 cross the finish line: 결승선을 통과하다

서술형 실전문제
p.102~103

01 have you ever been to Jeju-do?

02 Jeju-do

03 She is planning to go to Jeju-do this summer.

04 Kevin is the youngest of his family members. / Kevin is younger than any other family member. / Kevin is younger than all the other family members. / No other family member is younger than Kevin. / No other family member is as[so] young as Kevin.

05 Is the chair which you are sitting on comfortable?

06 which(혹은 that), than, whose

07 who laughs last laughs best

08 is a story which expresses traditional beliefs

09 ⓐ go ⓑ going ⓒ goes

10 The first race takes place in the Atacama Desert in Chile which is the driest desert in the world.

11 In   12 on earth is as[so] cold as Antarctica

13 Take part in, which(혹은 that), to test your limits, make your own history

03 Mina는 이번 여름에 제주도를 방문할 계획이다.

04 young은 1음절 형용사이므로 -est를 붙여 최상급을 만든다.

05 which 뿐만 아니라 that도 가능하다.

06 첫 번째 빈칸은 선행사가 사물인 the town이므로 관계대명사 which 혹은 that을 쓰는 것이 옳으며, 마지막 빈칸은 이어서 나오는 명사 smile이 있으므로 소유격 관계대명사를 쓰는 것이 옳다.

07 best는 well의 최상급이다.

08 신화란 전통적인 믿음을 표현하는 이야기이다.

09 ⓐ 주어가 복수이므로 go ⓑ keep+Ving: 계속해서 V하다 ⓒ 주어가 단수이므로 goes

10 사물이 선행사이므로 which를 대신하여 that을 사용하여도 무관하다.

11 in fact: 사실

12 질문: 어떤 사막이 지구에서 가장 추운가? 답: 지구에 있는 어떤 사막도 남극만큼 춥지 않다.

13 4 Deserts Race가 사물이므로 관계대명사 which 혹은 that을 사용한다.

창의사고력 서술형 문제
p.104

|모범답안|

01 (1) flying yoga   (2) joining her yoga class
   (3) scary   (4) exercise more

02 (1) who teach English to students
   (2) who cut other people's hair
   (3) that deals with large amounts of information
   (4) which operates with an engine
   (5) who invented the first airplane

03 (1) Roses are the most beautiful flowers on earth.
   (2) Cheese cake is the most delicious food in the world.
   (3) No other food is spicier than curry to me.
   (4) This metal is the hardest material in the world.
   (5) This sofa is softer than any other sofa in the hall.

01 오늘 나는 Suji와 플라잉 요가에 대해 이야기를 나누었다. 나는 그것을 TV에서 본 적이 있다. 놀랍게도 그녀는 최근에 그것을 배우며 즐기고 있었다. 그녀는 그녀의 요가 수업에 가입할 것을 제안하였지만 그것은 내게 너무 두려워 보였다. 비록 나는 그녀의 제안을 받아들이지 않았지만 운동을 더 할 것을 결심했다.

단원별 모의고사
p.105~108

01 temperature   02 (1) direction   (2) scary
(3) boiling   (4) temperature   03 ①

04 (1) This novel was written about a series of historical facts.
   (2) The race takes place every spring.
   (3) The cat was found in the middle of the road.

05 ③   06 She likes badminton best.

07 ⑤   08 ⑤   09 ④   10 Have you ever done it on a real mountain?   11 ②

12 (E) → (C) → (D) → (A) → (B)   13 ③

14 ②   15 ③, ④   16 is the month that comes before   17 It is one of the worst experiences of my life.   18 ③   19 ④

20 It takes seven days to finish a race.   21 ②

22 colder than, as[so] cold as   23 ⑤

24 ③   25 who[that], test, limits, take part

26 (C) → (A) → (B)

01 어떤 물건이나 장소가 얼마나 뜨거운지 또는 차가운지의 정도의

02 direction: 방향 scary: 무서운, 두려운 boiling: 끓는 temperature: 온도, 체온

03 주어진 문장에서 head는 '~를 향해서 가다'라는 의미로 사용되었으므로 이와 같이 쓰인 것은 ①번이다. ②번과 ③번은 '머리', ④번과 ⑤번은 '책임자'라는 의미로 쓰였다.

05 (A) 뒤에 동사원형 play가 이어지므로 'Do', (B) '누구와 함께 주로 운동하니?'라고 묻고 있으므로 'with' (C) and 뒤에 동사가 이어져야 하므로 'ride'가 적절하다.

06 Jean이 여가 시간 활동으로 가장 좋아하는 운동은 배드민턴이다.

07 나머지는 모두 flying yoga를 가리키지만 ⓔ는 가주어 it을 나타낸다.

08 (A)와 나머지는 모두 '무서운'을 의미하지만 ⑤번은 '멋진, 아주 좋은'을 의미한다.

09 ④ Mike가 Suji와 함께 요가 수업을 받을 것이라는 진술은 바르지 않다.

12 (E) 주말 계획 설명 → (C) 자주 배드민턴을 치는지 질문 → (D) 대답 및 가장 좋아하는 여가 활동 설명 → (A) 누구와 함께 운동하는지 질문 → (B) 대답

13 위 문장은 'You borrowed his pen.'에서 온 것이고, 아래 문장은 'You lent him your pen.'에서 왔다. 따라서 각각 소유격 관계대명사와 목적격 관계대명사를 쓰면 된다.

14 형용사의 최상급은 정관사 the와 함께 쓴다.

15 선행사가 사물이며 관계대명사가 이끄는 절에 목적어가 빠져 있으므로, 목적격 관계대명사 which 혹은 that을 쓸 수 있다.

16 8월은 9월 앞에 오는 달이다.

17 bad의 최상급은 worst이다.

18 물이 떨어져 간다고 했으므로 충분히 물을 마셨다는 것은 어색하다.

19 ① 모래는 사방으로 뻗어 있고, ② 뜨거운 태양 때문에 바람도 뜨겁다고 하였으며, ③ 목이 마른 이유가 오랜 시간 걸어서인지 더운 바람 때문인지 알 수 없고, ⑤ 사막 레이스는 총 1000km 경주이다.

20 하나의 경주를 완주하는 데에 일주일이 걸린다고 하였다.

21 기간을 나타내고 있으므로 전치사 for를 쓰는 것이 옳다.

22 남극에 있는 사막은 지구상에서 가장 추운 곳이라고 하였다. 비교급과 원급을 이용한 최상급 표현으로 빈칸에 알맞은 말을 쓴다.

23 사람들이 사막 레이스에 참가하는 이유는 알 수 없다.

24 사람들이 경주에 참가하는 이유는 자신의 한계를 시험하고 자신만의 역사를 만들 기회가 되기 때문이다. 글을 읽고 나머지 질문에는 답할 수 없다.

25 anyone은 사람을 가리키며 동사 want를 바로 받아주므로 주격관계대명사를 쓰는 것이 옳다.

26 사막에 있다는 상상을 하는 주어진 문장 → (C) 사막이 뜨거워 물을 마시려고 배낭을 여는 내용 → (A) 물이 거의 없음을 확인하고 한 방울만 마신 채 계속 걷는 내용 → (B) 앞서 나온 모든 상황이 나쁜 꿈같지만 사막 레이스에 참가하는 사람들에게는 꿈이 아니라는 마무리로 이어지는 것이 자연스럽다.

Summer on a Stick

Reading

교과서

확인문제   p.112

1 T   2 F   3 T   4 F   5 F

확인문제   p.113

1 T   2 F   3 F   4 F   5 T

교과서 확인학습 A   p.114~115

01 hot days, are   02 stay cool   03 make
04 pineapple, kiwis, cup, makers   05 Steps
06 Cut, into small pieces   07 Peel, slice them
08 Put, pieces into   09 Add
10 Blend until, smooth   11 Pour, into
12 Add, slices   13 Close
14 Put them, for about   15 Finished
16 Enjoy, on a stick   17 Tips
18 are an excellent source of
19 more vitamin C than
20 when, a cold, try   21 Share
22 make your own   23 Share
24 use   25 cut them into
26 put them into, with   27 will be pretty

교과서 확인학습 B   p.116~117

1 The hot days of summer are here.
2 How can we stay cool?
3 Let's make ice pops together!
4 You need: 1/2 pineapple, 2 kiwis, 1 cup of apple juice, ice pop makers
5 Steps
6 Cut the pineapple into small pieces.
7 Peel the kiwis and slice them.
8 Put the pineapple pieces into the blender.

9 Add the apple juice.

10 Blend until the mix is smooth.

11 Pour the mix into the ice pop makers.

12 Add the kiwi slices.

13 Close the ice pop makers.

14 Put them in the freezer for about three hours.

15 Finished!

16 Enjoy your summer on a stick!

17 Health Tips

18 Pineapples are an excellent source of vitamin C.

19 They have more vitamin C than oranges.

20 So when you have a cold, try pineapples.

21 Share Your Ideas!

22 How will you make your own ice pops?

23 Share Your Ideas!

24 I will use kiwis and strawberries.

25 I will cut them into big pieces.

26 I will put them into the ice pop makers with apple juice.

27 I think my ice pops will be pretty.

서술형 실전문제

p.118~119

01 (1) freezer (2) slice (3) Pour (4) source

02 blender 03 pineapple

04 (1) Put the garbage into the trash can.

 (2) Dive into the water and swim with her.

05 (1) when (2) until (3) and

06 (1) Cut a carrot into small pieces.

 (2) I think (that) the book will be very useful.

07 pieces 08 peel

09 We have to pour the apple juice into the blender.

10 the ice pop makers

11 smooth, blending

12 vitamin C

13 He will use kiwis and strawberries to make his own ice pops.

14 that 15 Jinsu, it looks pretty!

01 slice: 얇은 조각, freezer: 냉동고, source: 원천, pour: 붓다, 따르다

02 부드러운 음식이나 음료를 섞기 위한 전기 기기: blender(믹서)

03 두껍고 거친 표면을 가졌으며 많은 즙이 있는 달콤한 노란색의 과육과 맨 윗부분의 뻣뻣한 나뭇잎을 가진 큰 열대 과일

04 garbage: 쓰레기 trash can: 쓰레기통 dive into: ~로 다이빙하다

05 (1) 주말에 집에 있을 때 주로 무엇을 하니? (2) 비가 그칠 때까지 기다리자. (3) 집중해라. 그러면 너는 그것을 더 잘 이해할 것이다.

06 cut something into pieces: ~을 잘게 자르다 useful: 유용한

07 작은 조각으로 잘라 자른 조각들을 믹서기에 넣는 것이다.

08 무언가의 껍질을 제거하는 것은 '벗기다'이다.

09 질문: 우리는 사과 주스를 어디에 부어야 하나요?

10 막대 아이스크림 틀을 냉동고에 넣는 것이다.

11 얼마나 오래 섞어야 하는지에 대한 질문에, 부드러워 보이면 섞는 것을 멈춰도 좋다고 대답한다. stop Ving: V하는 것을 멈추다

12 파인애플은 비타민 C가 풍부하다.

13 진수는 막대 아이스크림을 만들기 위해서 키위와 딸기를 사용할 것이라고 하였다.

14 완전한 문장을 이끌면서 동사 think의 목적어 역할을 하므로 명사절을 이끄는 접속사 that이 들어가는 것이 옳다.

단원별 예상문제

p.120~124

01 peel 02 slice 03 smooth 04 ③

05 ① 06 (1) cut (2) put (3) mix (4) stay

07 ③ 08 ①

09 (1) Clean the room, or your mom will be upset.

 (2) Unless you clean the room, your mom will be upset.

10 ② 11 (1) me to eat regularly (2) me to make more friends. 12 ⑤ 13 Mother Theresa is looked up to by people around the world.

14 ③ 15 am, will call, will take part in

16 enjoy 17 ④ 18 ④ 19 We have to peel the kiwis. 20 We put the ice pop makers in the freezer. 21 ④ 22 ④

23 kiwis and strawberries 24 파인애플에 비타민 C가 풍부해서 감기에 도움이 되므로 25 ③ 26 ⑤

27 ⑤ 28 We close the ice pop makers.

29 You finished making ice pops. 30 ③

31 When you have a cold, try pineapples. 32 big pieces, kiwis and strawberries 33 ④

34 ③ 35 ③ 36 We put them in the freezer for about three hours.

01 과일이나 야채 등의 외면을 벗겨내는 것은 peel(껍질을 벗기다)이다.

02 더 큰 조각에서 잘라낸 음식의 얇고 평평한 조각을 나타내는 말은 slice(얇은 조각)이다.

03 주어진 단어는 반의어 관계를 나타낸다. smooth: 부드러운, rough: 거친

04 pour: 쏟다, 붓다

05 보기의 close는 '닫다'라는 동사로 이처럼 쓰인 것은 ①번이다.

06 stay: 유지하다, mix: 섞다, cut A into B: A를 B(상태)로 자르다, put A into B: A를 B에 넣다

07 blend: 조화되다, 어울리다, 섞다

08 ①번은 to부정사의 형용사적 용법이고, 나머지는 모두 to부정사의 부사적 용법 중 목적을 나타낸다.

09 (1) 명령문+or ~는 '~해라, 그렇지 않으면'이라는 의미이다.
   (2) Unless는 접속사로 '~하지 않으면'이라는 의미로 사용된다.

10 보기와 ②에서 사용된 현재완료는 '계속'이다. ① 결과, ③, ④ 경험, ⑤ 완료로 쓰였다.

11 advise와 tell은 모두 to부정사를 목적격 보어로 취하는 동사이다.

12 speak well of: ~에 대해 좋게 말하다

13 look up to: ~을 존경하다

14 첫 번째 빈칸에는 주격 관계대명사, 세 번째 빈칸에는 목적격 관계대명사의 자리이다. 각각 사람 선행사이므로 who를 쓸 수 있으며, 두 번째 빈칸에는 의문사 who가 들어가는 것이 옳다. 사람이고 주격이므로 관계대명사 who가 들어가야 알맞다

15 조건의 부사절에서 현재시제로 미래를 나타내지만, 명사절 접속사 if는 미래를 의미하기 위해서 미래시제를 사용해야 한다.

16 어떤 것을 경험할 때 만족과 즐거움을 발견하는 것은 '즐기다'이다.

17 파인애플 주스가 아닌 사과 주스가 필요하다.

18 부사는 주격보어가 될 수 없다. 따라서 smooth가 옳다.

19 질문: 키위를 자르기 전에 무엇을 해야 하나요?

20 질문: 우리는 막대 아이스크림 틀을 어디에 두나요?

21 이어지는 답변이 막대 아이스크림을 만드는 방법에 관한 것이므로 how가 옳다.

22 진수가 사과 주스를 사용하는 이유는 알 수 없다.

23 키위와 딸기를 가리키는 말이다.

24 감기에 걸렸을 때 파인애플을 먹어 보기를 권하는 이유는 파인애플에 비타민 C가 풍부해서이다.

25 몇 개의 아이스크림 제조기가 필요한지는 알 수 없다.

26 파인애플을 믹서에 넣고 사과 주스를 추가한 후 부드러워질 때까지 섞은 후에 막대 아이스크림에 혼합물을 넣어주는 순서가 옳다.

27 밑줄 친 for는 기간을 나타내는 전치사로 '~ 동안'이라는 의미로 사용된다. ① ~에 대해, ② [~을 돕기] 위해, ③ [고용 되어] ~을 위해[~에서], ④ ~에 찬성[지지]하는

28 질문: 키위 슬라이스를 추가한 다음에 무엇을 하나요?

29 아이스크림을 만드는 것을 끝냈다는 의미이다.

30 파인애플은 오렌지보다 더 많은 비타민 C를 가지고 있다. 따라서 오렌지는 파인애플보다 비타민 C를 덜 가지고 있는 것이다.

31 have a cold: 감기에 걸리다

32 밑줄 친 ⓒ는 큰 조각의 키위와 딸기를 의미한다.

33 진수는 자신의 막대 아이스크림이 예쁠 것이라고 하였지만 맛있을 것이라고 언급하지는 않았다.

34 과일들을 섞기 위하여 믹서가 필요하다.

35 복수명사를 지칭하므로 them이라고 쓰는 것이 옳다.

36 질문: 막대 아이스크림 틀을 냉동실에 얼마나 오랫동안 두어야 하나요?

Come One, Come All

01 far   02 hometown   03 ①
04 (1) neighborhood   (2) parade   (3) advertise
(4) pile   (5) regularly   05 ①   06 ⑤
07 (1) sled   (2) colorful   (3) arrow

01 주어진 단어는 반의어 관계를 나타낸다. far: 먼, near: 가까운

02 '당신이 태어나거나 자란 도시나 마을'을 가리키는 것은 hometown(고향)이다.

03 ①번 문장에서 sail은 '돛'을 의미한다. rake: 갈퀴로 긁다, 긁어모으다

04 neighborhood: 근처, 이웃, parade: 퍼레이드, 행진, advertise: 광고하다, pile: 더미, regularly: 규칙적으로

05 주어진 문장에서 live는 형용사로 '실황인, 라이브의'를 의미하며 이와 같은 의미로 쓰인 것은 ①번이다. 나머지는 모두 '살다'나 '살아 있다'를 의미한다.

06 주어진 문장에서 cross는 '건너다'와 '십자, X표'를 의미한다.

07 sled: 썰매, colorful: 형형색색의, arrow: 화살

01 disappear   02 (1) live   (2) fireworks   (3) almost
(4) artwork   03 (1) to end   (2) more and more
(3) come out   (4) out of hand
04 (1) When will the music festival be held?
   (2) I enjoyed decorating the Christmas tree.
   (3) People gathered together to see the singer.
05 (1) People celebrate the festival everywhere for
      two days.
   (2) It was amazing to see my favorite singer in
      person.
   (3) People watch the artists shaping their works
      from beginning to end.

01 주어진 단어는 반의어 관계를 나타낸다. appear: 나타나다, disappear: 사라지다

02 live: 라이브의, 실황인, almost: 거의, fireworks: 불꽃놀이, artwork: 예술 작품

03 from beginning to end: 처음부터 끝까지, more and more: 더욱 더, come out: 나오다, out of hand: 손을 쓸 수 없는

04 hold: 개최하다, decorate: 장식하다, gather: 모이다, 모으다
05 (2) in person: 직접 (3) from beginning to end: 처음부터 끝까지

Conversation

핵심 Check   p.130~131

1 (1) How can I get to
(2) Cross the street, go straight
(3) Is there a hospital / just around
2 (1) take about half an hour
(2) How long will it take to / by bus
(3) How long will it take to decorate the classroom / take about two hours

교과서 대화문 익히기

Check(√) True or False   p.132

1 T   2 F   3 T   4 F

교과서 확인학습   p.134~135

Listen and Speak 1-A
How can I get to the library / Cross, go straight, make

Listen and Speak 1-B
What's up / free / Why, ask / having / Let's, near / How can I get there from the school / Come out, go straight, Make a left, on your left / Let's meet / See, then

Listen and Speak 1-C
How can, get to / Go straight, make, be on your right / far from / not

Listen and Speak 2-A
be late for / How long will it take to get to the theater / take about, by bus / almost

Listen and Speak 2-B
excited / Me, too, advertise / about making / post them, neighborhood / How long will it take to / take about / come to

Real Life Talk
get to / over there / Take, get off / How long will it take to get there / take about / the festival / it's a lot of fun / have a great time

시험대비 기본평가   p.136

01 It will take about 5 minutes by car.
02 (B) → (E) → (C) → (D) → (A)
03 ⓒ → and   04 ⑤

02 (B) 길 묻기 → (E) 길 안내하기 → (C) 거리가 먼지 질문 → (D) 대답 → (A) 감사 표현
03 between A and B: A와 B 사이에

시험대비 실력평가   p.137~138

01 How long will it take to get to the theater?
02 ①   03 why don't we have lunch together?
04 ⑤   05 advertise   06 ⓐ the school festival
ⓑ the posters   07 ⑤
08 He will go there by bus.
09 Because he heard (that) it's a lot of fun.
10 He should take the number 11 bus.
11 (A) get   (B) Go straight   (C) a right   (D) one block   (E) fron

02 by bus: 버스로
03 how about ~?=why don't we ~?= ~하는 게 어때?
04 위 대화를 읽고 Emma가 Ming's까지 가는 데 걸리는 시간은 알 수 없다.
05 '사람들이 물건을 사게 만들도록 물건에 대해 대중에게 이야기 하다'를 가리키는 말은 advertise(광고하다)이다.
07 Andy와 Mike가 그들의 이웃들과 포스터를 게시할 것이라는 설명은 대화의 내용과 일치하지 않는다.
11 Green Street까지 직진하세요. 우회전하세요. 한 구역 곧장 간 후 길을 건너면 마켓이 당신 앞에 있을 것입니다.

서술형 시험대비   p.139

01 How can I get to the library?
02 make a left 또는 turn left   03 ⓐ → excited
04 They are going to advertise the school festival.
05 They are going to make posters.
06 (A) Go straight to 1st Street and make a right
(B) left

01 이어지는 대답으로 보아 길을 묻는 질문이 적절하다.
02 make a left: 왼쪽으로 돌다
03 exciting: 흥분시키는, excited: 신나는, 흥분한
04 Andy와 Mike는 학교 축제를 홍보할 것이다.
05 Andy와 Mike는 포스터를 만들 것이다.
06 극장에 가기 위해 1st Street까지 곧장 간 후 오른쪽으로 돌면 왼쪽에 있다.

Grammar

p.140~141

핵심 Check

1 (1) It, to exercise　(2) It, to drive　(3) to lie

2 (1) felt, follow(ing)　(2) saw, enter(ing)

　(3) made[had], clean

시험대비 기본평가

p.142

01 (1) get → to get　(2) to changing → to change

　(3) said → say(또는 saying)

　(4) to dance → dance(또는 dancing)

02 (1) fall 또는 falling　(2) to go

　(3) break 또는 breaking　(4) to play

03 (1) I heard the baby cry(ing).

　(2) It is a good idea for you to wake up early.

　(3) Emma saw them swim(ming) around the island.

　(4) People watch the artists create their works

　　from beginning to end.

01 (1) 가주어 it에 의미상의 주어 'for+목적격'이 쓰였으므로 진주어로 to부정사를 쓰는 것이 옳다. (2) to부정사의 형태는 'to+동사원형'이다. (3), (4) 지각동사의 목적어가 목적격보어의 행위의 주체가 될 경우 목적격보어로 원형부정사나 현재분사를 쓰는 것이 옳다.

02 (1), (3) 지각동사의 목적격보어는 목적어와의 관계가 능동일 경우 원형부정사나 현재분사가 쓰인다. (2), (4) 진주어로 to부정사를 쓸 수 있다.

03 (1), (3) '아기가 우는 소리', '그들이 수영하는 것'은 모두 목적어가 목적격보어의 주체가 되므로 목적격보어로 원형부정사나 현재분사를 쓰는 것이 옳다. (2) 일찍 일어나는 것의 주체가 '너'이므로 의미상의 주어로 '너'를 명시하여 for you를 써야 한다. (4) 미술가들이 작품을 만드는 것을 지켜보는 것이므로 목적어로 the artists, 목적격 보어로 create their works를 쓴다.

시험대비 실력평가

p.143~145

01 ③　　**02** ②　　**03** ④

04 It is wrong to tell a lie.　**05** ⑤　**06** ③

07 ④　　**08** It is dangerous to ride a motorcycle without a helmet.　**09** ④　**10** ①

11 ②　　**12** anybody go(ing) out　**13** ②

14 ③　**15** ⑤　**16** It is a lot of fun to ride a horse.　**17** ④　**18** ⑤　**19** ③

20 I saw her call(ing) someone.　**21** ①, ④

22 ⑤　　**23** I saw the boy fall(ing) off the tree yesterday.　**24** using his phone　**25** It is not safe to stay here.

01 ③ 모두 가주어 It이지만 ③번은 인칭대명사 It이다. 전자는 해석되지 않지만 후자는 '그것'이라고 해석된다.

02 see는 지각동사로 목적격보어로 원형부정사 혹은 현재분사, 과거분사를 받을 수 있다. 친구들이 축구를 하는 주체가 되므로 play(ing)가 빈칸에 들어가는 것이 적절하다.

03 '이 책을 읽는 것'이 주어이므로 to read this book이라고 쓰고 어려웠다는 것은 과거이므로 was difficult를 쓴다.

04 '거짓말을 하는 것'을 진주어로 하여 문장을 만든다.

05 make가 사역동사로 쓰였으므로 목적격보어로 원형부정사 형태를 쓰는 것이 옳다.

06 '부부가 싸우는 소리', '집이 흔들리는 것'이므로 ③번이 옳다.

07 listen to는 지각동사이다. 따라서 목적격보어로 원형부정사나 현재분사를 쓰는 것이 옳다.

08 to가 필요하다.

09 '최선을 다하는 것'이 주어이므로 to do your best를 써서 진주어를 만들고 가주어 It을 쓴 것이 답이다.

10 남자가 차에 타는 것이므로 get 혹은 getting을 쓰는 것이 옳다. dormitory: 기숙사

11 모두 주어로 쓰인 to부정사이지만 ②번은 부사로 쓰인 to부정사로 감정의 원인을 나타낸다.

12 누가 나가는 것을 보지 못했다는 의미이다. anybody는 go out의 주체가 되므로 go out 혹은 going out을 쓸 수 있다.

13 hear는 지각동사이며 you가 들어오는 것이므로 원형부정사 혹은 현재분사를 목적격보어로 써야 한다.

14 (A), (C) 목적어와의 관계로 보아 지각동사의 목적격보어로 원형부정사나 현재분사를 쓰는 것이 옳으며, (B) 진주어이므로 to부정사를 쓰는 것이 옳다.

15 주어진 문장의 It은 가주어이다. ①, ② 시간, 명암을 나타내는 비인칭 주어, ③, ④ 인칭대명사, ⑤ 가주어

16 '말을 타는 것'이 주어이므로 가주어 it을 활용하여 문장을 만든다.

17 '나는 Brad가 길을 걷고 있는 것을 보았다'가 옳다.

18 make는 목적격보어로 원형부정사를 취하여 사역동사의 의미를 갖는다.

19 네가 창문을 닫는 것을 내가 보았다는 의미가 된다. 따라서 ③번이 가장 적절하다.

20 '그녀가 누군가에게 전화하는 것'이므로 목적어로 her, 목적격보어로 call 또는 calling을 쓸 수 있다.

21 It is fun 다음에는 진주어로 동명사를 쓸 수도 있으며, see는 지각동사에 해당하므로 목적격보어로 원형부정사나 현재분사를 쓴다.

22 to부정사의 형태는 'to+동사원형'이다.

23 '나는 그 소년이 어제 나무에서 떨어지는 것을 보았다'라고 쓸 수 있다.

24 using을 대신하여 use를 써도 무방하다.

25 가주어 it과 진주어로 to부정사를 이용하여 문장을 만든다.

01 you ride(또는 riding) a bike yesterday

02 It is bad to run on the stairs.

03 Did you see the accident happen?

04 It was good

05 It is not a good idea to allow students to use cell phones in school.

06 saw her cross(ing) the street

07 It is rude of you not to bow politely.

08 (1) To save water is important.
　　(2) It is important to save water.

09 open(ing) the window

10 It is difficult to shoot an arrow.

11 to reduce food waste in school cafeteria

12 musicians play(ing) beautiful live music, play(ing) catch, sing(ing) a song

13 It is easy to look up a word in a dictionary.

14 I heard someone play(ing) the piano.

15 It is important to be honest and fair.

16 잘못된 곳: to do → do(ing) 고친 이유: 지각동사의 목적격 보어로 원형부정사나 현재분사를 쓰는 것이 옳다.

17 It is not easy to be a doctor.

18 to watch them move the table

19 I felt someone follow(ing) me yesterday.

01 어제 네가 자전거를 타는 것을 보았기 때문이라고 답할 수 있다.

02 stairs: 계단

03 '사고가 발생하는 것을 보았니?'라는 문장으로 쓸 수 있다. happen: 발생하다

04 to부정사를 맨 뒤로 보낸 것으로 보아 가주어 it을 써야 함을 알 수 있다.

05 allow+목적어+to부정사: 목적어가 V하도록 허락하다

06 Susan이 길을 건너는 것을 보았다고 답하는 것이 적절하다. 'Susan이 길을 건너는 것'이므로 지각동사의 목적격보어로 원형부정사나 현재분사를 사용하여 답한다.

07 '예의 바르게 인사하지 않는 것'이 주어이다. to부정사의 부정은 to V 앞에 부정어를 써서 나타내므로 진주어를 not to bow politely라고 쓰는 것이 옳다.

08 '물을 절약하는 것'이 주어이므로 to save water라고 쓴다.

09 어떤 남자가 창문을 여는 것을 보았지만 그가 누구인지는 모른다고 답할 수 있다. 지각동사 see의 목적어로 창문을 여는 주체

인 a man이 쓰이고 있으므로 원형부정사나 현재분사를 목적격보어로 쓰는 것이 옳다.

10 'To shoot an arrow is difficult.'라고 써도 무방하다.

11 학교에서 음식물 쓰레기를 줄이려는 것이 힘들었다는 대답이 들어가는 것이 자연스럽다.

12 공원에서 너는 음악가들이 아름다운 즉석 연주를 하는 것을 들을 수 있다. 또한 너는 아이들이 캐치볼 놀이를 하고, 커플들이 노래를 부르는 것을 볼 수 있다.

13 difficult의 반의어는 easy이므로 사전에서 단어를 찾는 것은 쉽다고 답할 수 있다. 'To look up a word in a dictionary is easy.'라고 써도 좋다.

14 '누군가가 피아노를 연주하는' 소리이므로 목적어와 목적격보어로 someone play(ing) the piano를 쓰는 것이 옳다

15 fair: 공정한

16 해석: Brady는 Clara가 무언가를 하는 것을 보았고 그녀가 무엇을 하는지 궁금했다.

17 to become a doctor로 써도 무방하다.

18 move를 대신하여 moving을 써도 무방하다.

19 feel은 지각동사로 목적어와 목적격보어를 취하는 동사이다. '누군가가 나를 따라오는 것'이라고 하였으므로 목적어로 someone을 쓰고 목적격보어로
follow 혹은 following을 쓰는 것이 옳다.

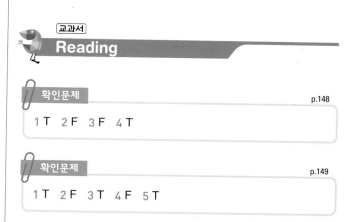

확인문제   p.148

1 T 2 F 3 F 4 T

확인문제   p.149

1 T 2 F 3 T 4 F 5 T

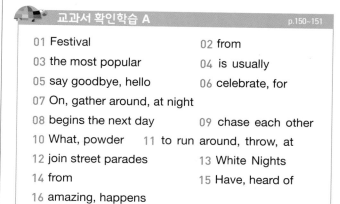

교과서 확인학습 A   p.150~151

01 Festival   02 from

03 the most popular   04 is usually

05 say goodbye, hello   06 celebrate, for

07 On, gather around, at night

08 begins the next day   09 chase each other

10 What, powder   11 to run around, throw, at

12 join street parades   13 White Nights

14 from   15 Have, heard of

16 amazing, happens

17 does not get completely   18 During, hold

19 starts in, lasts, about

20 there is, almost every night

21 popular, celebration   22 appears on the river

23 begin, follows   24 hear, playing

25 Snow Festival   26 from

27 my favorite season because of

28 starts in the last week, goes on

29 The largest event   30 shape, into, other

31 watch, shaping, from, to   32 favorite activity

33 to fly through, on

25 Kiruna Snow Festival

26 Ebba from Kiruna, Sweden

27 Winter is my favorite season because of the Kiruna Snow Festival.

28 The festival starts in the last week of January and goes on for five or six days.

29 The largest event is the snow design competition.

30 The artists shape huge piles of snow into animals, buildings, and other beautiful artworks.

31 People watch the artists shaping their works from beginning to end.

32 My favorite activity is the dog sled ride.

33 It is amazing to fly through a world of snow on a dog sled.

교과서 확인학습 B   p.152~153

1 Holi, the Festival of Colors

2 Amala from Delhi, India

3 Holi is the most popular festival in my country.

4 It is usually in March.

5 During the festival, we say goodbye to cold winter and hello to warm spring.

6 We celebrate the festival everywhere for two days.

7 On the first day, people gather around a big fire at night and sing and dance.

8 The main event begins the next day.

9 Children and adults chase each other with *gulal*.

10 What is *gulal*? It is blue, yellow, green and pink powder.

11 It's a lot of fun to run around and throw colorful powder at everyone.

12 We also join street parades!

13 White Nights Festival

14 Victor from St. Petersburg, Russia

15 Have you heard of the *White Nights*?

16 Every summer, this amazing thing happens in my hometown.

17 The night sky does not get completely dark.

18 During that time, we hold the White Nights Festival.

19 It usually starts in May and lasts for about a month.

20 During the festival, there is a ballet or an opera almost every night.

21 The most popular event is the Scarlet Sails celebration.

22 A boat with red sails slowly appears on the river.

23 Soon, fireworks begin and a water show follows.

24 You can also hear musicians playing beautiful live music.

시험대비 실력평가   p.154~157

01 ④   02 to run   03 ③

04 Holi is the most popular festival in India.

05 gather   06 ⑤   07 ②

08 the White Nights   09 ⑤

10 We can see a ballet or an opera almost every night.   11 shape (또는 shaping)   12 ②

13 ⑤   14 It lasts five or six days.   15 ②

16 ④   17 ⑤

18 chase[chasing] each other with gulal

19 We should go to the festival on the second day.

20 play(ing)   21 every summer   22 ⑤

23 ④   24 ②   25 ⑤

26 shaping their works   27 ④   28 ③, ⑤

01 at night: 밤에, throw something at someone: ~에게 ~을 던지다

02 가주어 it이 쓰이고 있으므로 진주어를 써야 한다. 병렬로 연결된 동사 throw의 형태로 미루어 보아 to run을 쓰는 것이 옳다.

03 주요 행사는 다음 날에 시작된다고 하였다. 따라서 ③번은 일치하지 않는다.

04 인도에서 가장 인기 있는 축제는 '홀리'라고 하였다.

05 사람들이 한 무리로 모이는 것은 gather이다.

06 colorful powder를 던진다고 하였다.

07 (A)에서 쓰인 현재완료는 '경험'이다. 따라서 '~에 가본 적이 있다'는 경험을 나타내는 has been to가 옳다.

08 '이 놀라운 것'이라는 것은 '백야'를 의미한다.

09 (C)는 '개최하다'는 의미로 쓰였다. ①, ③ ~을 쥐다, 잡다, ② 지탱하다, ④ (수화기를 들고) 기다리다, ⑤ 개최하다

10 축제 동안 거의 매일 밤 발레나 오페라가 있다고 하였다.

11 지각동사 watch의 목적격보어 자리이다. 목적어와 능동 관계에

있으므로 원형부사 혹은 현재분사를 쓴다.

12 (A) 명사구가 이어지고 있으므로 because of (B) 복수명사가 이어지고 있으므로 other (C) 놀라움을 유발하는 것이므로 현재분사 amazing을 쓰는 것이 옳다.

13 ⑤ 몇 명의 미술가가 눈 디자인 대회에 참가하는지는 알 수 없다.

14 축제는 5~6일 동안 지속된다고 하였다.

15 (A) 출신을 나타내는 전치사 from, (B) 월, 연도 앞에는 전치사 in, (C) 특정 기간을 나타내어 '~ 동안'이라는 의미는 during

16 ④ 축제 첫 날 밤에 사람들이 큰 모닥불 주변에 모여 노래하고 춤을 춘다고 하였다.

17 join은 타동사이므로 전치사 없이 목적어를 취한다. 따라서 join이라고 쓰는 것이 어법상 옳다.

18 축제 마지막 날인 둘째 날에는 어린이들과 어른들이 gulal을 지니고 서로를 쫓아다니는 모습을 볼 수 있다.

19 둘째 날에 주요 행사가 있다고 하였다. 따라서 주요 행사만 보고 싶다면 둘째 날 축제에 가야 한다.

20 목적어와 능동 관계에 있으므로 지각동사 hear의 목적보어로 원형부사나 현재분사를 쓸 수 있다.

21 백야 축제는 매년 여름마다 거행된다고 하였다.

22 배가 어디에서 오는지는 알 수 없다.

23 배가 서서히 나타난다고 하였으므로 ④번은 옳지 않다.

24 go on: 계속되다

25 ⑤ 눈 덩어리를 동물 모양으로 만드는 사람들은 미술가들이라고 하였다.

26 지각동사 see의 목적격보어 자리이므로 shape their works라고 써도 좋다.

27 ④ 미술가들은 눈덩이로 동물, 건물, 다른 아름다운 작품의 모양을 만든다고 하였다.

28 밑줄 친 (A)는 가주어 it이다. ①, ④ 인칭대명사 ② 비인칭 주어

서술형 시험대비
p.158~159

01 They celebrate the festival for two days.

02 gather around, sing and dance

03 is a lot of fun to run around and throw, colorful powder at everyone.

04 India in March

05 It is blue, yellow, green and pink powder.

06 St. Petersburg, Russia

07 It usually starts in May and lasts for about a month.

08 The night sky does not get completely dark.

09 There are a ballet or an opera almost every night and the Scarlet Sails celebration.

10 slowly appear(ing) on the river

11 to fly

12 Winter is Ebba's favorite season because of the Kiruna Snow Festival.

13 Kiruna, the snow design competition

14 It lasts for five or six days.

15 I am watching the artist shaping a huge pile of snow into an elephant.

01 축제는 이틀 동안 지속된다고 하였다.

02 gathering around, singing and dancing이라고 써도 좋다.

03 가주어를 이용하여 문장을 다시 쓸 수 있다.

04 홀리 축제를 보려면 3월에 인도로 가야 한다.

05 gulal은 파랑, 노랑, 초록, 분홍의 가루라고 하였다.

06 러시아 상트페테르부르크가 글쓴이의 고향이다.

07 빈도부사의 위치는 보통 일반동사 앞, be동사나 조동사 뒤이다.

08 밤하늘이 완전히 어두워지지 않는 것이 백야이다.

09 축제 행사로는 발레, 오페라, 붉은 돛 축하 행사가 있다고 하였다.

10 배가 강 위에 서서히 나타나는 것을 보았다고 쓸 수 있다. '배가 나타나는 것'이므로 지각동사의 목적어로 원형부사나 현재분사를 쓰는 것이 옳다.

11 진주어이므로 to fly를 쓴다.

12 키루나 눈 축제 때문에 Ebba는 겨울을 가장 좋아한다고 하였다.

13 키루나 눈 축제를 보기 위해서 키루나를 방문할 것이라면 축제에서 가장 큰 행사인 눈 디자인 대회를 보아야 한다고 말하는 것이 옳다.

14 축제는 5일이나 6일 동안 계속된다고 하였다.

15 '미술가가 ~을 바꾸는 것'이므로 목적어로 the artist, 목적격보어로 shaping ~을 쓰는 것이 옳다.

영역별 핵심문제
p.161~165

01 dark 02 ① 03 ④

04 (1) Go straight, make (2) each other (3) get off

05 ② 06 (1) Where is your hometown?

(2) It is across from the museum.

(3) My friends gathered to celebrate my birthday.

07 How can I get there from the school?

08 ④ 09 I hope many people come to the festival. 10 ⑤ 11 ⑤ 12 ④

13 ⑤ 14 ⑤ 15 ② 16 ④

17 to see him shouting at someone 18 ③

19 ⑤ 20 to hearing → to hear

21 It is exciting to learn English. 22 ②

23 ③ 24 I felt someone touch(ing) my shoulder. 25 celebrate 26 ④

27 ③ 28 ⑤ 29 ③

30 We can see the artists shape huge piles of snow into animals, buildings, and other beautiful artworks. 31 ④

32 It is interesting to watch the artists shaping their works from beginning to end. 33 sled

01 주어진 단어는 반의어 관계를 나타낸다. dark: 어두운, bright: 밝은

02 '따라가서 잡으려고 노력하다'를 가리키는 말은 chase (뒤쫓다)이다.

03 ④번 문장에서 chase는 '뒤쫓다'를 의미한다.

04 make a left: 왼쪽으로 돌다, each other: 서로, get off: 내리다

05 주어진 문장에서 sail은 '돛'을 의미하며 이와 같은 의미로 쓰인 문장은 ②번이다. 나머지는 모두 '항해하다'를 의미한다. retirement: 은퇴, navigator: 항해사, extend: 펼치다

06 hometown: 고향, across from: ~ 건너편에, celebrate: 축하하다

08 민수는 학교에서 나와서 Green Street까지 곧장 간 후 왼쪽으로 돌아야 음식점을 찾을 수 있다

10 Andy와 Mike가 포스터를 어디에서 만들지는 알 수 없다.

11 ⑤번을 제외한 나머지는 모두 감사에 대한 대답 표현이다.

12 (A)는 수원 화성에 어떻게 가는지 질문하는 문장이므로 get(도착하다)이 적절하다. (B) get on the bus: 버스를 타다, get off the bus: 버스에서 내리다 (C) 그곳까지 가는 데 소요 시간을 질문하고 있으므로 'How long will it take to ~?'가 적절하다.

13 Mina가 수원 화성 축제에 방문해 본 적이 있는지는 알 수 없다.

14 빈칸에는 목적격보어로 원형부정사를 쓰는 동사가 들어가야 한다. encourage는 목적격보어로 to부정사를 사용하는 동사이다.

15 모두 날씨, 날짜, 거리, 명암, 시간 등을 표현할 때 쓰이는 비인칭 주어 it이지만 ②번은 가주어 it이다.

16 누군가가 문을 열고 나가는 것이므로 open the door와 go out의 주체는 someone이 된다. 따라서 ④번이 옳다.

17 그가 누군가에게 소리 지르는 것을 보는 것은 놀라움을 주었다고 답하는 것이 자연스럽다.

18 ③ 소년들이 공을 차는 주체가 되므로 kick 혹은 kicking을 쓰는 것이 옳다.

19 밑줄 친 부분은 진주어로 쓰인 to부정사이다. 각각의 to부정사는 ① 목적격보어로 쓰인 명사적 용법 ② 부사적 용법 중 목적 ③ 명사를 꾸미는 형용사 ④ 동사의 목적어로 쓰인 명사적 용법 ⑤ 진주어로 쓰인 to부정사이다.

20 진주어는 to부정사이다. 따라서 to hear로 쓰는 것이 옳다.

21 '영어를 배우는 것'이 주어이므로 to learn English를 진주어로 하여 문장을 만든다.

22 ⓒ listen to는 지각동사이므로 tell 혹은 telling을 쓰는 것이 옳다. ⓓ 지각동사 see가 쓰였으므로 목적격보어로 원형부정사나 현재분사를 쓰는 것이 옳다.

23 첫 번째 빈칸은 진주어 자리이므로 to부정사를 쓰는 것이 옳으며, 두 번째 빈칸에는 지각동사의 목적격보어가 들어가야 하므로 ③번이 옳다.

24 '누군가가 내 어깨를 만지는 것'이므로 목적어로 someone, 목적격보어로 touch(ing)을 쓰는 것이 옳다.

25 중요한 행사나 명절을 위해 특별한 무언가를 하는 것은 '축하하다, 기념하다(celebrate)'이다.

26 아이들과 어른들이 gulal을 지니고 서로를 쫓아다닌다는 말이 먼저 나온 후 gulal이 무엇인지 설명해 주는 것이 자연스럽다.

27 ⓑ는 진주어로 쓰인 to부정사로 명사적 용법이다. 따라서 ③번이 옳다. ① 부사 용법 중 목적 ② 감정의 원인 ④ 형용사적 용법 ⑤ 부사적 용법 중 형용사 수식

28 축제에 있는 사람들이 얼마나 많은 양의 gulal을 가지고 있는지는 알 수 없다.

29 go on은 '계속되다'는 의미이다. 따라서 continue가 옳다.

30 눈 디자인 대회에서는 미술가들이 거대한 눈 덩어리를 동물, 건물, 다른 아름다운 작품의 모양으로 만드는 모습을 볼 수 있다. shaping을 써도 무방하다.

31 가장 큰 행사는 개썰매 타기가 아니라 눈 디자인 대회라고 하였다.

32 지각동사 watch의 목적어와 목적격보어가 능동 관계에 있으므로 shape를 써도 무방하다.

33 '눈 위로 미끄러지는 데 사용되는 작은 탈 것'은 '썰매'이다.

단원별 예상문제 p.166~169

01 bank(오른쪽 맨 위 건물) 02 Go straight two blocks and make a left. The bakery is between the hospital and the bus stop. 03 ⑤ 04 How long will it take to get there? 05 ① 06 (A) make posters (B) their neighborhood (C) about three hours (D) the (school) festival 07 ④ 08 ⑤ 09 1st Street까지 곧장 간 후 우회전하면 오른쪽에 우체국이 있다. 10 Is it far from here? 11 ③ 12 ③ 13 I heard Kevin speak(ing) French. 14 ② 15 ⑤ 16 It is a good chance to hear her play(ing) the violin. 17 Do you see a boy swim(ming) in the lake? 18 ① 19 ④ 20 ⑤ 21 ② 22 gulal

03 길을 묻는 질문에 소요 시간을 답하고 있으므로 ⑤번은 어색하다.

06 Andy와 Mike는 이번 주 금요일의 학교 축제로 매우 신이 났다. 이를 홍보하기 위해 그들은 포스터를 만들고 근방에 포스터를 붙이기로 결정한다. 포스터를 만드는 데 약 세 시간이 걸릴 것이다. 그들은 많은 사람들이 축제에 와서 즐기기를 원한다.

07 주어진 문장은 길을 안내해 주는 표현이므로 길을 묻는 표현 다음에 이어지는 (D)가 적절하다

08 ⓐ의 get은 '도착하다'라는 의미로 이와 같이 쓰인 것은 ⑤번이다. ①번은 '가져오다', ②번은 '타다', ③, ④번은 '받다'는 의미로 쓰였다.

11 진주어로 to부정사를 쓸 수 있으며 지각동사의 목적격보어로 원형부정사나 현재분사를 쓰는 것이 옳다.

12 모두 가주어 it이지만 ③번은 It was ~ that 강조 용법이다.

13 'Kevin이 프랑스어를 말하는 것'이므로 목적어로 Kevin, 목적격보어로 speak(ing) French를 써야 한다.

14 '목표를 설정하고 최선을 다하는 것'은 to set a goal and (to) do your best이다. 따라서 ②번이 옳다.

15 watch는 지각동사이며 목적어와 목적격보어의 관계가 능동이므로 원형부정사나 현재분사를 쓰는 것이 옳다.

16 '그녀가 바이올린을 연주하는 것'이므로 목적어로 her, 목적격보어로 play(ing) the violin을 써서 문장을 만든다.

17 '한 소년이 수영하고 있는 것'이므로 목적어로 a boy, 목적격보어로 swim(ming)을 쓰는 것이 옳다.

18 빈칸 ⓐ에는 전치사 of가 들어간다. ① get tired of: ~에 싫증이 나다 ② come up with: ~을 떠올리다 ③ look after: ~을 돌보다 ④ look up to: ~을 존경하다 ⑤ put off: ~을 미루다

19 백야에 대해 들어봤느냐는 질문에 - [C] 백야 설명 (this amazing thing이 'the White Nights' 지칭) - [A] 백야 기간 동안 축제를 옒 - [D] 축제 기간에 행사를 하고, 가장 인기 있는 축제는 '붉은 돛 축하 행사'임 - [B] 붉은 돛 축하 행사 설명

20 축제에 몇 명의 음악가들이 있는지는 알 수 없다.

21 홀리 축제를 이틀 동안 기념한다고 말한 후 첫째 날과 둘째 날에 어떤 행사가 있는지에 대한 설명이 이어지는 것이 자연스럽다.

22 형형색색의 가루는 gulal이다.

서술형 실전문제
p.170~171

01 They are going to have lunch together at the new Chinese restaurant, Ming's.

02 They are going to meet at 12 o'clock.

03 학교에서 나와서 Green Street까지 곧장 간 후 왼쪽으로 돌면 왼쪽에 있다.

04 call(ing) / called

05 It is essential to improve my English skill.

06 to have a balanced diet

07 Did you see the cat jump(ing) up onto the chair?

08 I saw the boy swimming in the pool.

09 It's a lot of fun to run around and throw colorful powder at everyone.

10 join street parades

11 People in India celebrate Holi in March.

12 It is in Gangneung.

13 We can see people swim(ming) at the beach.

14 It is soft and sweet.

04 someone은 나의 이름을 부르는 주체가 될 수 있으므로 현재분사나 원형부정사를 쓰고, 나의 이름은 '불리는 것'이므로 called를 쓰는 것이 옳다.

05 improve: 향상시키다

06 균형 잡힌 식사를 하는 것은 정말로 중요하다고 답할 수 있다. 다섯 단어이므로 to부정사로 만들어 답한다.

07 고양이가 의자로 뛰어오른 것을 보았는지 묻는 말로 쓸 수 있다.

09 'To run around and throw colorful powder at everyone is a lot of fun.' 혹은 'Running around and throwing colorful powder at everyone is a lot of fun.'으로 써도 무방하다.

10 이어지는 대답이 행진을 설명하는 말이므로 '거리 행진에 참가했니?'라고 묻는 것이 옳다.

11 홀리 축제는 3월에 있다고 하였다.

12 오죽헌은 강릉에 있다.

13 사람들이 해변에서 수영하는 것을 볼 수 있다.

14 감자떡이 어떤지를 묻는 말이다. 글쓴이는 감자떡이 부드럽고 달콤하다고 하였다.

창의사고력 서술형 문제
p.172

|모범답안|

01 Come out from the school and go straight to Green Street. Make a left, and the restaurant will be on your left.

02 (1) You can see many children chasing each other.
   (2) I can see many merchants selling their things.
   (3) I can hear people laughing happily at a festival.

03 (1) It is important to do your homework.
   (2) It is necessary to obey the school rules.
   (3) It is essential to pay attention to what a teacher says.
   (4) It is dangerous to run in the hall.

단원별 모의고사
p.173~176

01 ②   02 ②   03 ⑤

04 (1) threw (2) competition (3) huge

05 (1) go on (2) More and more (3) because of

(4) in front of 06 It will take about 15 minutes by bus.   07 이곳에서 수원 화성에 가는 것

08 off   09 ⑤

10 (1) How long does it take to get to school from your house?
   (2) How can I get to the bank?
   (3) Cross the street and go straight one block.
   (4) It will take about 10 minutes by subway.

11 (C) → (B) → (D) → (A)   12 ①   13 ④

27

14 ②　　　15 She heard the rain fall(ing) on the roof.　　　16 ③　　　17 ①, ②, ④

18 James felt something biting his arm.

19 ④　　　20 ②　　　21 ②　　　22 ③

23 It is amazing to fly through a world of snow on a dog sled.

01 '눈 위에서 미끄러지기 위해 사용되는 작은 탈 것'을 가리키는 말은 sled(썰매)이다.

02 주어진 문장에서 hold는 '개최하다, 열다'를 의미하며 이와 같은 의미로 쓰인 것은 ②번이다. ①, ③, ④번은 '잡다, 쥐다'를 의미하며 ⑤는 '맡다, 보유하다'를 의미한다. ⑤ 내 자리 좀 맡아 주실래요?

03 이어지는 대화로 보아 길을 묻는 표현이 적절하다. ⑤번은 소요 시간을 묻는 표현이다.

04 throw: 던지다, competition: 경쟁, 대회, huge: 거대한

05 go on: 지속되다, 계속되다, more and more: 더욱 더, because of: ~ 때문에, in front of: ~ 앞에

08 get off: 내리다

09 교실 장식의 소요 시간은 언급되지 않았다.

11 (C) 계획 질문 → (B) 계획 설명 → (D) 소요 시간 질문 → (A) 소요 시간 대답

12 학교에 어떻게 가는지 묻고 있으므로 ①번이 적절하다.

13 (a)는 부사로 쓰여 '거의, 대략'을 의미하며 이와 같은 의미로 쓰인 것은 ④번이다. 나머지는 모두 전치사로 '~에 관하여, ~에 대해'를 의미한다.

14 ② 지각동사의 목적격보어는 목적어와 능동의 관계에 있을 경우 원형부정사나 현재분사를 쓴다. 따라서 sing 혹은 singing을 쓰는 것이 옳다. pound on: ~을 마구 두드리다

15 '비가 지붕 위로 떨어지는 소리'이므로 목적어로 the rain, 목적격보어로 fall(ing)을 쓰는 것이 옳다.

16 두 문장 모두 지각동사의 목적격보어로 원형부정사나 현재분사를 쓸 수 있다. irritate: 짜증나게 하다

17 빈칸에는 목적격보어로 원형부정사를 취할 수 있는 동사가 와야 한다. 따라서 사역동사와 지각동사가 옳다.

18 '무언가가 그의 팔을 무는 것'이므로 목적어로 something, 목적격보어로 biting 혹은 bite을 써서 문장을 만든다.

19 (A) 명사가 따라오고 있으므로 전치사 During, (B) appear는 자동사이므로 수동태로 쓸 수 없다. (C) 연주자들이 연주를 하는 주체가 되므로 지각동사의 목적격보어로 원형부정사나 현재분사를 쓴다.

20 ② 밤하늘이 완전히 어두워지지 않는다고 하였으므로 무언가를 보는 것이 어렵다는 것은 글의 내용과 일치하지 않는다.

21 due to: ~ 때문에

22 눈 디자인 대회에서는 예술가들이 눈으로 특정한 모양을 만들며 겨룬다고 하였다.

23 fly through: ~을 날다

교과서 파헤치기

단어 TEST Step 1   p.02

01 미친 듯이, 열렬하게   02 던지다
03 단연, 틀림없이   04 청중, 관람객   05 재미있는, 우스운
06 기린   07 벽, 담   08 집회장, 홀
09 피아니스트, 피아노 연주자
10 고치다, 낫게 하다   11 만남, 모임
12 헝가리   13 기계, 기계장치
14 (많은 사랑을 받는) 우상
15 놓치다, 그리워하다   16 환상적인
17 자리, 좌석   18 자유   19 배드민턴
20 발명하다, 창안하다   21 본래의
22 벼룩시장   23 소리치다, 괴성을 지르다   26 인사
24 얼룩말   25 서명   26 인사
27 창조물, 창작   28 작곡가   29 준비하다
30 움직임   31 공연, 연극, 실행 32 최근의
33 얼굴; ~을 마주 보다[향하다]   34 ~와는 달리
35 딸기   36 악보   37 종이접기
38 점점 높이다   39 격려하다, 힘을 북돋우다
40 동시에, 한꺼번에 41 누르다   42 기억해서, 외워서
43 ~에 열중하다, ~에 열광하다

단어 TEST Step 2   p.03

01 softly   02 amazing   03 fan
04 signature   05 grape   06 vacation
07 greeting   08 drummer   09 single
10 fall   11 strawberry   12 concert
13 prepare   14 breath   15 composer
16 movement   17 ballet   18 note
19 performance   20 recent   21 novel
22 creation   23 unlike   24 face
25 miss   26 liberty   27 scream
28 invent   29 heal   30 machine
31 definitely   32 madly   33 flea market
34 original   35 sheet music   36 audience
37 fantastic   38 cheer up
39 hold one's breath   40 at once
41 press down   42 build up   43 in person

단어 TEST Step 3   p.04

1 concert, 연주회, 음악회   2 composer, 작곡가

3 breath, 숨, 호흡   4 pianist, 피아니스트
5 flea market, 벼룩시장   6 fall, 떨어지다
7 signature, 서명   8 idol, 우상   9 performance, 공연
10 hall, 홀, 집회장   11 heal, 고치다, 낫게 하다
12 original, 본래의   13 prepare, 준비하다
14 audience, 청중, 관람객   15 ballet, 발레
16 creation, 창조물

대화문 TEST Step 1   p.05~06

Listen & Speak 1 A

How's, going / fun, read lots, of / Which book, like
best / like, best

Listen & Speak 1 B

what are, going to, this Saturday / I'm going to, fan
meeting / a big fan / Which member, like best / like,
best, sing, well / drummer, fantastic, want to join /
love to, can't wait

Listen & Speak 1 C

like sports / Yes, do / Which sport, like best / tennis
best, exciting

Listen & Speak 2 A

Why, all those / going to sell, flea market / old
clothes, too / why don't you join

Listen & Speak 2 B

why, many paper flowers / for, mom's birthday /
beautiful, Where, get / made / good / taking a paper
folding class / going, the perfect gift / hope, too

Listen & Speak 2 C

Which country, want to visit / to visit Canada / Why
do you want to / Because, want to see

Real Life Talk

with the school radio show, your English teacher,
with / everyone, happy to be / Let's talk, what's your
favorite band / Definitely / like, too. Which song, like
best / most of, like, best / Why do you like it /
Because, makes, feel better, down. Let's listen to

대화문 TEST Step 2   p.07~08

Listen & Speak 1 A

Jack: Hi, Sumin. How's the book club going?
Sumin: It's fun . I read lots of interesting books.
Jack: Which book do you like best?
Sumin: I like Charlotte's Web best.

Listen & Speak 1 B

Amy: Jiho, what are you going to do this Saturday?

Jiho: I'm going to Blue Sky's fan meeting with my friends.

Amy: Wow, I'm also a big fan of the band.

Jiho: Really? Which member do you like best , Amy?

Amy: I like Lucy best . She sings really well.

Jiho: I like the drummer, Mike, best. He's fantastic! Do you want to join us?

Amy: Sure, I'd love to. I can't wait!

Listen & Speak 1 C

A: Do you like sports?

B: Yes , I do.

A: Which sport do you like best?

B: I like tennis best . It's so exciting!

Listen & Speak 2 A

B: Why do you have all those old clothes?

G: I'm going to sell them at the flea market.

B: Really? I have some old clothes , too.

G: Then why don't you join me this Saturday?

B: Okay.

Listen & Speak 2 B

Sujin: Tom, why do you have so many paper flowers ?

Tom: They're for my mom's birthday.

Sujin: They're so beautiful . Where did you get them?

Tom: I made them.

Sujin: Wow, you're really good.

Tom: Thanks. I'm taking a paper folding class these days.

Sujin: They are going to be the perfect gift for your mom.

Tom: I hope so, too.

Listen & Speak 2 C

A: Which country do you want to visit for your dream vacation?

B: I want to visit Canada.

A: Why do you want to visit Canada?

B: Because I want to see Niagara Falls.

Real Life Talk

Mina: Good afternoon, friends. I'm Mina with the school radio show. Today Mr. Smith, your English teacher, is here with us. Hi, Mr. Smith.

Mr. Smith: Hello, everyone . I'm happy to be here with you.

Mina: Let's talk about music. Mr. Smith, what's your favorite band?

Mina: Oh, I like them, too. Which song do you like best?

Mr. Smith: I like most of their songs, but I like Hey Jude best .

Mina: Why do you like it?

Mr. Smith: Because the song makes me feel better when I'm down.

Mina: That's great! Let's listen to the song.

본문 TEST Step 1 p.09~10

01 favorite, idol, will answer

02 often show, for   03 scream madly

04 Others, hours, take

05 some, even, another

06 recent creation, way   07 begin with, in

08 loved by, first 09 about, in, close

10 find, let's take, in   11 All, are filled

12 Unlike, side, faces

13 way, can, handsome, better   14 sheet music

15 play, memory

16 slowly by, touching

17 hold, breath, miss, note   18 up, down, at,

19 makes, powerful, rich

20 pays attention, movement

21 long beautiful, flies

22 like watching, at once   23 flies, ends

24 scream, throw, clothing, stage

25 goes wild   26 amazing star 27 His, born in

28 first, playing, when

29 later became, composer   30 think of, as

31 don't, give, listen

32 If, today's, will, original

본문 TEST Step 2 p.11~12

01 favorite, idol, Many, will

02 often show, love

03 scream madly at

04 Others, take pictures of

05 travel to, to see, favorite star

06 recent creation, way

07 begin with, in

08 loved by, not the first

09 How about, in, Not

10 To find, let's take, in   11 All, are filled

12 Unlike other concerts , faces, audience

13 way, can see, handsome, better

14 doesn't, any sheet music

15 begins to, from memory

16 slowly by softly touching

17 hold their breath, to miss a single note

18 builds up, press down, at once

19 makes, powerful, rich

20 pays attention to, body movement

21 long beautiful, flies

22 like watching, at once   23 flies, ends

24 scream, throw, clothing, onto the stage

25 goes wild   26 Who, amazing star

27 was, was born in

28 started playing, when he was seven

29 later became, composer   30 think of, as

31 Why don't, listen

32 If, like, idols, will love, original idol

19 이것은 음악을 아주 힘 있고 풍성하게 만든다.

20 청중들은 그의 모든 작은 몸짓에 주의를 집중한다.

21 그의 길고 아름다운 머리카락이 사방에 날린다.

22 이것은 마치 피아노와 발레 공연을 동시에 보는 것 같다.

23 시간은 쏜살같이 흐르고 연주회가 끝난다.

24 사람들은 소리를 지르며 꽃과 옷을 무대로 던진다.

25 콘서트홀은 열광의 도가니가 된다!

26 이 놀라운 스타는 누구였을까?

27 그의 이름은 Franz Liszt였고 그는 1811년에 헝가리에서 태어났다.

28 그는 7살에 처음 피아노를 치기 시작했다.

29 Liszt는 나중에 훌륭한 피아니스트이며 작곡가이자 선생님이 되었다.

30 그러나 많은 사람들은 그를 첫 번째 아이돌이라고 생각한다.

31 그의 음악을 한번 들어보는 게 어떤가?

32 만약 당신이 요즘의 아이돌을 좋아한다면, 원래의 아이돌도 좋아할 것이다.

1 여러분은 가장 좋아하는 K팝 아이돌이 있는가? 많은 학생들이 "그렇다."라고 답할 것이다.

2 이 학생들은 종종 자신들의 스타를 향해 큰 애정을 보인다.

3 어떤 학생들은 콘서트에서 미친 듯이 괴성을 지른다.

4 어떤 학생들은 스타의 사진을 찍기 위해 몇 시간을 기다린다.

5 어떤 학생들은 심지어 가장 좋아하는 스타를 보기 위해 다른 도시로 여행을 가기까지 한다.

6 아이돌이 최근의 창조물일까? 아니다!

7 아이돌은 1960년대의 The Beatles부터 시작됐을까?

8 그들은 많은 사람에게 사랑받았지만, 최초는 아니다.

9 1950년대의 Elvis Presley는 어떤가? 완전히 헛짚었다.

10 답을 찾기 위해서 1845년에 빈에 있는 한 콘서트홀로 타임머신을 타고 가 보자.

11 모든 좌석이 꽉 차 있다.

12 다른 연주회와는 달리 피아노의 옆면이 청중을 향해 있다.

13 이렇게 함으로써, 청중은 잘생긴 185cm의 피아니스트를 더 잘 볼 수 있다.

14 그는 어떠한 악보도 가지고 있지 않다.

15 그는 기억으로 연주하기 시작한다.

16 그는 건반을 부드럽게 누르면서 천천히 시작한다.

17 모든 사람들이 단 하나의 음도 놓치고 싶지 않아서 숨을 죽인다.

18 그는 속도를 점점 올리고, 그의 긴 손가락으로 많은 건반을 한꺼번에 누른다.

1 Do you have a favorite K-pop idol? Many students will answer, "Yes."

2 These students often show great love for their stars.

3 Some scream madly at concerts.

4 Others wait hours to take pictures of their stars.

5 Some students even travel to another city to see their favorite stars.

6 Are idols a recent creation? No way!

7 Did idols begin with The Beatles in the 1960's?

8 They were loved by many, but they were not the first.

9 How about Elvis Presley in the 1950's? Not even close.

10 To find the answer, let's take a time machine to a concert hall in Vienna in 1845.

11 All the seats are filled

12 Unlike other concerts, the side of the piano faces the audience.

13 This way, the audience can see the handsome 185cm pianist better.

14 He doesn't have any sheet music with him.

15 He begins to play from memory.

16 He starts slowly by softly touching the keys.

17 All the people hold their breath because they don't want to miss a single note.

18 He builds up speed, and his long fingers press down on many keys at once.

19 This makes the music very powerful and rich.

20 The audience pays attention to his every little body movement.

21 His long beautiful hair flies everywhere.

22 It's like watching a piano and ballet performance at once.

23 Time flies and the concert ends.

24 People scream and throw flowers and pieces of clothing onto the stage.

25 The concert hall goes wild!

26 Who was this amazing star?

27 His name was Franz Liszt and he was born in 1811 in Hungary.

28 He first started playing the piano when he was seven.

29 Liszt later became a great pianist, composer and teacher.

30 But many people think of him as the first idol.

31 Why don't you give his music a listen?

32 If you like today's idols, you will love the original idol.

7. powerful, rich

8. ended, went wild

Real Life Talk - Step 2

A: Which, like

B: like, best

A: Why, like

B: Because, great

A: Which song, best

B: cheers me up

Think and Write

1. Dear

2. my, big fan of

3. all of, love, best.

4. that, acting, real

5. How, prepare for

6. in person, will ask, more questions

7. hope to

8. Love

Read And Write

1. Our Time

2. performed, successfully

3. was different from

4. side, faced, audience

5. could see, this way.

6. sheet music, from memory.

Real Life Talk - Step 2

1. A: Which singer do you like best?

2. B: I like John Lennon best.

3. A: Why do you like him?

4. B: Because he is a great singer.

5. A: Which song do you like best?

6. B: I like Imagine best. It cheers me up.

Think and Write

1. Dear Sandra,

2. Hello, my name is Jina and I'm a big fan of you.

3. I watched all of your movies and I love "Into the Sky" best.

4. I think that your acting is so real.

5. How do you prepare for your roles?

6. If I meet you in person, I will ask you many more questions.

7. I hope to see you soon.

8. Love , Jina

Read And Write

1. The Star of Our Time

2. Yesterday Franz Liszt performed his piano concert very successfully in Vienna.

3. This concert was different from others.

4. The side of the piano faced the audience.

5. They could see Liszt better this way.

6. He didn't have any sheet music and played from memory.

7. His music was so powerful and rich.

8. When the concert ended , the concert hall went wild .

10 marathon, 마라톤　　11 traditional, 전통적인

12 protect, 보호하다　　13 race, 경주　　14 desert, 사막

15 throat, 목구멍　　16 train, 훈련하다

단어 TEST Step 1　　p.21

01 선수, 육상 경기 선수	02 도달하다, ~에 이르다
03 장비, 설비	04 기대하다	05 온도
06 무서워하는	07 놀라운	08 무서운, 두려운
09 참가자	10 젖은, 축축한	11 목구멍
12 얼다, 얼어붙다	13 한계, 제한; 제한하다
14 태우다, 타다	15 요청하다; 요구, 요청
16 보호하다	17 바람이 (많이) 부는	18 치다, 때리다
19 상상하다	20 줄넘기	21 사서
22 굽다	23 경주, 경쟁	24 암벽 등반
25 훈련하다; 기차	26 끓는, 끓어오르는	27 행성
28 전통적인	29 보통의, 평범한	30 타격, 펀치
31 힘든, 어려운	32 배낭	33 던지다
34 매달다	35 계속되다	36 ~에 참가하다
37 ~까지	38 사실은, 실제로	39 생계를 위해
40 일련의	41 일어나다, 개최되다
42 ~가 떨어지다, 바닥나다	43 ~을 돌보다

단어 TEST Step 2　　p.22

01 desert	02 direction	03 traditional
04 finish line	05 boiling	06 Antarctica
07 backpack	08 field	09 throw
10 relay	11 dry	12 marathon
13 planet	14 mean	15 hang
16 tough	17 bat	18 ride
19 gym	20 kick	21 ordinary
22 punch	23 giant	24 sand
25 uniform	26 temperature	27 equipment
28 freeze	29 protect	30 participant
31 athlete	32 limit	33 throat
34 wet	35 take part in	36 in the middle of
37 a series of	38 take place	39 be out of
40 go on	41 take care of	42 up to
43 in fact		

단어 TEST Step 3　　p.23

1 giant, 거대한　　2 Antarctica, 남극대륙

3 participant, 참가자　　4 librarian, 사서

5 athlete, (운동) 선수　　6 temperature, 온도

7 gym, 체육관　　8 freeze, 얼다, 얼어붙다　　9 boil, 끓다

대화문 TEST Step 1　　p.24~25

Listen & Speak 1 A

in your free time / often bake, How about / usually watch movies

Listen & Speak 1 B

happy, It's / What are you going to do / going to play badminton / play, often / my favorite free time activity / Who, usually play with / What do you do in your free time / often go, ride my bike

Listen & Speak 1 C

what, for a living / doctor / in your free time / I often play table tennis

Listen & Speak 2 A

have you ever been to / I have, went, What about / I've never been there, going / I'm sure, a lot

Listen & Speak 2 B

have you ever heard of / I've seen, were hanging / Guess, learning, these days / looked so scary / a little scared, enjoying / I think, should exercise, too / want to join / scary for, play basketball

Listen & Speak 2 C

Have you ever ridden / I have / When, ride a horse / Last summer

Real Life Talk

in your free time / often go rock climbing / What mountain, go to / usually do, gym near / Have you ever done / Not yet, hope to do / really cool, come and join / going this Saturday / sounds great / going to love

대화문 TEST Step 2　　p.26~27

Listen & Speak 1 A

Tony: Bomi, what do you do in your free time?

Bomi: I often bake cookies. How about you, Tony?

Tony: I usually watch movies.

Listen & Speak 1 B

Jean: I'm so happy. It's Friday!

Tom: What are you going to do on the weekend, Jean?

Jean: I'm going to play badminton.

Tom: Do you play badminton often?

Jean: Yes, it's my favorite free time activity.

Tom: Who do you usually play with?

Jean: My dad. What do you do in your free time?

Tom: I often go to the Han River and ride my bike.

Listen & Speak 1 C

Minsu: Ms. Allen, what do you do for a living?

Allen: I'm a doctor.

Minsu: What do you do in your free time?

Allen: I often play table tennis .

Listen & Speak 2 A

Mina: Tom, have you ever been to Jeju-do?

Tom: Yes, I have. I went there last winter vacation. What about you?

Mina: I've never been there, but I'm going there this summer.

Tom: That's great! I'm sure you'll like it a lot.

Listen & Speak 2 B

Suji: Mike, have you ever heard of flying yoga?

Mike: Yeah! I've seen it on TV. People were hanging in the air!

Suji: Guess what? I'm learning it these days.

Mike: Really? It looked so scary. Do you like it, Suji?

Suji: At first, I was a little scared, but now I'm enjoying it.

Mike: Sounds great! I think I should exercise more, too.

Suji: Do you want to join my yoga class?

Mike: No, that's too scary for me. I'll just play basketball.

Listen & Speak 2 C

A: Have you ever ridden a horse?

B: Yes, I have.

A: When did you ride a horse ?

B: Last summer .

Real Life Talk

Hojin: Judy, what do you do in your free time?

Judy: I often go rock climbing with my dad.

Hojin: What mountain do you go to?

Judy: No, Hojin. I usually do it at a gym near my house.

Hojin: I see. Have you ever done it on a real mountain?

Judy: Not yet. But I hope to do it someday.

Hojin: That's really cool. Can I come and join you next time?

Judy: Sure. I'm going this Saturday.

Hojin: That sounds great.

Judy: You're going to love it.

본문 TEST Step 1   p.28~29

01 Imagine, middle, great

02 on, every direction

03 feels like, fire   04 burns, face, throat

05 open, backpack, drink   06 almost, out of

07 wet, drop, keep going

08 Sounds like   09 dream, take part

10 series, races across, toughest

11 Each race, long, takes   12 takes place, in

13 the driest, in

14 fact, hasn't rained, for   15 goes to, in

16 the windiest desert

17 third, heads to, in

18 the hottest, deserts   19 reach up to

20 travels, coldest, earth

21 throw boiling, freezes

22 the greatest, take part   23 Not, exactly

24 participants, ordinary, like   25 So why, do

26 librarian from, says

27 chance, limits, own

28 Anyone, crosses, anything

본문 TEST Step 2   p.30~31

01 Imagine, in the middle of

02 go on and on   03 feels like, giant, fire

04 burns your face, throat

05 open your backpack to drink

06 almost, out of water

07 wet, with a drop of, keep going

08 Sounds like, bad dream

09 who take part in

10 a series of four races across, toughest deserts

11 Each race is, long, takes   12 takes place, in

13 the driest   14 In fact, hasn't rained, for

15 goes to, in   16 the windiest desert on earth

17 heads to   18 the hottest of, four deserts

19 reach up to

20 Finally, travels to the coldest desert

21 throw boiling water into freezes

22 the greatest runnners, take part in, right

23 Not, exactly   24 the participants are ordinary, like

25 why, do it   26 a librarian from France

27 a chance to test your limits, make

28 who crosses, can do anything

본문 TEST Step 3   p.32~33

1 당신이 아주 큰 사막의 한 가운데에 있다고 상상해 봐라.

2 모래 벌판이 사면팔방으로 계속 이어진다.

3 태양은 거대한 불덩이 같다.

4 뜨거운 바람이 당신의 얼굴과 목구멍을 태운다.

5 당신은 물을 좀 마시려고 배낭을 연다.

6 오, 이런! 물이 거의 떨어져 간다.

7 당신은 물 한 방울로 목을 적시고 계속 간다.

8 나쁜 꿈인 것 같은가?

9 글쎄, '4 Deserts Race'에 참가하는 사람들에게 이것은 꿈이 아니다.

10 '4 Deserts Race'는 세계에서 가장 험한 사막들을 가로지르는 연속된 4개의 경주이다.

11 각 경주는250킬로미터이고 7일이 걸린다.

12 첫 번째 경주는 칠레에 있는 아타카마 사막에서 열린다.

13 그곳은 세계에서 가장 건조한 사막이다.

14 실제로 아타카마 사막의 어떤 곳에는 400년간 비가 내리지 않았다!

15 다음 경주는 중국에 있는 고비 사막으로 이어진다.

16 그곳은 세상에서 가장 바람이 많이 부는 사막이다.

17 세 번째 경주는 이집트에 있는 사하라 사막으로 향한다.

18 그곳은 네 개의 사막 중 가장 뜨겁다.

19 온도가 섭씨 50도까지 올라갈 수 있다.

20 마지막으로 경주는 세상에서 가장 추운 사막인 남극 대륙으로 향한다.

21 이곳에서 끓는 물을 공중에 던지면, 그것은 얼어버린다!

22 세상에서 가장 훌륭한 달리기 주자들만 '4 Deserts Race'에 참가할 수 있다, 맞는가?

23 꼭 그렇진 않다.

24 많은 참가자들은 당신과 나와 같은 평범한 사람들이다.

25 그러면 그들은 왜 그것을 하는가?

26 프랑스 출신의 사서인 Adrianna는 말한다.

27 "그것은 당신의 한계를 시험하고 당신만의 역사를 만들 기회예요.

28 결승선을 넘는 사람은 어떤 것이든 할 수 있어요."

1 Imagine you are in the middle of a great desert.

2 The sands go on and on in every direction.

3 The sun feels like a giant ball of fire.

4 The hot wind burns your face and throat.

5 You open your backpack to drink some water.

6 Oh, no! You're almost out of water.

7 You wet your throat with a drop of water and keep going.

8 Sounds like a bad dream?

9 Well, this is not a dream for the people who take part in the 4 Deserts Race.

10 The 4 Deserts Race is a series of four races across the world's toughest deserts.

11 Each race is 250 kilometers long and takes seven days.

12 The first race takes place in the Atacama Desert in Chile.

13 It is the driest desert in the world.

14 In fact, it hasn't rained in some parts of the Atacama Desert for 400 years!

15 The next race goes to the Gobi Desert in China.

16 It is the windiest desert on earth.

17 The third race heads to the Sahara Desert in Egypt.

18 It is the hottest of the four deserts.

19 Temperatures can reach up to 50℃.

20 Finally, the race travels to the coldest desert on earth, Antarctica.

21 If you throw boiling water into the air here, it freezes!

22 Only the greatest runners on the planet can take part in 4 Deserts Race, right?

23 Not exactly.

24 Many of the participants are ordinary people like you and me.

25 So why do they do it?

26 Adrianna, a librarian from France, says,

27 "It's a chance to test your limits and make your own history.

28 Anyone who crosses the finish line can do anything."

Real Life Talk - Step 2

1. in your free time

2. often play

3. Have, played

4. haven't

5. Have, played

6. Yes, I have

7. hit a home run

8. have

Think and Write

1. Day, class

2. was held on

3. exciting

4. played basketball, jump rope

5. ran a relay race

6. jump rope, relay race

7. won, 100m race

8. got, highest score, became, overall

9. All the classes

단어 TEST Step 1 p.40

01 조각, 일부, 부분	02 시원한, 냉정한, 멋진
03 추운, 찬; 감기	04 자르다 05 단계
06 파인애플	07 껍질을 벗기다; 껍질 08 믹서
09 냉동고	10 원천, 근원 11 대략, 약
12 조언, 비결	13 매끄러운, 부드러운
14 섞다, 혼합하다	15 ~인 채로 있다, 남다, 머무르다
16 시도하다, 해보다	17 더하다, 추가하다
18 얇게 썰다(베다); 얇은 조각	19 비타민
20 나누다, 공유하다 21 건강	
22 혼합(물); 섞다, 혼합하다	23 우수한, 훌륭한
24 붓다, 따르다 25 끝내다, 마치다	26 딸기
27 ~까지 28 막대기, 지팡이	29 필요하다
30 ~을 만드는 기계(사람, 회사)	
31 예쁜, 귀여운; 꽤, 상당히	32 자기 자신의, 고유한
33 (문, 가게를) 닫다, (눈을) 감다	34 막대 아이스크림
35 사과 주스 36 시원함을 유지하다	37 감기에 걸리다
38 A를 B에 넣다 39 2분의 1	
40 A를 B(상태)로 자르다	41 ~을 섞다
42 A를 B에 붓다 43 한 잔(컵)의 ~	

구석구석지문 TEST Step 2 p.39

Real Life Talk - Step 2

1. G: What do you do in your free time?

2. B: I often play sports.

3. G: Have you ever played table tennis?

4. B: No, I haven't.

5. G: Have you ever played baseball?

6. B: Yes, I have.

7. G: Have you ever hit a home run?

8. B: Yes, I have.

Think and Write

1. A Happy Day for Class 3

2. The school sports day was held on May 14th.

3. It was very exciting.

4. Students played basketball and did group jump rope.

5. They also ran a relay race and a 100m race.

6. Class 2 won the group jump rope, and Class 1 won the relay race.

7. Class 3 won the basketball game and the 100m race.

8. They got the highest score and became the overall winner.

9. All the classes had great fun.

단어 TEST Step 2 p.41

01 apple juice	02 share	03 strawberry
04 enjoy	05 excellent	06 finish
07 close	08 stick	09 health
10 mix	11 ice pop	12 kiwi
13 maker	14 need	15 pour
16 orange	17 pretty	18 until
19 own	20 peel	21 freezer
22 slice	23 smooth	24 blend
25 piece	26 add	27 source
28 blender	29 tip	30 cut
31 try	32 stay	33 cool
34 pineapple	35 step	36 piece
37 pour A into B	38 a half(=one half)	
39 stay cool	40 cut A into B	41 have a cold
42 mix up	43 put A into B	

단어 TEST Step 3 p.42

1 excellent, 훌륭한, 우수한   2 share, 공유하다

3 peel, 껍질을 벗기다   4 blender, 믹서

5 smooth, 매끄러운   6 stick, 막대기   7 step, 단계

8 tip, 조언, 비결   9 cut, 자르다   10 slice, 얇은 조각

11 mix, 혼합   12 vitamin, 비타민

13 pineapple, 파인애플   14 pour, 붓다, 따르다

15 add, 더하다   16 strawberry, 딸기

23 Share your Ideas

24 use, strawberries.

25 cut them into big pieces

26 put them into, with apple juice

27 I think, will be pretty

본문 TEST Step 1   p.43~44

01 hot days, are   02 can, stay cool

03 Let's make, together

04 need, of, makers

05 Cut, into, pieces

06 Peel, slice them

07 Put, pieces into   08 Add, juice

09 Blend until, smooth

10 Pour, into, makers   11 Add, slices

12 Close, pop   13 Put in, for about

14 Finished, Enjoy, on, stick   15 Health Tips

16 excellent source, vitamin

17 more vitamin, than

18 when, cold, try   19 Share, Ideas

20 will, your own   21 Share your

22 will use, strawberries

23 cut, into, pieces   24 put into, with

27 think, will be

본문 TEST Step 2   p.45~46

01 hot days of, are

02 How can, stay cool

03 Let's make, together

04 need, pineapple, kiwis, cup, makers

05 Steps   06 Cut, into small pieces

07 Peel, slice them

08 Put, pieces into the blender

09 Add, apple juice

10 Blend until, smooth

11 Pour, into, ice pop makers   12 Add, slices

13 Close, ice pop makers

14 Put them, for about   15 Finished

16 Enjoy, on a stick   17 Health Tips

18 are an excellent source of vitamin

19 more vitamin C than oranges

20 when, have a cold, try

21 Share, Ideas   22 How will, make your own

본문 TEST Step 3   p.47~48

1 더운 여름날이 왔어요.

2 우리는 어떻게 시원하게 지낼 수 있을까요?

3 막대 아이스크림을 함께 만들어 봐요!

4 여러분은 필요해요: 파인애플 1/2개, 키위 2개, 사과 주스 1컵,
   막대 아이스크림 틀

5 단계

6 파인애플을 작은 조각으로 자르세요.

7 키위의 껍질을 벗기고 얇게 자르세요.

8 파인애플 조각들을 믹서에 넣으세요.

9 사과 주스를 첨가하세요.

10 혼합물이 덩어리 없이 골고루 잘 섞일 때까지 섞으세요.

11 혼합물을 막대 아이스크림 틀에 부으세요.

12 키위 조각을 추가하세요.

13 막대 아이스크림 틀을 닫으세요.

14 약 세 시간 동안 그것들을 냉동고에 넣으세요.

15 끝났어요!

16 막대 위의 여름을 맛보세요!

17 건강 조언들

18 파인애플은 비타민 C의 훌륭한 원천이에요.

19 파인애플에는 비타민 C가 오렌지보다 더 많이 들어 있어요.

20 그러니 감기에 걸리면 파인애플을 먹어 보세요.

21 여러분의 생각을 나누세요!

22 여러분은 어떻게 막대 아이스크림을 만들 건가요?

23 여러분의 생각을 나누세요!

24 저는 키위와 딸기를 사용할 거예요.

25 저는 그것들을 크게 자를 거예요.

26 그것들을 사과 주스와 함께 막대 아이스크림 틀에 넣을 거예요.

27 제 막대 아이스크림은 예쁠 것 같아요.

본문 TEST Step 3 - Step 4   p.49~52

1 The hot days of summer are here.

2 How can we stay cool?

3 Let's make ice pops together!

4 You need: 1/2 pineapple, 2 kiwis, 1 cup of apple
   juice, ice pop makers

5 Steps: Cut the pineapple into small pieces.

6 Peel the kiwis and slice them.

7　Put the pineapple pieces into the blender.

8　Add the apple juice.

9　Blend until the mix is smooth.

10　Pour the mix into the ice pop makers.

11　Add the kiwi slices.

12　Close the ice pop makers.

13　Put them in the freezer for about three hours.

14　Finished! Enjoy your summer on a stick!

15　Health Tips

16　Pineapples are an excellent source of vitamin C.

17　They have more vitamin C than oranges.

18　So when you have a cold, try pineapples.

19　Share Your Ideas!

20　How will you make your own ice pops?

21　Share Your Ideas!

22　I will use kiwis and strawberries.

23　I will cut them into big pieces.

24　I will put them into the ice pop makers with apple juice.

25　I think my ice pops will be pretty.

단어 TEST Step 1　　　　　　　　　　　　　　　p.53

01 화살	02 근처, 이웃, 인근	03 나타나다
04 어두운	05 해결하다	06 장식하다
07 먼, 멀리	08 폭죽, 불꽃놀이	09 따르다
10 모이다, 모으다	11 형태, ~ 모양으로 만들다	
12 놀라운	13 거대한	14 지속하다
15 광고하다	16 대회, 시합, 경쟁	17 축제
18 썰매	19 거의	20 완전히
21 게시하다	22 음악가	23 축하하다, 기념하다
24 야외의	25 뒤쫓다	26 더미
27 예술 작품	28 가루	29 성인, 어른
30 형형색색의	31 개최하다	32 던지다
33 고향	34 빵집, 제과점	35 서로
36 손을 쓸 수 없는	37 처음부터 끝까지	38 A와 B 사이에
39 지속되다, 계속되다		40 ~ 때문에
41 더욱 더	42 ~의 오른편에	43 ~ 앞에

단어 TEST Step 2　　　　　　　　　　　　　　　p.54

01 bakery	02 celebrate	03 colorful
04 parade	05 take	06 during
07 sail	08 artwork	09 chase
10 hold	11 hometown	12 boat
13 cross	14 live	15 near
16 powder	17 outdoor	18 block
19 pile	20 adult	21 throw
22 decorate	23 gather	24 advertise
25 solve	26 last	27 appear
28 neighborhood	29 competition	30 firework
31 huge	32 arrow	33 completely
34 follow	35 more and more	
36 get off	37 each other	38 in front of
39 because of	40 next to	41 go on
42 between A and B		
43 from beginning to end		

단어 TEST Step 3　　　　　　　　　　　　　　　p.55

1 lift, 들어올리다　　2 adult, 어른　　3 chase, 뒤쫓다

4 artwork, 예술 작품　　5 competition, 대회, 경쟁

6 festival, 축제　　7 sled, 썰매　　8 last, 지속하다

9 hometown, 고향　　10 gather, 모이다　　11 hold, 개최하다

12 pile, 더미   13 advertise, 광고하다

14 shape, ~ 모양으로 만들다   15 celebrate, 축하하다

16 decorate, 장식하다

Listen and Speak 1-A

How can I get to the library / Cross, go straight, make a left / Thank you

Listen and Speak 1-B

What's up / Are, free this Saturday / Why do, ask / about having lunch / Let's try, Chinese restaurant, near / How can I get there from the school / Come out, go straight, Make a left, be on your left / All right. Let's meet at / See you then

Listen and Speak 1-C

Excuse me, can, get to / Go straight, make a right, will be on your right / Is, far from / No, not / Thank you

Listen and Speak 2-A

hurry up, going to be late for / How long will it take to get to the theater / take about, by bus / almost ready

Listen and Speak 2-B

excited about, this Friday / Me, too, can, do to advertise / about making / can post them, neighborhood / How long will it take to / take about three hours / I hope, come to the festival

Real Life Talk

Excuse, How can, get to / easy, over there / I do / Take, get off / How long will it take to get there / take about 20 minutes / very much / problem, Are, going, the festival / its's a lot of fun / I hope, have a great time

---

Listen and Speak 1-A

Sora: Excuse me. How can I get to the library?

Tom: Oh, the library? Cross the street and go straight two blocks. Then make a left.

Sora: Thank you very much.

Listen and Speak 1-B

Minsu: Hi, Emma. What's up?

Emma: Hey, Minsu. Are you free this Saturday?

Minsu: Yes. Why do you ask?

Emma: Well, how about having lunch together?

Minsu: Sure.

Emma: Let's try the new Chinese restaurant, Ming's.

It's near the school.

Minsu: Okay. How can I get there from the school?

Emma: Come out from the school and go straight to Green Street. Make a left, and the restaurant will be on your left.

Minsu: All right. Let's meet at 12 o'clock.

Emma: Wonderful. See you then.

Listen and Speak 1-C

A: Excuse me. How can I get to the post office?

B: Go straight to 1st Street and make a right. It will be on your right.

A: Is it far from here?

B: No, it's not.

A: Thank you very much.

Listen and Speak 2-A

Amy: Jinho, hurry up. We're going to be late for the movie.

Jinho: Okay. How long will it take to get to the theater?

Amy: It will take about 15 minutes by bus.

Jinho: All right. I'm almost ready.

Listen and Speak 2-B

Andy: I'm so excited about the school festival this Friday.

Mike: Me, too. What can we do to advertise it, Andy?

Andy: How about making posters?

Mike: Great idea. We can post them in our neighborhood.

Andy: Right. How long will it take to make them?

Mike: Well, it will take about three hours.

Andy: Okay, I hope many people come to the festival.

Real Life Talk

Man: Excuse me. How can I get to Suwon Hwaseong from here?

Mina: It's easy. Do you see the bus stop over there?

Man: Yes, I do.

Mina: Take the No. 11 bus and get off at the sixth stop.

Man: How long will it take to get there?

Mina: It will take about 20 minutes.

Man: Thank you very much.

Mina: No problem. Are you going there for the festival?

Man: Yes. I heard it's a lot of fun.

Mina: I hope you have a great time.

01 Festival, Colors   02 from Delhi
03 most popular, my   04 is usually in
05 During, say, hello
06 celebrate, everywhere for
07 On, gather around, at
08 main, begins, next
09 chase each other
10 What, green, powder
11 run around, throw, at
12 also join, parades
13 White Nights   14 from, Petersburg, Russia
15 Have, heard of
16 Every, amazing, happens
17 get completely dark   18 During, hold
19 in, lasts, about
20 there, almost every
21 most popular, celebration
22 with, appears on   23 begin, follows
24 also hear, playing   25 Kiruna, Festival
26 from Kiruna   27 favorite, because of
28 starts, last, goes on
29 largest event, competition
30 shape, into, other
31 watch, shaping, from, to
32 activity, sled ride   33 to, through, on

01 Festival of Colors
02 from Delhi, India
03 the most popular festival
04 is usually in March
05 During, say goodbye, hello, warm spring
06 celebrate, for two days
07 On, gather around, at night, sing and dance
08 main, begins the next day
09 chase each other with
10 What, powder 11 to run around, throw, at everyone
12 also join street parades
13 White Nights   14 from, Russia
15 Have you heard of
16 amazing, happens
17 does not get completely dark   18 During, hold
19 usually starts in, lasts for about
20 During, there is, almost every night
21 most popular, celebration

22 appears on the river
23 fireworks begin, follows
24 also hear, playing   25 Snow Festival
26 from Kiruna, Sweden
27 my favorite season because of
28 starts in the last week, goes on for
29 The largest event, competition
30 shape huge piles, into, other
31 watch, shaping, from beginning to end
32 favorite activity, dog sled ride
33 It, amazing to fly through, on

1 홀리, 색의 축제
2 인도, 델리의 Amala
3 '홀리'는 우리나라에서 가장 인기 있는 축제예요.
4 그것은 보통 3월에 있어요.
5 축제 기간 동안에, 우리는 추운 겨울에게 작별 인사를 하고 따뜻한 봄을 맞는 인사를 해요.
6 우리는 이틀 동안 어디서든 축제를 기념해요.
7 첫째 날, 사람들은 밤에 큰 모닥불 주변에 모여 노래하고 춤을 춰요.
8 주요 행사는 다음 날에 시작돼요.
9 어린이들과 어른들이 'gulal'을 지니고 서로를 쫓아다녀요.
10 'gulal'이 무엇이냐고요? 그것은 파랑, 노랑, 초록, 분홍의 가루예요.
11 주변을 뛰어다니며 형형색색의 가루를 모든 사람들에게 던지는 것은 정말 재미있어요.
12 우리는 거리 행진에도 참가해요!
13 백야 축제
14 러시아, 상트페테르부르크의 Victor
15 '백야'에 대해 들어 봤나요?
16 매년 여름, 이 놀라운 일이 나의 고향에서 벌어져요.
17 밤하늘이 완전히 어두워지지 않아요.
18 그 시기 동안, 우리는 백야 축제를 열어요.
19 축제는 보통 5월에 시작되고 약 한 달 동안 지속돼요.
20 축제 기간 동안 거의 매일 밤 발레나 오페라 공연이 있어요.
21 가장 인기 있는 행사는 '붉은 돛 축하 행사'예요.
22 빨간 돛을 단 배가 강 위에 서서히 나타나요.
23 곧 불꽃놀이가 시작되고 물 쇼가 이어져요.
24 또한 여러분은 음악가들이 아름다운 라이브 음악을 연주하는 것을 들을 수 있어요.
25 키루나 눈 축제
26 스웨덴, 키루나의 Ebba
27 겨울은 키루나 눈 축제 때문에 내가 가장 좋아하는 계절이에요.
28 축제는 1월 마지막 주에 시작해서 5일이나 6일 동안 계속돼요.

29 가장 큰 행사는 '눈 디자인 대회'예요.

30 미술가들이 거대한 눈 덩어리를 동물, 건물, 다른 아름다운 작품의 모양으로 만들어요.

31 사람들은 미술가들이 그들의 작품을 만드는 것을 처음부터 끝까지 지켜봐요.

32 내가 가장 좋아하는 활동은 개썰매 타기예요.

33 개썰매를 타고 눈 세상을 날아가는 것은 정말 놀라워요.

본문 TEST Step 4-Step 5
p.66~69

1 Holi, the Festival of Colors

2 Amala from Delhi, India

3 Holi is the most popular festival in my country.

4 It is usually in March.

5 During the festival, we say goodbye to cold winter and hello to warm spring.

6 We celebrate the festival everywhere for two days.

7 On the first day, people gather around a big fire at night and sing and dance.

8 The main event begins the next day.

9 Children and adults chase each other with *gulal*.

10 What is *gulal*? It is blue, yellow, green and pink powder.

11 It's a lot of fun to run around and throw colorful powder at everyone.

12 We also join street parades!

13 White Nights Festival

14 Victor from St. Petersburg, Russia

15 Have you heard of the White Nights?

16 Every summer, this amazing thing happens in my hometown.

17 The night sky does not get completely dark.

18 During that time, we hold the White Nights Festival.

19 It usually starts in May and lasts for about a month.

20 During the festival, there is a ballet or an opera almost every night.

21 The most popular event is the Scarlet Sails celebration.

22 A boat with red sails slowly appears on the river.

23 Soon, fireworks begin and a water show follows.

24 You can also hear musicians playing beautiful live music.

25 Kiruna Snow Festival

26 Ebba from Kiruna, Sweden

27 Winter is my favorite season because of the Kiruna Snow Festival.

28 The festival starts in the last week of January and goes on for five or six days.

29 The largest event is the snow design competition.

30 The artists shape huge piles of snow into animals, buildings, and other beautiful artworks.

31 People watch the artists shaping their works from beginning to end.

32 My favorite activity is the dog sled ride.

33 It is amazing to fly through a world of snow on a dog sled.

구석구석지문 TEST Step 1
p.70

Listen and Speak 2 - C

1. will, do, class party
2. make sandwiches
3. How long, take to
4. Maybe, take about an hour

Think and Write

1. Love
2. live in
3. There are, neighborhood
4. a lot of, to swim
5. famous *hanok* in
6. is called, was born
7. The most famous food
8. Come and enjoy

Project Culture

1. to introduce
2. is held in, in July
3. many interesting events
4. see people do
5. it, to do, painting
6. Lastly, outdoor concert
7. hear musicians play

구석구석지문 TEST Step 2
p.71

Listen and Speak 2 - C

1. A: Chris, what will you do for the class party?
2. B: I'll make sandwiches.
3. A: Great idea. How long will it take to make them?
4. B: Maybe it'll take about an hour.

Think and Write

1. I Love Gangneung
2. I live in Gangneung.
3. There are beautiful beaches in my neighborhood.

4. It's a lot of fun to swim at the beach.

5. There is a famous hanok in Gangneung.

6. It is called Ojukheon. Yulgok was born there.

7. The most famous food in Gangneung is potato tteok.

8. It is soft and sweet. Come and enjoy Gangneung!

Project Culture

1. I want to introduce Boryeong Mud Festival.

2. It is held in Daecheon Beach in July.

3. There are many interesting events in the festival.

4. First, you can see people do Ssireum in mud.

5. Also it is fun to do colorful mud body painting on your body.

6. Lastly, there is an outdoor concert.

7. You can hear musicians play beautiful musics.

MEMO

MEMO

적중100

영어 기출 문제집

정답 및 해설

동아 | 이병민